RECENT SOVIET PSYCHOLOGY

RECENT SOVIET PSYCHOLOGY

Edited with an introduction by
N. O'CONNOR, M.A., Ph.D.
*Social Psychiatry Research Unit, Institute of Psychiatry,
The Maudsley Hospital, London*

Translated from the Russian by
Mrs. RUTH KISCH, Dr. R. CRAWFORD
and
H. ASHER, B.A., Lecturer in Physiology
The Medical School, Birmingham

LIVERIGHT
PUBLISHING CORPORATION
NEW YORK

Copyright

©

1961

Pergamon Press Ltd.

Library of Congress Card Number 60-16487

PRINTED IN THE UNITED STATES OF AMERICA

VAN REES PRESS • NEW YORK

TABLE OF CONTENTS

6   CONTENTS

PREFACE

ALTHOUGH TRANSLATIONS of Russian work in experimental psychology have been made by Simon and by Wortis, there is still insufficient opportunity for the English-speaking psychologist to know this work as fully as he would like. The present set of translations is to be welcomed as a new attempt to break the barriers between the work in Russian psychological laboratories and that in our own. It is to be hoped that future publication in English of Russian experimental researches within a short time of their being carried out will make it impossible for the English-speaking student of psychology to be ignorant of what is happening in the psychological laboratories of that country.

One can easily exaggerate the importance of differences in underlying philosophy as a factor in creating separation between the Russian- and the English-speaking currents in experimental psychology. These differences may help to create differences in the type of problems which will be attacked experimentally but not much in the methods of attack. In the laboratory, we are neither idealists nor empiricists nor dialectical materialists, but experimentalists with a range of experimental techniques accepted on both sides.

The element of isolation created by differences in language and in restricted opportunities for social intercourse has been more serious. It has had one effect which cannot be regretted: that experimental enquiry in Russia has been directed towards some problems that have been relatively neglected in our own experimental laboratories. I find myself particularly interested in their work on language development and on conscious control. Incorporation of this interest into the work in psychological laboratories in America and Great Britain will lead to the enrichment of our experimental psychology.

That the breaking down of the barriers of our mutual isolation will lead to corresponding enrichment of the Russian tradition in experimental psychology is also to be supposed, although it is for them to judge in what directions they can profit by our different experimental programmes. A wider use of statistical methods may be one. In the interesting article by B. M. Teplov on the analysis of personality in terms of Pavlov's distinction between different properties of the nervous system, there is mentioned an unsolved problem which awaits experimental investigation, that of whether "mobility" is a single property. This appears to be the sort of problem for which factor-analysis is the most rigorous and most economical method.

It is obvious that we know too little about Russian experimental psychology; it seems equally obvious that they do not know enough about the experimental psychological work of the English-speaking world. There are few references to British or American publications in these papers, and those few neither recent nor widely representative. Plainly there is a barrier to be overcome on both sides. This series of translations makes a contribution to overcoming one side of the barrier; it is to be hoped that our Russian colleagues will make equal efforts to overcome it from their side. The result we must hope for is not only increased fruitfulness of psychological research, but also the promotion of a mutual understanding which will contribute to the great cause of World Peace.

Department of Education,   R. H. THOULESS
17, Brookside, Cambridge

RECENT SOVIET PSYCHOLOGY

INTRODUCTION

Method of Selection

SIMON (1) AND WORTIS (2) have already published books on post-war psychology and psychiatry in Russia so this book is less an introduction than a report of current Russian psychological research. It consists of selected essays from "Problems of Psychology" (Voprosy Psikhologii), one of the chief psychological journals of the U.S.S.R. Russian psychological literature, unlike Russian psychology itself, has a brief and mainly post-war history, journals such as "Problems of Psychology" and "Isvestiya", the journals of the Pedagogical Institute, having commenced publication in 1955 and 1954 respectively. Thus the presentation of material has been primarily through psychological congresses and a limited number of books Of such congresses there were at least three before 1955, but the Academy of Pedagogical Sciences has more recently arranged psychological congresses on an annual basis. Increasingly articles have been published rather than given as lectures and now that journal publication has become regular there is a need to review the current literature.

Both the two previous collections were somewhat in the nature of reports of work which until then had not been known in England. At the time of publication, only a limited number of experts had more than a fanciful notion of the scope of Russian psychological work. These books helped to introduce everyday Russian psychology to English readers. Both were written in a period when western experts felt obliged either wholeheartedly to attack the methods, the philosophy or the social attitudes of their Russian colleagues, or vigorously defend them. A somewhat more objective mutual appraisal has recently become possible. This collection of articles is published with this fact in mind. The selection of the articles has been made jointly. A list was recommended for consideration by the Psychology Section of the Moscow Academy of Sciences and a further selection of these was then made by the writer after seeking advice from colleagues. Naturally such a selection was biased in favour of reports which might appeal to English readers. In this respect it is possible that some of them may be less representative of Russian interests than they otherwise would be. However, Russian colleagues have been frequently consulted and at all times their views have been taken into account.

In this introduction an attempt is made to discuss previous attitudes to Russian psychological literature on the part of English-speaking specialists, Russian attitudes to their own psychology and finally the fields of interest of Russian psychology as represented in this collection.

It is necessary, however, to make some fairly general observations about the articles included. In language, interests and method of reporting results, Russian practice frequently differs considerably from English. The same is true of course of French and German conventions, although this fact seems to arouse less comment. In reports of experimental work readers must expect fairly lengthy discussions of theory. The division between journals reporting experiments and journals reporting discussions of theoretical models or literature is not characteristic of Russian psychological literature. There may be many reasons for this and European, including English, journals are in this respect more akin to Russian journals than are the American. Because there are relatively few journals all types of articles are published together. Exceptions to this rule are beginning to appear and as Mintz [3] notes, philosophical articles by physiologists have recently appeared in "Questions of Philosophy" rather than in physiological or psychological journals.

This division of fields of interest is not yet, however, very common and as a result a number of articles may seem overlengthy by English standards. Translators have usually succeeded in providing a satisfactory English equivalent but this does not mean that they have been able to achieve the concise clarity which editors of English scientific journals take as their objective. Fortunately the considerable services of a number of bilingual collaborators have been available in reviewing translations. For this reason it is hoped that little awkwardness of expression remains and that in most cases accuracy and clarity of translation have been achieved. It may fairly be said therefore that any unclarity of expression is to be attributed to the originals. In general the principles of selection which have been followed are: the interest of the subject matter, the degree to which the report is representative of Russian psychological thought and the adequacy of the experimental method. Articles of a philosophical nature without experimental findings have been excluded.

There is naturally a very considerable variation in individual work, but work can often be traced to three main sources. These are the tradition of physiological work beginning with Sechenov and Pavlov, the work originated by Vigotskii and carried on by Luria, Leont'ev and their colleagues, and finally the work of the Uznadze school in Georgia. The more physiological aspects of Pavlov's work are reported generally in the *Journal of Higher Nervous Activity* and are not included here. Experiments on animal conditioning are therefore not included.

The papers included in this volume are chosen almost exclusively from Voprosi Psychologii and an effort has been made to represent the major divisions of Soviet Psychology. Thus material is given showing work in the fields of educational psychology, Pavlovian typology, thinking, speech, sensation and perception and attitudes or set. In addition, work on verbal control of behaviour in subnormal patients is included.

Attitudes to Soviet Psychology

Attitudes adopted by expositors and critics of Russian psychology have not always been directly relevant to the scientific questions involved. In this respect, like all such attitudes and resulting statements, they are apt to give rise to hypercritical reactions among Russian psychologists. The expression of attitudes of a fundamentally philosophical nature is, of course, calculated to give rise to an opposition of principles. Such oppositions are rarely resolved because their precise relationship with the subject matter of a particular science can seldom be accurately specified.

It seems unprofitable therefore to emphasise the points of philosophical disagreement between, let us say, nominalism or positivism on the one hand and dialectical materialism on the other, although these differences may be important. It would seem more valuable at present to collect examples of experimental work. In this way it may become possible to judge the extent to which principles of scientific method influence the ingenuity, scope and decisiveness of psychological experiments. The success of experimental work can be judged not only by its basic assumptions but also by its elegance, exactitude and ingenuity. Such qualities can be appreciated by working scientists who may very well disagree profoundly about interpretations and even about the hypotheses which gave rise to the experiment in the first place.

In a science such as psychology, standards of experimental performance based on criteria such as exactitude and ingenuity are of vital significance. Commonsense and everyday expectations march so closely with experimental findings that it is easy to mistake the one for the other. In judging a body of experimental work from a country whose national

growth, development and system of government have each become a bat-
tle-ground of opposite opinion it is doubly important to look for examples
of adequate method and good and ingenious experimentation. In this
respect we are at once on somewhat less controversial ground. It may
appear to Murray, May and Cantril (1959) for example, that there is too
much unanimity of doctrinal foundation among Soviet psychologists.
However, the value of Russian psychology must depend on its interest
and fruitfulness and ultimately on its usefulness to psychologists and
others. If such standards are high, observations about a medieval attitude
of mind become irrelevant if not misleading.

Russian psychologists would certainly be willing to be judged by similar criteria, and those who have become known in England, either through
visits or by their publications, have earned the respect of their English
colleagues. This is not to say that all Russian psychology is first-class
and without deficiencies. It has a number of shortcomings of which psychologists in the U.S.S.R. are aware. For example, apart from some interesting work in the field of education, there has been very little development in social psychology. There has also been a tendency in some University departments, though not in all, to capitalize the very valuable
inheritance of Pavlovian techniques perhaps to the exclusion of other
sources. More recently this unbalance has been corrected and Russian
psychology has begun to spread into many different fields. Professor
Smirnov, for example, in a speech delivered at the opening of the 1959
Congress of Psychologists in Moscow, spoke of the need to develop industrial psychology, so far only studied to a limited extent in Russia.
Other shortcomings for example of quality of work, exist in all countries
and their existence need not surprise the sophisticated. Unfortunately it
sometimes happens that higher standards are demanded of work from
abroad than at home. This common attitude must not be allowed to ob-
scure the fact that although the studies presented in subsequent pages
may not all be of equal merit, many are of considerable interest.

Many of the critical attitudes adopted towards Soviet psychology in
the past have been connected with what is believed to be State interference
with theoretical issues. Criticisms have commonly been levelled at the
intelligence-testing controversy and the 1936 Decree concerning it which
has since been published in English by Wortis [2]. This is usually quoted
as an example of the way in which a State based on Communist or Marxist
doctrine brings pressure to bear on scientists. It must be said at once that
from the point of view of an old established country in which social pressures are very much implicit rather than explicit, Soviet experience in

the social sciences appears to demonstrate a more overt from of pressure. At the same time a good case can be made for saying that the pattern and method of direction of research in England are not basically dissimilar from those in Russia. In England, however, the pattern is better understood, works more smoothly and results in fewer extreme trends.

If we turn to the administrative application of theories, a case in point might be the use of intelligence tests for selection at 11-plus. In recent years emphasis on the value of intelligence testing in grammar school selection has been reduced. Inefficiency in selection by this method has been acknowledged and a number of local education authorities have reviewed their selection policy in favour of comprehensive schools. This means delaying selection and increasing educational opportunity. The positions of Britain and Russia on this question have therefore gone through similar phases. Britain has been slower, less decisive and less complete. In keeping with its philosophical tradition it has also remained more empirical. In its discussion it has tended to ignore theory and to concentrate on the technicalities of measurement, of practice effects, of normality of distribution of samples and similar questions. However, in practical and administrative development the trends have been similar. In effect it could be argued that behind the reduction in emphasis on intelligence and selection lies the development of a more liberal educational policy in both countries.

Obviously much more could be said about this question but it is perhaps enough to show that it is possible to over-emphasize the differences in social structure between Western countries and Russia so far as the relationship between political or administrative and academic questions are concerned. For a further example we might look to the United States of America, where the State of Tennessee once passed an Act forbidding the teaching of Evolution in High Schools. This Act was soon disputed and the outlook of Tennessee High School pupils is at present somewhat more informed than it was in the 1920s when the Act was passed. The Americans took a very short time to reject the implications of the Act in practice. The Russians took somewhat longer to develop a more liberal approach to the question of individual ability. The reasons for this are complex because the question is by no means so clear-cut. Russians do not accept the prevalent English view of a given quantum of intelligence present from birth or from an early age. However, theoretically speaking the statement of such a view would not be followed by shocked silence or violent condemnation on political grounds. Most Russian psychologists would regard such a view as backward-looking but would argue against it on the basis of evidence. It might be said, therefore, that we should not too readily criticise the limitations on academic freedom in Russia today. They do not seem to exist in any greater degree than in England or America, whatever may have been true of certain Institutes during the war and shortly after.

For quite another reason also, it might be said that research trends in the two economically and socially different countries have a certain communality of pattern. This is because research, whether for health, education or war, is frequently inspired by the need to answer practical questions. Often practical questions do not differ greatly from country to country despite considerable differences in social organisation. It is even true that social pressures much discussed by contemporary sociologists act in a similar manner in both countries in so far as the social organisation of groups remains the same and even when the class structure has changed radically. At present Russian academic opinions reflect experimental results about as much as our own do here.

It is hoped therefore that the time has now come when English readers can examine these reports as they would if reading an English journal and not be confused by the political aura which the undoubtedly widely different systems of government often seem to impose on our thinking. Without withdrawing any of the force of this observation it must none the less be said that the starting-point and the conclusions of Russian experiments are frequently very different from our own. These differences are discussed in the next section.

Russian Attitudes and Sets in Psychology

Reports of visits to Russia have recently described a decrease in the partisan expression of philosophical views. There has been a tendency to move away from philosophical prolegomena in journal articles and towards a direct discussion of experimental material. This tendency is a natural response to increasing involvement with the subject matter of the science and its technical problems as well as a result of increasing liberal trends in the Universities. It also reflects an increase in the complexity of the material studied.

As the number of scientists has increased their studies have in some cases departed so far from their sources that they represent a completely novel trend. Such new investigations may have originally resulted from some suggestions for example made by Pavlov, but their development usually leads them into fields of experiment where Pavlov did not go.

Thus the work of Luria and Zaporozhets on the verbal control of motor behaviour has origins in both Vigotskii and Pavlov but is very dissimilar from any work carried out by either. This is less true of work done in Georgia along the lines suggested by Uznadze. However, the studies of Sokolov on orienting reflexes and nearly all material concerned with the interaction of verbal and non-verbal cues is novel although deriving to some degree from earlier work or suggestions of Ivanov-Smolenskii and Krasnagorskii.

This writer is not competent to trace the foreign sources of current Russian influences in psychology. Obviously earlier German psychological literature has had a part to play and the great impact of Pavlov is universally acknowledged. The work of Uznadze has something in common with German work by Willmott and Kohler. As in many such cases it is profitless to dispute priority because ideas are often developed in many places contemporaneously when a subject reaches a critical stage of development.

Work in Russian psychology, as in English psychology, depends very much on the ability and interests of particular people and groups of people. Thus, just as the tradition of statistical analysis in University College, London, resulted in generations of studies concerned with the factor analysis of cognitive abilities, so in Koltushy studies concerning the conditioning of physiological processes continue.

In Leningrad, in Anan'ev's Institute, studies are almost entirely centred on the analysis of learning processes, especially those concerned with space perception. In Moscow several other areas of study are directed by such workers as Leont'ev studying acoustic analysis, Luria the verbal control of voluntary behaviour, Smirnov the study of memory, Sokolov the analysis of inhibition and orienting reflexes, and Teplov the analysis of types of nervous system and their flexibility.

In Tbilisi the development of the ideas of Uznadze seems to proceed rather independently of the fields of interest of Moscow psychologists. It is, however, connected with their work by reason of their common interest in the structure of language and its relation to thought.

In addition to these activities other studies connected with psychiatry and with physiology are also going on. The work of Gershuni in Leningrad and Mme. Zimkina also in Leningrad, Schwarz and Anokhin in Moscow and Mme. Traugott in Leningrad should be mentioned.

This is not by any means a complete list even of the psychological studies which are going on. Rubinstein, until his death last year, continued his studies of philosophical aspects of psychology in Moscow and

Zaporozhets collaborates with a number of workers all studying child development. Apart from those mentioned there are a great number of allied physiological and psychiatric studies which were partially touched on by Ivanov-Smolenskii.

In all these schools, or fields of investigation, most of which are represented in this volume, the writer has found extremely little mechanical or hide-bound application of dialectics. During a recent visit to most of the laboratories listed, Pavlov's name was often mentioned, Sechenov's and Vigotskii's from time to time but the names of Marx and Engels scarcely at all. Russian psychologists may apply dialectical principles in their thinking about problems but for the most part, both in groups and as individuals, they do not refer to the relationship between a prevailing philosophy and individual experiments any more than would English or American psychologists. Rubinstein is an exception because his work is directly centred on just such topics.

No Russian opinion on this important question has been made known in the last few years, although in the past both Anan'ev and Rubinshtein have expressed their views concerning both dialectical materialism and Lenin's principles of reflection from his study "Materialism and Empirio-Criticism".

When Professor Leont'ev and Professor Luria were asked to express their views on this general topic they were able to make the following observations: "The significance of the principle of reflection for psychology is that it affords an approach to psychical processes and phenomena as something which gives the subject a correct (or relatively correct, capable of becoming more complete and more correct) picture of what exists outside his consciousness. Here, of course, the term "reflection" does not have the same meaning as when we speak, for example, of the reflection of an object in a mirror. Psychical reflection is a reflection which is vital and active. It is not simply a physical reflection, an epiphenomenon. On the contrary, it fulfils an important function in life, in behaviour: by orienting the subject in the surrounding world it enables him to adapt himself to that world and to change it.

"Psychical reflection is not added to the processes of life from outside: it is a phenomenon of life itself, developing in the course of evolution. Transition from primitive to higher forms and levels of reflection takes place as a result of development of the subject's vital, practical connections with the surrounding world. In man it reaches the highest possible level—the level of consciousness. Man's activity is linked both with inevitable reflection of the external conditions affecting him and the reality of which he is conscious through language, pictorial representation and other media for the transmission of the collective experience of society, the experience of preceding generations of mankind. This, too, is the level of creative reflection. It acquires its creative character by virtue of the fact that man becomes capable of activity in the pattern of reflection, of consciousness —of working with images and conceptions. It is for this reason that man is capable of encompassing both the past and the future in thought; he penetrates into the atom, hidden from the eye, and into the infinitely remote cosmos. He is aware also of himself, his consciousness, his internal world.

"For psychology the principle of reflection is an active methodological principle, guiding research to the causal and genetic explanation of psychical processes and phenomena. It frees psychology from simplified mechanical interpretations and from the sterile phenomenologism, which isolates consciousness."

Certainly the supposed structure of theoretical surveillance has had but small effect in creating uniformity except within any one department. Areas of work are unexplored but this appears to be a question of individual ingenuity rather than of general decision. This fact reveals the basic difficulty of imposing any widely generalised discipline on a particular set of facts. If the discipline is based on these facts it may reflect them closely. If it is not it may still reflect a widespread feature of events in all allied fields. None the less the knowledge of facts in a field dissimilar from that on which the generalisation was based will behave to a large extent randomly in respect of this theory. It thus happens that any point of view not tailored to a particular set of data cannot readily be imposed on such data. Individual ingenuity and inspiration as well as knowledge of the facts may thus become of prime importance in any study, whatever the theoretical direction. It is for this reason perhaps that no amount of stress on the social determinants of individual behaviour in Marxist theory has resulted in any studies of social conditioning of groups by Russian psychologists. Instead, equally interesting aspects of children's learning and control of voluntary behaviour have been worked out, for example by Zaporozhets, Luria and others.

This is simply to note that the interaction of individual scientists with their problems often follows the logic of data and interest rather than that of dogma. By dogma used in this sense I do not mean only Marxism but the mechanical and unthinking application of any principle whatsoever. It is for ourselves and our Russian colleagues to decide whether Dialectical Materialism as a theory is a useful theory in its application to psychology. So long as its implications are worked out flexibly and with an eye to their effectiveness in producing useful and ingenious experimentation there can be no possible objection to it. Often, of course, such broad general theories follow on the development of a particular science, rather than giving rise to it.

So far as the Russian use of dialectical materialism is concerned one is left with the impression that its application has gone beyond the stage of the use of phrases as dialectic pronouncements and has become part of the mental equipment of working scientists much as nineteenth-century empiricism and positivism lies behind the thinking of many English scientists. As a result articles appear as reports of investigations together with discussions of the results and are not now commonly preceded by remarks concerning the relevance of dialectical precepts to the matters under investigation. Such theories as those of mental reflection and the primacy of matter certainly influence thought but they have become as implicit as positivism is in Britain. However, artificial connection between statements of fact and principles of theory are less and less obvious. Where connections are presumed to exist good reason is usually given for using the hypothesis. As a result there is less artificiality in the connection of hypotheses and conclusions.

The scope of Russian psychological work has recently been reviewed in an introductory speech to the Moscow Psychological Conference this year. Professor Smirnov, who made the report, looked forward to an extensive development of industrial psychology. Also, indications of this talk were that problems of memory, thinking and fatigue in school children would receive the same extensive attention which they had already had in psychological laboratories. Likewise, as a result of the aftermath of the war the rehabilitation of cases of brain injury would continue to be important. Professor Smirnov drew attention to the lack of development of a psychology of unconscious behaviour and emotional development.

Like many other psychologists in Russia he proclaimed his dissatisfaction with Freudian theory. Bassin [4] also interprets the history of Freud's thought as showing a departure from its original sound beginnings. The rejection of psycho-analysis in any of its current developed forms is based on two objections: its idealistic character and its tendency to use a physiology involving an altogether too mechanical theory of brain localisation. There is common ground for example, between Russian work and Freudian observations in the acceptance of the principle of the pathogenic nature of the conflict of drives. But subsequent Freudian theory is regarded as both too unrelated to physiology and too crude in its interpretation of the interaction of sub-cortical drives and conscious sets of ideas or voluntary actions.

A discussion of this kind indicates that Russian psychologists have certain quite clear theoretical predilections in favour, for example, of physiologically based explanations rather than molar psychological ones. They also appear to prefer dynamic rather than mechanical brain localisation theories. Such views can be argued to be consistent with Dialectical Materialist theory, but they are also Pavlovian views. What has yet to emerge, in the opinion of this writer, is a dialectical approach to questions of social psychology in which Russian psychology has so far produced no great experimenter and no firm tradition. Presumably such work when it does commence will be tied to an already existing body of methodology of a Marxist kind and perhaps to the outstanding work of educationists and psychologists such as Makarenko and Uznadze. However, as yet no established body of experiments has appeared in the literature.

The question of what attitude Russian psychologists have towards their subject must therefore be answered in two ways. Soviet psychologist show a preference for physiological work and explanatory hypotheses which derive in large part from Pavlov. Their attitude might also be said to conform to dialectical materialist principles. However, although such principles exert an influence on thinking they only partly determine, for example, the selection of subject matter for research. Russian psychologists therefore are free to conduct a wide range of experiments many of which might be criticised because as yet they are not closely tied to physiological explanations. At the same time they tend to select subjects for investigation which exploit their national traditions, and in north-west Russia these are primarily physiological. As one might expect, traditions and experiments have a different character in parts of Russia far from Leningrad and Moscow, such for example as Georgia.

McLeish [5] draws attention to the discussions which he says preceded the current position in Russian psychology. Despite a debate which centred round idealism and empiricism as methodological faults, Kornilov tried to hammer out another contradiction, that between psychology as physiology or as independent of physiology. Whilst partly solving the problem in favour of a complex view of mental process, it might be said that the full and completely satisfactory resolution remains to be achieved. For example, the failure to develop an adequate stand on social and cultural questions leaves Russian psychologists with an incomplete development of their own field. In the view of this writer it is possible that Russian psychologists and sociologists may soon provide a more complete psychology by entering this area of research. If they do it is possible that they will do so taking account of Vigotskii's view that facts are sometimes independent of the theories which give rise to them.

It is clear that there exists now a body of experiments in the U.S.S.R. about which we know rather little. Such work deserves our attention irrespective of its theoretical principles and presuppositions. If, in fact, it is of interest to us either as suggesting new approaches to research or new subject matter, it will then be open to English readers to consider what is the nature and quality of the ideas which gave rise to the experiments which have been done.

N. O'CONNOR

REFERENCES

1. Psychology in the Soviet Union. (1957). Ed. Brian Simon. Routledge and Kegan Paul, London.
2. Soviet Psychiatry. (1950). Ed. J. Wortis. Williams & Wilkins, Balt.
3. MINTZ, A. (1958) Recent Developments in the U.S.S.R., *Ann. Rev. Psychol.,* Vol. 9, 453–504.
4. BASSIN, F. V. (1958–9). Freud in the Light of Contemporary Scientific Discussion, translated from *Vopr. psi.,* Nos. 5 and 6, 1958. *Soviet Psychology Information Bulletin,* Vol. 6, Nos. 1 and 2, Soc. Cult. Rel. with U.S.S.R., London, 1959.
5. MCLEISH, J. (1955). *N* .terials on Soviet Psychology. *S.C.R. Psychol. Bull.,* Vol. 2, No. 3, 8–12.
6. MURRAY, H. A., MAY, M. A. and CANTRIL, H. (1959). *The American Psychologist,* Vol. 14, 303–307.

TYPOLOGICAL PROPERTIES OF THE NERVOUS SYSTEM AND THEIR PSYCHOLOGICAL MANIFESTATIONS *

B. M. TEPLOV

Institute of Psychology, R.S.F.S.R. Academy of Paedagogic Sciences, Moscow

1

STUDY of the individual differences in people is one of the most important tasks of psychology. Its importance became particularly evident as soon as psychological science set itself to become a science that could be usefully applied in practical work (educational and child psychology, the psychology of work, pathopsychology).

Individual differences include, of course, some that can be established with relative ease, such as differences in knowledge, in capabilities or customs. Usually, however, when individual differences are being discussed, it is a question of other, more fundamental and permanent properties. They are the properties that are concerned in the chapters of psychology textbooks dealing with temperament, character and capabilities.

These chapters are usually among the least substantial in textbooks of psychology and contain but few scientifically established principles, so that they have little to offer that is of use in practical work, although their content would appear to be concerned with problems of great importance in life. Furthermore, they have hardly any connection with the content of the rest of the course of general psychology.

It should be stated that the psychological differences in individuals do not constitute the entire contents of these chapters in psychology. They are usually contained in a section dealing with the psychology of personality. Most Soviet psychologists are agreed that the psychology of personality is not merely a question of psychological differences between individuals. The problems of the psychology of personality are first and foremost problems of general psychology and only in a subordinate way they are problems of "individual" or "differential" psychology. Inadequate

---

* Voprosy Psikhologii, No. 5, pp. 108–130, 1951.

[21]

development in problems connected with the general psychology of personality is undoubtedly one of the reasons for the patently unsatisfactory position in the development of problems of individual psychological differences.

One must of course recognize that some place is always given in the chapters in courses of psychology dealing with separate psychical processes to the question of individual differences i.e. differences in sensitivity, in perception, in types of memory and quality of thought. As a rule, however, these individual differences are left quite unconnected either with one another or with the individual differences in temperament, character and capabilities discussed in the psychology of personality.

The doctrine of individual differences, as it is presented in textbooks and courses of psychology, lacks not only system but even simple coherence. Actually, there are no logical grounds for use of the expression "doctrine of individual differences". There are a certain number of empirically established facts on this subject (some of them very valuable), but there is no solid framework of any sort, psychological or physiological, into which these odd pieces of information can be fitted.

Successes in the study of individual psychological differences depend to a considerable degree on the development of general psychological theory, and above all, of course, on the development of general problems in the psychology of personality, but they will also depend on the creation of a system of psychology which will eliminate the gap which now exists between the two parts of this science, namely the psychology of psychic processes and the psychology of personality *. This important section is still in an obviously unsatisfactory state, a fact which is fully realized by Soviet psychologists (see the resolution of the Congress on the Psychology of Personality [28]).

In Western European and American psychology of the last decades the problems of individual differences have usually been tackled by the so-called "test method". Here there is fundamental divergence between Soviet psychologists and the supporters of "testology", as this sphere of the activity of Western psychologists may be termed.

---

* There is no doubt about the existence of this gap although the authors of textbooks and courses in psychology have avoided contrasting psychical processes and psychical properties of personality in chapter headings. For example, in the textbook of psychology for educational institutes published in 1956 under the editorship of A. A. Smirnov, A. N. Leont'ev, S. L. Rubinstein and B. M. Teplov, the fifth section, "Psychical properties of personality" is notable both for its modest proportions and its complete lack of connection with the preceding sections [48].

These tests are more or less short, strictly standardized examinations, the results of which can, in one way or another, be expressed in numerical form and are generally submitted to statistical treatment. There can be no objection in principle to "short examination", to standardized examination conditions, to the attempt to express the results in numerical form or to statistical treatment of the results. There must, however, be objection for another reason, namely, that an overwhelming majority of the tests have no firmly established scientific basis.

One of the best known tests is Rorschach's test: the subject is shown ink blots of "chance" shape and is asked to say what he "sees" in these blots. It is difficult to take exception to the fact that certain features of the imagination, of fantasy, may be revealed in a test of this nature, but it is even more difficult to believe that this test can claim to reveal the fundamental properties of the personality of man in all their multiformity. And it is still more difficult to believe that tens of thousands of man-days have been spent on the development of a technique for the preparation of these blots, on the development of standard conditions for the conduct of the tests with them, on the discovery of methods for expression of the results of such test in numerical form — in the form of "marks", and on the elaboration of methods for the statistical treatment of these results. It is difficult to believe that there are not a few individuals whose main specialization is the conducting of Rorschach tests. Finally, of course, one cannot but protest against the fact that "selections" of any kind, on which the future of individuals may not infrequently depend, should be effected by means of Rorschach or other similar kinds of tests.

A considerable proportion of these tests are "tests" which have been arrived at quite empirically, and their significance had, as it were, to be proved statistically as a result of their massive application. We suggest, however, that if the physiological or psychological meaning of a test is not clear to us, if the test is a "blind test", then no statistical treatment of massive application of such a test, however complicated or clever it may be, will yield scientifically meaningful results. "Blind tests" cannot be made to "see" merely by their combination with statistical methods.

This also applies in all respects to the reliance placed on test examinations for the calculation of correlations (statistical and probability relationships) between the results obtained with different tests. Since the time of the publication of Spearman's book on the abilities of man (1927 [70]) there has been a conviction that the "structure of the personality" could be discovered by purely test methods through special (usually very complicated) mathematical operations with correlation coefficients (so-called "factor analysis"). An enormous amount of time and effort has been spent on the carrying out of test investigations designed for treatment by the methods of factor analysis. The results so far obtained are less than modest. Some, possibly most, of these examinations have been conducted on lines of blind empiricism, while others have been based on conceptions founded partly on everyday observations and partly on idealistic speculative constructions such as the typology of Jung or Kretschmer. Neither of these lines has made any original contribution to the understanding of the nature of individual differences. Neither could they yield results of scientific value as they are based on the tacit assumption that it is possible to start with the discovery and perfecting of intricate methods for the mathematical treatment of experimental results without any strict investigation of what the properties are that it is desired to test or of what methods are suitable for the testing of these properties.

Occasional test of undoubted scientific importance have been suggested in this field of testological investigation. These must, of course, be investigated and used. But "testology" as a whole has not revealed any useful paths to an understanding of individual psychological differences. Scientifically, it has proved barren and in practical application it has sometimes proved definitely harmful.

All the above is intended to show that the search for ways of determining the individual psychological differences in people by objective methods with sound theoretical foundations is one of the most important tasks in contemporary psychology.

The present paper will discuss one of the possible ways in which this problem can be solved. The group of psychologists who, for the last four to five years, have been carrying out research under my direction in the laboratory of the Institute of Psychology, R.S.F.S.R. Academy of Pedagogic Sciences, has been working on such lines.

The object of this collective was to obtain an understanding and, if possible, more exact definition of some of the individual psychological differences in people by investigation of the typological properties of higher nervous activity.

I have several times already had occasion to describe the general trend and nature of our research (see [60], [61], [63], [64], [72]). The main results obtained by our group up to the middle of 1955 were reflected in the collected papers, "The Typological Features of the Higher Nervous Activity of Man". I shall now deal only with some questions of principle connected with the general course of our work.

2

Two approaches to the scientific definition of individual differences are possible.

(1) One can proceed from the quantitative depiction of certain properties (stature, weight, extent of expiration etc.; the sensivity of each of the analysers, speed of memorizing and retentiveness etc.).

(2) One can proceed from the grouping of individuals by types such as athletic, asthenic and pyknic builds or by types of memory such as visual, auditory, motor or graphic and verbal abstract.

The former approach is naturally termed the analytic and the latter, the synthetic approach. Neither can, from its unilateral approach, furnish a complete answer to the problem. The first method yields quite a lot of useful empirical pieces of information, but these alone can only give disjointed "catalogues" of individual features. The second method gives very rapid results which are seemingly effective and appear to be close to life, but ultimately it leads to an impasse. Such conceptions as Jung's introvert and extrovert types or the cyclothymic and schizothymic types of Kretschmer, typology which has enjoyed exceptional popularity in Western psychology during the last few decades, arose in connection with this method. The effort to carry out objective investigations on individual differences, based on integrated types of this kind which, however, do not lend themselves to scientific analysis, led to the production of "irrational" methods, such as the above-mentioned Rorschach test, methods with false semblances of objectivity due entirely to the use of the complicated apparatus of mathematical statistical methods for the treatment of the results.

It cannot be denied that the second method implies an approach which is genuinely scientific and has no connection with "irrational" methods. It is possible in this way, by prolonged and intensive scientific work, to arrive at the establishment of psychological types" which can be made the object of scientific analysis. The investigations of Myasishchev and Kovalëv [38], [39], [23], for example, were carried out by this method, which is an essential, but not the only possible way. Our collective follows the first method, but our work is based on the physiological conceptions of the typological properties of the nervous system described by Pavlov. The ultimate aim is the fusion of the two methods or, more correctly, the meeting of the workers digging the tunnel from the two ends.

One of the decisive merits of the Pavlov doctrine of nervous system types lies in the fact that Pavlov understood types of nervous activity as "different combinations of the basic properties of the nervous system" [43; III, Bk. 2, 267]. In this conception lies the scientific importance and the great future of the Pavlov doctrine of types.

It should be noted, however, that in the literature on higher nervous activity the word "type" is used in another as well as this, its main sense, namely type as the characteristic "pattern" or "picture" of the behaviour of animals or man. Kupalov [30] was the first to direct attention to the difference in these two meanings, and this question has been analysed by me elsewhere [63]. In analysing the history of the development of the doctrine of types of higher nervous activity in animals during the life of Pavlov, I attempted to show that there was a gradual transition from predominant use of the general "picture" of animal behaviour for determination of nervous system types to strictly experimental indices of definite properties of nervous processes [63: 7].

Towards the end of his life Pavlov became convinced that the basic properties of the nervous system on which the theory of animal types must be based were the following three: (1) strength of the nervous processes; (2) their mobility; and (3) the balance between processes of excitation and inhibition. In his well-known work, "The General Types of Higher Nervous Activity of Animals and Man" [43: III, Bk. 2, 267], Pavlov summarized the experimental methods used for the determination of these properties in dogs by the classical salivary method. Concerning "types", Pavlov wrote the following in this paper: "The possible variations in the basic nervous processes and the possible combinations of these variations should produce types of nervous system numbering as least 24 by arithmetical calculation, but actually very much fewer, namely four sharply defined, easily recognizable types and, what is important, differing in their capacities for adaptation to the surrounding medium and in their resistances to pain-producing agents" [43: III, Bk. 2, 290].

What were the reasons that compelled Pavlov to select 4 types from 24 (at a modest calculation!) possible combinations of basic properties?

(1) "Sharply defined and immediately recognizable". This argument arises from the conception of type as a "model" of behaviour. As, however, I have shown elsewhere [63: 23 – 30], even in experimental dogs typical pictures of behaviour are not direct and unequivocal indications of the types of higher nervous activity, understood as complexes of certain properties of the nervous system, a fact which Pavlov himself noted and stressed repeatedly. Nevertheless, this argument can, of course, be a serious scientific argument in relation to application of the theory of "four types" to man.

(2) "Capacity for adaptation to the surrounding medium". This argument cannot be deliberately transferred from dogs to man: in man the capacity for adaptation to the surrounding medium is very definitely determined by factors different from those operating in the case of animals.

(3) "Resistance to pain-producing agents". This basis is difficult to subvert on any *a priori* theoretical grounds. Yet the following fact merits attention. Numerous attempts have been made to establish connections between certain diseases and types of higher nervous activity. When such works are examined carefully, it is found that this connection—were it indeed demonstrated by the investigators—was not so much between the disease and the types as a characteristic complex of properties as between the disease and a certain property or certain properties. Davidenkov, for example, observed a connection between inertia of the nervous system and neuroses (the main purveyors of neuroses were pre-eminantly the most inert natures) [10; 67]; Chernorutskii [65], and Langbelonogova and Kok [31] detected some connection between hypertensive and ulcerative disease and weakness and imbalance of the nervous system. The question arises whether it would not be more advantageous to direct one's efforts to determination of the particular property of the nervous system which, *a priori* could play some part in the development of a particular disease instead of attempting which is extremely difficult and only provisionally successful — to classify the patients according to the "four types".

The idea of the "four types" and their analogy with the four types of temperament was developed by Pavlov before maturation of his doctrine of the basic properties of the nervous system, which was reflected in the last papers by the great physiologist. It is understandable, therefore, that the first serious attempts to apply the Pavlov doctrine of types of nervous system to man were made on the basis of the schema of the "four types" rather than on doctrine of definite properties of the nervous system.

These first serious attempts were linked with the name of Ivanov-Smolenskii and with the investigations of his co-workers. In his laboratories four "types of closing activity", distinguished mainly by the rapidity of the formation of positive and inhibitory conditioned connections, were identified by means of the motor method with speech, alimentary or orienting reinforcement: these types were labile, inert, excitable and inhibitory. The experimental investigations of Novikova [42], Kotlyarevskii [25], Pen [49] and others may be recalled in this connection. These experimental works were carried out in the late twenties (the last two were published in 1933 but "were finally formulated in 1932". See [17:7]).

It can be assumed that the four-member classification of "types of closing activity in the child", suggested by Ivanov-Smolenskii, was developed on the basis of the four-member classification of types of nervous system in animals, proposed by Pavlov in 1927. Ivanov-Smolenskii and his co-workers advanced a step, however, by suggesting an experimental criterion for differentiating two balanced types and introducing the terms "labile" and "inert" to designate them, terms which Pavlov subsequently used to denote the two opposite poles in the parameter of mobility.

During the period between 1927 and 1935 Pavlov made several re-examinations of the principles for the classification of types of higher nervous activity as he tried to gain as deep an understanding as possible of the basic properties of the nervous system and the interrelationships between them. The history of Pavlov's development of the doctrine of nervous system types, an outline of which I have tried to give in one of our papers [63: 6-23], presents an instructive picture of the great scientist's untiring creative research. During this period Pavlov discovered the third basic property of the nervous system—its mobility. The last clasification given by Pavlov is built primarily on the principle of the strength of the nervous system as the most important of its properties, the principle of balance of the nervous processes, on which his 1927 classification was constructed, being shifted to second place (see my paper mentioned above, p. 77 et seq.). The 1935 classification differed in principle from the 1927 classification (as also from earlier draft classifications of types). In the 1935 classification the types were consistently described for the first time as "complexes of the basic properties of the nervous system"; here too the experimental methods for the determination and investigation of each of these properties were systematized for the first time.

The number "four", however, remained in 1935 as in 1927, as did also the relationship of these four types with the names of the temperaments which have come down from antiquity (although not from Hippocrates, as is generally thought) *. This fact, which is quite unreal from the physiological standpoint, has had a very harmful effect on development of the application of Pavlov's doctrine of types of nervous system to man.

* The doctrine of the four temperaments was developed in late antiquity, several centuries after Hippocrates. In the writings of Hippocrates himself we find only reference to the presence of four fluids in the body of man and to the fact that man's health depends on correct proportions between these fluids ("On the Nature of Man"; 4), with also the conception of "melancholia": "Prolonged suppression of fear and grief are the signs of melancholia" ("Aphorisms", VI, 23; see [7: 198–199 and 723]). For the history of the doctrine of temperaments in the science of antiquity see, for example, Siębek [69: 278 et seq.].

A completely erroneous conviction was created, particularly in those who attempted to apply the Pavlov theory for practical purposes in medicine and education, that it was a question of dividing people (particularly patients and children) into four types more or less corresponding to the four traditional temperaments. It was often found (and the frequency was greater, the more conscientiously the investigator approached the task) that most of the individuals examined did not fit into any of the four types: these individuals were designated "intermediate" types.

The experimental determination of types was generally effected by one or other variant of the Ivanov-Smolenskii method. Four types were determined by this method but, as has just been shown, these were quite different in content from the "four types" of which Pavlov wrote in his last classification which is expounded in all textbooks of physiology and psychology and which is tacitly accepted as beyond discussion and "final". This circumstance, which is vital to the whole sense of the matter, is not usually given any attention; it is assumed that the "four types" determined by the Ivanov-Smolenskii method are also the "Pavlov types".

From 1933 [17] right up to his last published statements on the subject, Ivanov-Smolenskii himself insisted on stressing that it was not types of higher nervous activity as a whole but merely types of closing activity in the cortex that were investigated in the studies made in his laboratories. In 1953 he wrote that the systematic classification of these types was based on the principles of balance and mobility [20; 47], while in countless textbooks, popular and other expositions of the Pavlov doctrine it has been constantly repeated that the first principle of Pavlov's classification of types was that of strength. Finally, it must be mentioned that it was no other than Ivanov-Smolenskii himself who, in a number of his published statements, laid special emphasis on the fact that the number of "typological variations" according to the Pavlov doctrine of types should not be limited to four (see [18: 80–81] and also [19] and [20]). There are therefore no grounds for considering that Ivanov-Smolenskii shared these mistaken views on the way to apply the Pavlov doctrine of types which we are discussing to man. Ivanov-Smolenskii* can, however, be reproved in that on none of the many occasions on which he expressed his views on these problems in print did he clear up the widely current "misunderstanding", which could not but lead to some discrediting of even the idea

---

* I had occasion to examine in detail some, in my opinion, erroneous positions taken up by Ivanov-Smolenskii in relation to the understanding of types of nervous system (see [63]). They do not, however, have any direct bearing on the problem with which we are now concerned.

of the importance of development in the application of Pavlov's doctrine of nervous system types to man.

In 1939 Krasnogorskii published in his book his classification of types (first suggested by him in 1931), based on the principle of relationship between the cortex and subcortex, the types being central, subcortical, cortical and anergic [26: 102–104]. This classification had nothing in common with the Pavlov classification, but it too retained the number "four", and it was regarded by many as the application of the Pavlov doctrine of types to children, inasmuch as its author, a pupil of Pavlov's, also worked by the conditioned reflex method. In 1952 Krasnagorskii described a new variant of the four-member classification of types, the general arrangement of which corresponded to the Pavlov classification, but one of the types (Pavlov's "impetuous" type) was now characterized by a thing which Pavlov did not have in mind, namely predominance of the subcortex over the cortex [27]. The interrelationship between cortex and subcortex is an important property of higher nervous activity. Krasnogorskii's merit is the stressing of this property. The investigation of this problem and the demonstration of its importance in relation to individual differences in people may constitute an interesting research problem. Yet why should a classification of types based solely on this property give exactly "four" types and why should these four types correspond in any sense with the four Pavlov types? Why with the introduction of a new property (predominance of the subcortex) into the Pavlov classification should the number "four" remain, enigmatically, unchanged, and even the type, distinguished by this new sign, still be termed "impetuous" or "choleric"?

It is possible to cite many similar examples of the use of schemas consisting of four types with the Pavlov names or with names borrowed after the Pavlov model from the traditional nomenclature of temperaments but without any attempt to retain the Pavlov content of the types. This, however, is hardly necessary. The works that have come from the laboratories of Ivanov-Smolenskii and Krasnogorskii are still the most influential.

We are of the opinion that Pavlov's discovery of the basic properties of the nervous system is of the greatest importance for the elucidation of the individual differences in men, and not at all his recognition of four types which correspond more or less with the traditional temperaments as the fundamental types. The number "four" is not the result of any scientific considerations.

It cannot even be said that it is a very fixed tradition in the science of the temperaments of man to distinguish exactly four temperaments.

It is true that Aristotle, Kant, Wundt, Ebbinghaus, Fontier and many others reckoned there were four temperaments (employing, incidentally, totally different principles of division). On the other hand, the great Roman physician, Galen, counted 13 temperaments (see [69: 284]), Höfding 8 [6: 341], Heymans 6 [71: 484], Ach [68: 314–324], Meiman 12 [37: 288] and so on*. Also, it would be quite unnatural to deduce the number of types of nervous system from the number of temperaments: temperament is the psychological manifestation of type of nervous system, and not the other way round.

The evidence afforded by study of animal types of nervous system indicates that types exist which do not correspond to any of the four Pavlov types, nor are yet intermediate types. Such, for example, are (1) the type with absolutely strong stimulatory and absolutely weak inhibitory processes, differing essentially—a fact recognized by Pavlov himself—from the ordinary "impetuous" (choleric) type, in which both processes are strong, absolutely, and the stimulatory process has only relative predominance over the inhibitory (for details, see [63: 78–79, 92]); (2) the unbalanced type with predominance of inhibition over excitation (*Ibid.* p. 86–90, 92); and (3) types which are unbalanced in respect of the mobility of the processes of excitation and inhibition (*Ibid.* pp. 90–91).

There is no reason whatever to believe that these types cannot be characteristic types in man also.

If a type is understood as a complex of the basic properties of the nervous system, then decision as to how many main types should be recognized and what these types should be will demand a study of the relationship between the individual properties and what combinations of the properties are the most natural, the most "typical". This question must be regarded as virtually unexplored. In the Pavlov classification of types provision is made only for the combination of inertia with strength and balance of the nervous system (phlegmatic type). There is, however, evidence that combination of inertia with imbalance and again with weakness of the nervous system are more common and "typical" phenomena than its combination with strength and balance [63: 96].

Our task is not merely to retain Pavlov's doctrine on types of higher nervous activity and to apply it to man, but to develop this doctrine creatively, recognizing clearly that it is its basic principles that really constitute Pavlov's guiding idea.

---

* In Soviet psychological literature some material on the history of the temperaments problem is to be found in the work of Eres' [13].

We consider it erroneous and harmful, practically, to think that the basic principle of Pavlov's doctrine of types is the recognition of "four types" analogous to the four traditional temperaments (and "intermediate" types between them). It is impossible, by reasoning on these lines, to escape from the circle of purely descriptive "typology". The conceptions on the basic properties of the nervous system, which were intended by Pavlov to be exact physiological conceptions, are converted by such an approach to the problem into several "metaphorical" conceptions, into a means of translating into everyday physiological language the social conceptions, but not scientific psychological conceptions, on the features of man's character. This approach to the question renders the discovery of methods for the objective examination of definite properties of the nervous system, a problem which is very complicated and difficult in its application to man, unnecessary. Any method, whether the collection of anamneses, superficial observation or rapid experiment by some kind of "portable" method, is suitable for the division of people into four types, based, of course, not on the physiological peculiarities of their nervous systems but on the most obvious vital indices or on the indices arrived at in "portable" psychological experiments provisionally accepted as "signs of division". In this approach the conception of type as "a complex of the basic properties of the nervous system" is in fact (irrespective of the intentions of the authors or their references to the principle of the Pavlov classification) replaced by a conception of type as a characteristic "standard pattern" of behaviour, as a typical mode of reaction. Sometimes the conception of type becomes tautological: man's belonging to a certain type is determined on the basis of a single behavioural characteristic which is typical of the individual, and this same characteristic is explained in a quasi physiological way as belonging to that type. Pavlov's conception of types of nervous system is discredited, and investigators who wish to defend the Pavlov view declare the conception of type to be "parasitic" and at variance with the Pavlov principle of determinism (see the paper by D. Zeidenberg-Solomonidis in the progressive French journal, *La Raison* [74]).

With such an approach Pavlov's doctrine on types loses its entire innovatory meaning.

We consider that the basis of principle in this doctrine lies in the discovery of those properties of the nervous system on which a classification of types can be produced. We regard it as essential, therefore, to proceed from "properties" to "types" and not from "types" to "properties".

While completely cognisant of the fact that this is an unusual course and that, far from promising rapid results, it suggests prolonged and difficult work, our collective's immediate aim was nevertheless to study in man the basic properties of the nervous system which might serve as parameters for classification. We did not consider it possible to proceed actively with the investigation of types as "complexes of these properties" until we had made a sufficient advance in the study of the individual pro- perties and the relationships between them.

3

The basic properties of the nervous system are not features or signs of the behaviour or character of man. They cannot be "observed" di- rectly. They must be discovered by special investigation.

What we can observe directly—the "pattern of behaviour" or the "actually occurring nervous activity"—is, in Pavlov's expression, "coal- escence of type features with changes determined by the external medium" [43: III Bk. 2, 334]. Our task was to separate "type features", that is, the basic properties of the nervous system, from this fusion. This was the rationale of our work. This task is, of course, a difficult one. But any task which is truly scientific and not simply descriptive is difficult.

Ivanov-Smolenskii rightly wrote: "While determination of nervous system types in animals is not always easy, in the case of man this task becomes immeasurably more complicated and presents extraordinary difficulties". And a little further on: "We would remind the reader yet again that Pavlov regarded the study of types of higher nervous activity, particularly in man, as a difficult and sometimes even an insurmountably difficult task" [18: 185 and 188] *.

It would of course be utterly wrong to draw pessimistic conclusions from Pavlov's words on the "*as yet almost* insuperable difficulty assoc- iated with determination of types of higher nervous activity" ([43: III, Bk. 2, 269]—my italics—B. T.). On the same page Pavlov also points to the means for "overcoming this difficulty": "the forms of our diag- nostic tests must be multiplied and varied as much as possible". Pavlov reckoned that it would be possible to separate the natural features, the true typological properties, from the "amalgam" by work on these lines.

This statement of Pavlov's has guiding importance for us also in our investigations on the properties of the human nervous system. For man,

* Cases are, unfortunately, not infrequently based on the authority of Ivanov- Smolenskii by those who have regarded the determination of nervous system types in man as a comparatively simple and easy task.

however, an incomparably greater variety of "diagnostic tests" than in
the case of animals is required.

We regard the properties of the nervous system as "natural properties"
but not necessarily as inherited properties; they may be the result of in-
trauterine development or again, of the developmental conditions during
the early period of life. In the context of our subject I have, therefore,
thought it correct to refrain from use of the term "genotype" which would
be a direct indication of the hereditary nature of type properties. In the
just expression used by Voronin in his review of a collection of papers
from our laboratory, the question of the hereditary nature of type properties in the case of man "has still purely theoretical significance" [5: 176].

We cannot, however, agree with Voronin that, while the argument
on the relationship between "genotype" and "phenotype" remains un-
settled, "the investigator should strive after the development of methods
for determining the individual features of the higher nervous activity of
man as it actually exists" and that "the investigator must deal with types
"overgrown" with conditioned connections and must study them just as
they are" [5: 176]. If we follow such a course, we obtain a typology which
operates by the Pavlov parameters of "natural properties" only in words,
but is actually investigating the "amalgam" in which these properties
are "latent" or "masked" by conditioned connections. Inasmuch as we
rejected the conception of "type" as fundamental and took the Pavlov
conception of the natural properties of the nervous system as our basic
conceptions, we thus recognized the groundlessness of a pessimistic attitude
to the possibility of separating these properties from the "amalgam" and
thus cut ourselves off from the path to simple and facile determination
of types "as they actually exist".

The difficult and tedious work of seperating the natural properties
of the nervous system from the "amalgam" is justified by the fact that,
in addition to yielding a description of the individual features in man and
their classification (this can achieved much more simply and much more
rapidly by the study of types "as they actually exist"), it opens up the
way towards an explanation of the origin of certain individual features
and towards the discovery of methods for individual approach to man—
in education in the case of children and adolescents and in the fixing of
the best regimes of work and living in the case of adults.

If we may have recourse to a very remote and coarse analogy, the
analysis of the natural properties of the nervous system can be likened
to a soil analysis. The immediate physiological basis of individual differences in personality is constituted by complex permanent systems of

connexions formed in the process of vital education in the widest sense of the latter word. But both the formation and the functioning of these systems of connections depend essentially on the natural properties of the nervous system, just as the nature of the growth on a particular area of ground depends essentially on the properties of the soil. No plant of any kind can, of course, grow on this area if the seeds of that plant have not fallen there. But the success and nature of the growth will depend in large measure on the properties of the soil. No psychological property can develop if it is not evoked in some way or other by the individual's life. But the effects of life impinge on different nervous systems in different individuals, fall on different "soils". So that to know the final result it is essential to know the properties of the "soil".

Our task is to find means for analysis of the properties of the "soil" and to demonstrate how these properties affect the "growth of the plants". This cannot be replaced by a description of the flora of the area and classification of the vegetational landscapes.

The true basic properties of the nervous system are the strength and mobility of the nervous processes. The third property mentioned by Pavlov—balance—is secondary, a derivative property, for the simple reason that here it is a question of balance in strength or mobility. Unless the strength and mobility of the nervous processes in a particular individual are known, it is impossible to speak in a strictly scientific sense, although not metaphorically or descriptively, of balance or imbalance in his nervous system.

It is now hardly a matter of doubt that there can be disequilibrium in the mobility of the nervous processes as well as in their strengths (Pavlov [43: III, Bk. 2, 268]; [44: III, 150–151]; Kupalov [29: 466–467]; Popesku-Nevianu [47: 64–65]; Rokotova [53]; Teplov [63: 90–91]). The only point in doubt is whether, in the case of disequilibrium in strength, there may be predominance of inhibition over excitation as well as predominance of excitation over inhibition (Pavlov [43: III, Bk. 2, 268 and 273]; Maizel' [34]; Teplov [63: 85–90]).

In the classification of types serious significance should be attached to the sign of disequilibrium—to a greater extent than was done by Pavlov in the last version of his classification of types, in comparison with earlier versions. Having, however, taken as our primary objective the study of the basic properties of the nervous system and not the investigation of types, we must obviously concentrate our attention on the examination of strength and mobility.

The following questions of general fundamental importance arise in connection with these basic properties of the nervous system.

First of all, there is the question of whether each of these properties
is a "single property" or one which, as a result of intensive investigation,
can be "split" into a group of similar properties.

We regard the strength of the nervous system as a "single property",
which is represented mainly by the "efficiency of the cerebral cells" (Pavlov
[43: III, Bk. 2, 344]). Two aspects can be distinguished in this property:
(1) "efficiency in the strict sense", that is, capacity for the prolonged
maintenance of concentrated excitation without exhibition of ultra-boun-
dary (prohibitive) inhibition; and (2) the ability to reveal no prohibitive
inhibition in response to the action of a single but, in the given conditions
(e.g. increased excitability as a result of caffeine administration), excessively strong stimulus. Methods for testing each of these two aspects of
the strength of the nervous system have been elaborated in our laboratory
by Rozhdestvenskaya [52, 51]. We do not yet have sufficient experimental
evidence to say whether the results of tests of these two basic indices of
the strength of the nervous system are always concurrent.

The question of the "complexity" of nervous system mobility, of its
various forms or aspects, was first raised in our laboratory in the work
of Ravich-Shcherbo [50]. An analysis of all the factual evidence and the
theoretical considerations which have been published on the question
of mobility allows of the possible conclusion that in the doctrine of higher
nervous activity the idea of mobility includes all the time characteristics
of the work of the nervous system and all aspects of this work in which
classification by speed can be applied. The indices of mobility, interpreted
in this wide sense may be: (1) the speed of first development of a nervous
process; (2) the speed of movement, irradiation and concentration of
nervous processes; (3) the speed of arrest of nervous processes; (4) the
speed of replacement of inhibition by excitation and of excitation by
inhibition; (5) the speed of formation of new positive and inhibitory conditioned connections; and (6) the speed of reaction change in the external
conditions, e.g. switching of the signal significance of stimuli, change
in the stereotype etc. (see Teplov [63: 60–72]). No systematic comparison
of these indices in the same subjects has as yet been made. Comparison
of the findings of different authors, obtained under different conditions
and on different subjects cannot reveal whether mobility is a single property
or not. This question remains open and can only be decided by experimental investigation.

Secondly, a very important question is that of the relationship between
strength and mobility. It has not, however, been investigated so far. The
importance of this question and the need to consider it in any attempt

to explain discrepancies between the various manifestations of mobility have been justly stressed by two authors who have given detailed critical analyses of our laboratory's published papers, Zimkina [15] and Voronin [5].

Thirdly, there is the question of whether the degree of concentration of the nervous processes and the firmness of connections can be regarded as an "independent" property of the nervous system, along with strength and mobility (see [63: 97–98]). The idea of "concentration" as an independent property belongs to P. S. Kupalov. It was, however, put forward by Kupalov merely as a hypothesis: "We were unable", he wrote, "to find the experimental forms which would enable us to draw any final conclusion" [30: 14]. M. N. Borisova has carried out special investigations in our laboratory on discrimination thresholds and thresholds for fine sensory differentiations which we regard as demonstrative of concentration of nervous processes (unpublished experiments). Even the experiments of this form have still not led to definite solution of the problem of the connection between strength and concentration of nervous processes. The idea of regarding "stability" as an independent property of the nervous system was suggested first by Asratyan and Yakovleva [66]. There is sharp discussion as to whether "stability of connections" is an independent property or one of the manifestations of inertia [63: 73–76]. A. N. Vasilev is now carrying out some experimental work in our laboratory which should introduce some clarity into this complex problem.

Fourthly, it is essential that we raise the question of the correctness of the widely held view on strength and mobility as positive qualities and weakness and inertia as qualities which are negative in all respects. The theoretical formulation of this view has been expressed in emphatic form by Davidenkov [10: 18]. In describing the separate types Pavlov himself expressed a somewhat similar view although, as I have tried to show in my previous papers, the theoretical analyses of the conceptions of weakness and inertia given by Pavlov were opposed to this view.

In psychology this widely held view has led to excessively simplified and actually harmful conceptions of the "possibilities" of individuals with weak or inert nervous systems: the strong type is the "good type" and the weak type is the "bad type", and so on.

We have been guided in our work by the hypothesis that the conceptions of weakness and inertia are not conceptions which are negative in their content (absence of strength or of lability). We postulate that weakness and inertia of the nervous system are properties which have both positive and negative aspects. The considerations which support this hypothesis as a whole have been developed in detail in some of my other papers [62, 63], According to our hypothesis, a weak nervous system is characterized not only by the negative property of a low limit of working capacity, but also by the positive property of high reactivity and, particularly, high sensitivity. The first step towards proof of this hypothesis was the work of Nebylitsyn, who demonstrated an inverse relationship between strength of nervous processes in the visual analyser and absolute visual sensitivity [40]. The positive properties of an inert nervous system are, according to this hypothesis, firmness of connections (unless it is proved that firmness is an independent quality) and more facile formation and maintenance of stereotypes.

We are of the opinion that the two parameters (strength-weakness and lability-inertia) should be regarded, not as two parameters of the degree of perfection of the nervous system, but as parameters which, at their opposite poles, depict qualitatively different means for the establishment of the organism's equilibrium with the medium. The fundamental point is not that all problems are dealt with easily by a strong nervous system, but that the strong nervous system deals with some problems better and the weak nervous system deals better with others, and when the same problem is to be solved the weak and strong nervous systems must approach it in different ways.

It is of interest to note that the two authors who had occasion to express their detailed views on this hypothesis (Zimkina [15] and Voronin [5]) advanced no arguments against it as a whole and gave completely opposite appraisals of its two parts. Voronin did not object to recognition of the weak nervous system, from the psychological and paedagogic standpoints, as a system of different "type" and not of different "level of perfection", but he doubted the advisability of a similar formulation of the problem in the case of inertia of the nervous system. Zimkina considers the positive assessment of the weak type of nervous system doubtful but agrees that "inertia of nervous processes, provided that it does not go beyond certain limits, is a basic, positive and very important property of the nervous system".

This difference of opinion between two competent physiologists is an indication that the material content of our hypothesis must be tested in intensive experimental work. The hypothesis in question suggests the direction that this work should take and offers a number of special subjects for experimental investigations.

Finally, the fifth point is the question of "general" and "special" (partial) properties of the nervous system.

When an individual is noted as having great mobility or strength of nervous processes in the visual region, does it follow that he must necessarily have great mobility or strength of the nervous processes in the auditory or motor region? Analysis of the vital facts led us to formulate the following hypothesis: there are, in addition to the general typological properties characterizing the nervous system as a whole, special (partial) typological properties peculiar to the individual analysers or individual cerebral systems.

This question was raised in relation to the mobility parameter in the investigation of Myasishchev and his group. This author emphasized the absence of any parallelism between "motor mobility" and "mobility of mental processes" and also between "intellectual and emotional mobilities" [38:49]. Popesku-Nevianu obtained experimental evidence which, he considers "proves definitely that there can be considerable differences between the levels of mobility in the general motor and speech motor analysers" [47: 64].

Nebylitsyn has recently carried out some experimental investigations in our laboratory in which he determined the strength of the cortical cells in the visual and auditory analysers by several methods in a small random group of subjects (25 individuals) [41]. The strength characteristics of the visual and auditory analysers were in agreement in 18 subjects (72 per cent) but in the remaining 7 there was discrepancy, sometimes quite marked, between the strength characteristics of the cortical cells in the two analysers.

This is only the first step in a reasonably exact experimental examination of the problem of general and special properties of the nervous system. It affords grounds for the conclusion that in most people (about 75 per cent) the strength of the cortical cells can be regarded as a property equally applicable to the visual and auditory analysers (and possibly to the nervous system as a whole), but that in some the visual and auditory analysers have quite different strength parameters.

4

Strength and mobility are properties of the nervous system and not properties of individuality. These are physiological and not psychological conceptions. Physiologically, they are of single significance, but have multiple significance psychologically. This means that different psychological features of individuality can emerge in the course of development under different conditions of life and education in the presence of a strong (or weak) and mobile (or inert) nervous system.

Yet these conceptions have very real explanatory significance in the psychology of personality or, more accurately, in questions of individual psychological differences in personality. According to the Marxist concept of determinism, external agencies affecting man always act through internal conditions, are always mediated through these internal conditions. This viewpoint has recently been developed in detail by Rubinstein ([56] and more particularly [57]). The inborn properties of the nervous system naturally constitute the most important element in these internal conditions.

I believe that Rubinstein is absolutely right in distinguishing two main aspects in the psychological features of personality, namely, character and capabilities [57]. The separation of these two aspects is effected by psychological, and not physiological, criteria. From this standpoint temperament cannot be regarded as a special, third psychological characteristic of personality. Temperament can only be regarded as a special problem within the problem of character.

At the present time all Soviet psychologists link temperament in one way or another with the typological properties of the nervous system (see Palei and Pshenichnov [45]; Kovalev [22: 9 and 18]; Kovalev and Myasishchev [23: 157]; Levitov [32: 2nd edition, 52]; and others). There are, however, different views on the relationship between temperament and character. Palei and Pshenichnov regard temperament as being independent of character. Levitov pronounces temperament to be outside the limits of character by analysing the relationship between temperament and character in the context of "character and other features of personality". It will be clear from what has been discussed above that a more correct view would appear to be that of Kovalev and Myasishchev, who suggest that "temperament is not something external in the character of man but forms an organic part of its structure" [23: 159]. A detailed discussion of this problem is beyond the scope of this paper.

I must, however, dwell a little on the content of the actual conception of "temperament".

In the development of this question psychologists came face to face with a sharp contradiction. There was in the history of psychology, on the one hand, a very long tradition whereby temperaments were described in terms of definite psychological features (although, incidentally, different authors based their descriptions of temperaments on completely different features). On the other hand Pavlov had in 1927 identified temperaments with types of nervous system, and indeed did this in very categorical form: "We can, with complete justification, transfer the types of nervous system established for dogs, ... to man. It is obvious that these types are what we term temperaments in man. Temperament is a general, over-all characteristic of each individual person, the general basic characteristic of his nervous system, and the latter gives a particular stamp to all the activity of each individual [43: III, Bk. 2, 85].

How are we to "graft" the psychological definition of temperament on to the Pavlov conception of it as type of nervous system, as the most fundamental characteristic of the nervous system? I submit that this problem cannot be solved by any *a priori* theoretical considerations if an attempt is made to base the determination of temperament simultaneously on certain psychological features and certain properties of the nervous system.

The solutions proposed for this problem have often taken quite ingenuous forms.

The chapter on temperaments in my textbook of psychology for middle schools will serve as an example. The following definition of temperament is given in the last (from the 5th to the 8th) editions of this textbook. "The term temperament is applied to the individual peculiarities of the individual as manifested in (1) emotional excitability..., (2) a more or less marked tendency to strong outward expression of feelings.., and (3) rapidity of the movements and general mobility [59: 5th edition, 239]. This definition made it possible to give a more or less balanced and brief description of each of the four traditional temperaments, to give typical "models" for the choleric, the sanguine and so on. But how are we to reconcile this definition with the statement on the next page that the characteristic features of the temperaments are explained by the properties of higher nervous activity which are the basis for the separation of the types of higher nervous activity (strength, balance and mobility)? Indeed, the tendency to powerful outward expression of the feelings and rapidity of movements may be the results of "habit-formation", of training during life, and are not in any way to be explained by properties of the nervous system. On the other hand, why were only "individual features" selected for the definition of temperaments? Surely the properties of the nervous system "give a particular stamp of some kind or other to all the individual's activity".

Very similar answers to this problem are given in the text-books of psychology by Ivanov [12: 343], Yegorov [12: 52], in the first edition of Levitov's book on character [32: 60] and in a number of other works.

A wider definition of temperament was given by those authors who included in it, along with emotional excitability (Kornilov) or simply "psychical excitability" (Yeres'), also "rapidity and strength of psychical processes" (Yeres' [13: 114]; Kornilov [24: 133]). "Rapidity and strength of psychical processes" is, of course, very similar to mobility and strength of nervous processes. But this terminological similarity may lead to error. Rapidity of mental processes is often determined directly by habit, training, skills and by the individual's knowledge in the particular field concerned. The expression "strength in the flow of mental processes" is difficult to understand, and it is even more difficult to correlate its content with the content of the physiological concept of strength of the nervous system.

Rubinstein's definition was an improvement on other psychological definitions: "Temperament is the dynamic depiction of the individual's psychical activity" [54: 656]—an improvement because it is wider in content. Neither, however, did it solve the problem which confronted psychologists after the appearance of Pavlov's conception of the identity of type of nervous system and temperament (or even of the direct dependence on temperament and type of nervous system). The value of the conception, "dynamic characteristic of psychical activity", lies not so much in its positive content as in the fact that it separates temperament from the content of the spiritual life of personality (attitudes to life, ideals, convictions etc.) which is not, of course, connected with temperament (with type of nervous system).

The least vulnerable and most correct in their basic conception are the definitions of temperament in which no description of its psychological characteristics is given and which merely indicate its dependence on type of higher nervous activity such as those of Zaporozhets [14: 175], Leites in the textbook of psychology of 1956 [48: 464] and Anan'ev [1: 45]). In their further explanation of temperaments, however, the authors of such definitions have been compelled to speak of the psychological content of this conception and, consequently, could not escape entirely from the difficulties connected with solution of the problem as formulated earlier. A serious attempt to examine some of these difficulties was made by Palei and Pshenichnov [45]. They were unable, however, to offer a complete answer to this problem—a matter for sympathy rather than blame.

It will be clear from what has been said that the concept of temperament should include the psychological manifestations relating to character and not to abilities, which are determined by the properties of higher nervous activity. It is probably true to say that the inborn character basis is most directly expressed in temperament.

This essentially formal definition of temperament is still, however, very remote from a genuinely psychological definition of temperaments.

If it is taken as a serious conception and not merely as a verbal formula that "temperament is the psychological manifestation of the general type of higher nervous activity (Yakusheva [67])—a view which was accepted by an overwhelming majority of Soviet psychologists as soon as it was put forward—then it is necessary, first, to have means to determine the properties of type and, secondly, to know what the psychological manifestations of the individual properties are, as well as those of types determined by combinations of these properties.

Usually, however, no one worries about this. It is tacitly assumed that these are matters which are self-evident or have been explained by someone at some time or other. Yakusheva, for example, determined temperament in schoolchildren by way of conversations and observations and drew therefrom some far-reaching conclusions on matters of principle concerning variability of temperament. The "diagnosis of temperament" in studies of this nature (they are very many; I have taken Yakusheva's paper merely as an example) are, however, made on the basis of certain psychological traits established by conversations and observations. How does the author know that these traits are actually "psychological manifestations" of the general type of higher nervous activity? The more fact that this question is apparently regarded by many investigators as unnecessary is in itself remarkable.

It is quite possible that the "psychological types" described in works of this kind (i.e. in most works on temperaments) merit full consideration and that their investigation will be quite useful. But what are the grounds for introducing the Pavlov conceptions of the properties of the nervous system types to support them? Would it not be better to do without "verbal" reliance on Pavlov and conduct the analysis on the purely psychological plane?

These doubts apply in even greater degree to many works in which types of higher nervous activity and not temperaments are discussed, but in which these types are determined solely on the basis of "vital indices", that is, more or less complex psychological manifestations of the personality. In these also it is generally assumed to be axiomatic that certain psychological traits are manifestations of the properties of nervous system types.

This does not, of course, mean that all works which in any way concern the properties of nervous system types and have been based on "vital indices" (i.e. by observation, interview, natural experiment etc.) are devoid of scientific significance.

Great attention should be paid to the communications on the "vital indices" of strength, balance and mobility of the nervous system made from their wide clinical experience by the leading workers in the former Pavlov neurological and psychiatric clinics (Birman [4]; Davidenkov [10];

Ivanov-Smolenskii [18]). The papers by these authors on the "vital indices" of the basic properties of the nervous system are reasoned hypotheses of great importance for the direction of experimental research on the subject.

A certain interest attaches to the works of the Leningrad psychologists, carried out under the direction of Samarin, which were based on prolonged observation and to some extent on natural experiment on infants, pre-school and primary school children (Gorbacheva [8] and [9]; Davydova [11]; Samarin [58]). The work of Umanskii [73] is an attempt at the more highly differentiated analysis of the indices of the individual properties of the nervous system in natural experiments with preschool children.

Others as well as myself are of the opinion that the scientific conception of investigations based on vital indices, such as that carried out by Leites [33] in our laboratory, is quite a legitimate one. The purpose of Leites' study was not to *use* certain psychological traits as indices of strength, mobility and balance which had been approved by someone or other at some time, but to *demonstrate* "any psychological features which could be accepted, even if only provisionally and hypothetically, as indices of the basic properties of types of nervous activity" [33: 300]. Such studies can only be built up by prolonged and careful investigation both of the psychological traits of the subjects (in this case school children of the upper forms) and of the details of their life, activity and the history of their development. The conditions required for integration of the psychological features observed as indices of particular typological properties of the nervous system have been analysed by me in greater detail elsewhere [63: 106–107]. At the present time such investigations have the same significance as those of the leaders of the Pavlov clinics mentioned earlier: they are capable of yielding hypotheses for the experimental elucidation of the properties of the nervous system. Their main purpose in the future will be the practical testing of the results of experimental investigations.

Useful in the same sense, too, are certain works in which temperaments or "types" as a whole are not examined, but only separate psychological features in man, which are analysed in relation to the doctrine of typological properties of the nervous system. Such, for example, is the work of Belyayeva-Eksemplyarskaya on individual differences in attention [3].

From the point of view of principle, those works, as yet very few, in which psychological features, as determined from vital indices, are correlated with experimentally determined properties of nervous system types, must be singled out.

Such, for example, is the investigation of Makogonova [35, 36], in which features attaching to the division of attention* were correlated with the indices of balance and mobility of the nervous processes, arrived at by the method of motor reactions with preliminary instructions.

Such also was the work of Il'ina [21], who made an attempt to distinguish in such a character trait as "sociability" what depended on properties of the nervous system (and particularly on mobility) and what did not depend on properties of the nervous system but was determined by the individual's system of relationships. Although the experimental determination of mobility by the skin-galvanic reflex method (on which alone Il'ina relied) cannot be accepted as sufficiently exact, this does not vitiate the fundamental importance of the conception of the study.

At the beginning of this section I mentioned Rubinstein's idea of two aspects in the psychological characterization of personality—character and abilities. Temperament, as the psychological manifestation of the properties of the nervous system, has a direct relationship with the inborn basis of character. On the other hand, the typological properties of the nervous system have a no less close relationship with the natural basis of capabilities, with what is generally termed "gifts".

This idea has been expressed by many Soviet psychologists in the last few years. Rubinstein expressed it in general form in 1952 [55: 226–227]. Myasishchev directed attention to the fact that the property of mobility was connected "in the closest manner" with the conception of capabilities [38: 56]. Some authors, without stressing this conception in its general form, do actually include it among the individual features on which capabilities or the typological properties of the nervous system depend. One of these is Platonov, who includes "features of the strength, mobility and balance of nervous processes" among the "individual psychological features of personality, the aggregate of which constitutes the age capabilities". In the second edition of his book on character, Levitov, in enumerating the "individual inborn features of the nervous system which influence the development of abilities" and "which are termed gifts", cites the features of higher nervous activity which constitute the basis of the Pavlov definition of typological properties of the nervous system [32: 2nd edition, 60].

I have on several occasions put forward the following hypothesis. "If general typological properties determine the temperament of man,

* The criterion in this was the degree of success attained in the work of radio school pupils when there was transition to a rate of receiving which made it necessary to receive a signal and to record the previous signal at the same time.

then particular properties will be of the greatest significance in the study of particular abilities" [63: 102] (see also [61: 41, and 64: 75]). This hypothesis is, however, too restricted. Special (partial) properties are, of course, linked with the problem of special abilities as well as with that of temperament. That much is certain. There are, however, general abilities as well as special. Consequently also, general properties of the nervous system are significant in relation to general abilities as well as in the problem of temperament. Clear confirmation of this is afforded by the work of Leites just mentioned [33]. Although his paper is entitled "An attempt at the psychological definition of Temperaments", the actual material contained in it indicates that there are manifestations of the basic properties of the nervous system—strength, balance and mobility—and typical combinations thereof in the general capabilities for mental work. The three young people described in the paper, who were classified by the author as having a strong balanced and mobile type, a strong unbalanced type and a weak type of nervous system respectively, were from the psychological standpoint examples both of three temperaments and of three qualitatively different "types" of general mental capabilities (and possibly more the latter than the former).

The typological properties of the nervous system enter into the composition of the natural basic elements in the development of capabilities which form part of the so-called "gifts". They may probably even be the most important element in the structure of these natural prerequisites of capabilities.*

Anan'ev has recently advanced theoretical considerations for a common natural basis in the development of character and abilities. In view of the importance of this opinion I take the liberty of citing a complete passage from Anan'ev's paper. "The successful developments that have followed the typology of higher nervous activity created by Pavlov enables us to turn afresh on new grounds to the problem of the connexion between character and aptitudes. It is well known that Pavlov's doctrine on types of higher nervous activity was applied by psychologists primarily for the investigation of character and temperament. The general types of nervous system came to be regarded as the substrate of temperament.

* On this basis, however, it is impossible to identify capabilities, i.e. the mental properties of personality, which are the result of development and education, with typological properties of the nervous system, which are only the natural basis for the development of capabilities. From this standpoint the following proposition which is given in editions 5 to 8 of my textbook of psychology for middle schools is erroneous: "The basic properties of nervous processes are perfected in the process of learning, which means that the corresponding capabilities are developed" [59: 5th edition, 232].

"The question arises whether the typology of higher nervous activity is the physiological basis for individual psychical properties generally, including also aptitudes. The experience accumulated from psychological investigations in the last five years makes it possible to answer this question in the affirmative (investigations of B. M. Teplov and his group). There are now a number of findings which point to a common natural basis for the development of character and aptitudes" [2: 94].

Acceptance of this theory, which we consider to be absolutely correct, presumes recognition of the multiple psychological significance of physiologically simple nervous system properties. Neglect of this latter consideration is one of the main reasons for the oversimplified, somewhat "vulgarized" approach in the application of Pavlov's typology to man, which we criticized earlier.

5

In summing up, I would like to draw attention to some general features which characterize the main trends of our work.

The path we are pursuing is not that of any purely empirical collection of individual psychological differences, a method merely descriptive or, what is worse, based on the quantitative analysis of texts. We would also wish to avoid subjectivism in the description and evaluation of these differences.

We are striving to obtain such information about the individual differences in people which will form some system. We are attempting to put forward hypotheses which can be verified experimentally.

We have chosen the path from the physiology of higher nervous activity to psychology. We do not consider that this is the only possible path, but we are firmly convinced that it is one of the possible paths.

The typological properties of the nervous system, which constitute the natural basis of individual psychological differences in the regions of both character (temperament) and capabilities, constitute the basic material of our research. Our first task (in the logical and not the chronological sense) is to obtain as clear an understanding as possible, in their application to man, of the physiological content of these properties and to find an adequate number of exact experimental methods to make it possible to examine each of these properties. There can be no question, in our opinion, of a single universal method in this field. The correlation of various methods is the approach which we at present consider the most important.

The task that is logically second is the examination of the psychological manifestations of each property separately and of the combinations of these properties that form the "types of nervous system". In practical work this second task should be carried out directly results of any significance have been obtained in the treatment of the first problem. Postponement of this second problem till after the first had been completely settled would be absurd from the standpoint of the basic conception of the work.

Our main line in the treatment of the second problem is from the simple to the complex although we can, by way of reconnaisance activities, make an attempt to apply the facts already ascertained by us (still very few) to the analysis of complex psychological features in the conditions of practical life. Our investigational method should ultimately lead to an understanding of the natural basis on which "psychological types" are built.

We are fully aware of the limits of the field we are investigating. Yet we know that this is an important region both theoretically and practically. We are endeavouring to work in this restricted field by the strictest and most exact methods possible as we are firmly convinced that psychology as a whole can become and indeed is becoming a strict and exact science.

Translated by DR. R. CRAWFORD

REFERENCES

1. ANAN'EV, B. G., (1949). Problema formirovaniya kharaktera (The Problem of Character Formation). Leningrad.
2. ANAN'EV, B. G., (1956). O vzaimosvyazyakh v razvitii sposobnostei i kharaktera, "Doklady na soveshch. po vopr. psikhologii lichnosti (Interconnexions in the Development of Capabilities and Character. Papers Delivered at the Congress on the Psychology of Personality). Moscow.
3. BELYAEVA-EKSEMPLYARSKAYA, S. N., (1957). Nekotorye individual'nye razlichiya vo vnimanii u shkol'nikov. "Materialy soveshch. po psikhologii (1–6 iyulya 1955 g.) (Some Individual Differences in Attention in School-children. Proceedings of Congress on Psychology. 1–6 July 1955). Moscow.
4. BIRMAN, B. N., (1951). Opyt kliniko-fiziologicheskogo opredeleniya tipov vysshei nervnoi deyatel'nosti. (Po materialam nervnoi klinika I. P. Pavlova). Zh. vyssh, nervn. deyat. 1: No. 6,
5. VORONIN, L. G., (1957). Za razvitiye obshchikh usilii fiziologov i psikhologov. (O sbornike "Tipologicheskiye osobennosti vyssh. nervn. deyat. cheloveka"). Vopr. psikhologii No. 1.
6. HÖFDING, G., (1914). Ocherk psikhologii, osnovannoi na opyte (Outline of Experimental Psychology). 6th Russian edition.
7. HIPPOCRATES, (1936). Selected Books (translation of V. I. Rudnev). Biomedgiz.
8. GORBACHEVA, V. A., (1954). Opyt izucheniya individual'no-tipicheskikh osobennostei detei trëkhletnego vozrasta (An Attempt at the Investigation of Individual Typical Features in Children of Three Years). *Izv. Akad. Ped. Nauk R.S.F.S.R.*, No. 52.
9. GORBACHEVA, V. A., (1954). Formirovaniye povedeniya detei v mladshei gruppe detskogo sada. *Izv. Akad. Ped. Nauk R.S.F.S.R.* No. 52, (Formulation of Behaviour in Young Kindergarten Children).

10. DAVIDENKOV, S. N., (1947). Evolyutsionno-geneticheskiye problemy v nevropatologii (Evolutionary Genetics Problems in Neuropathology). Leningrad.
11. DAVYDOVA, A. N., (1954). Opyt monograficheskogo izucheniya detei s chertami raznykh tipov nervnoi sistemy (Attempt at a Monographic Study of Children with Features of Different Types of Nervous Systems). *Izv. Akad. Ped. Nauk R.S.F.S.R.*, No. 52.
12. YEGOROV, T. G., (1955). Psikhologiya (Psychology). 2nd edition. Voyenizdat.
13. ERES', E. P., (1939). Issledovaniye temperamentov shkol'nikov. "Uch. zap. kaf. psikhologii Mos. gos. ped. inst. (Examination of the Temperaments of School-children. Scientific Papers of the Dept. of Psychology, Moscow Paedagogic Inst.). No. 1.
14. ZAPOROZHETS, A. V., (1953) Psikhologiya, Uchebnoye posobiye dlya doshkol'nykh ped. uchilishch (Psychology. A Textbook for Preschool Educational Institutions).
15. ZIMKINA, A. M., (1951). O tipologicheskikh osobennostyakh vyssh. nervn. deyat. cheloveka (Typological Features of the Higher Nervous Activity of Man). *Vopr. psikhol.* No. 1.
16. IVANOV, P. I., (1954). Psikhologiya (Psychology). Uchpedgiz.
17. IVANOV-SMOLENSKII, A. G., (1933). Osnovnye ustanovki i zadachi fiziologii i patofiziologii vyssh. nervn. deyat. rebënka v oblasti O.Z.Dn.P., sb. "Eksperimental'nye issledovaniya nervnoi deyatel'nosti rebënka (Status of and Problems in the Physiology and Pathophysiology of the Higher Nervous Activity of the Child in the Region O.Z.Dn.P. In a Collection "Experimental Investigations on the Nervous Activity of the Child".
18. IVANOV-SMOLENSKII, A. G., (1952). Ocherki patofiziologii vyssh. nervn. deyat. (Outline of the Pathophysiology of Higher Nervous Activity). 2nd Ed., Medgiz.
19. IVANOV-SMOLENSKII, A. G., (1952). *Zh. vyssh. nervn. deyat.* 2: No. 5.
20. IVANOV-SMOLENSKII, A. G., (1953). *Zh. vyssh. nervn. deyat.* 3: No. 1.
21. IL'INA, A. I., (1956). Nekotorye osobennosti proyavleniya obshchitel'nosti u shkol'-nikov v zavisimosti ot podvizhnosti nervnykh protsessov. "Dokl. na soveshch. po vopr. psikhologii lichnosti (Some Features in the Manifestations of Sociability in Schoolchildren in Relation to the Mobility of Their Nervous Processes. Papers Delivered at Congress on the Psychology of Personality). Moscow, 1956.
22. KOVALËV, A. G., (1953). *Uch. zap. L.G.U.*, No. 147.
23. KOVALËV, A. G., and MYASISHCHEV. V, N., (1957). Psikhicheskiye osobennosti cheloveka (Psychical Features of Man). Vol. 1 of Character. L.G.U. Press.
24. KORNILOV, K. N., (1946). Psikhologiya. Uchebnik dlya srednei shkoly (Psychology. A Textbook for Middle Schools).
25. KOTLYAREVSKII, L. I., (1933). Orientirovochno-issledovatel'skiye uslovnye re-fleksy na prostye i sinteticheskiye razdrazhiteli u detei shkol'nogo vozrasta, sb. "Eksperimental'nye issledovaniya vyssh. nervn. deyat. rebënka" (Orienting-investigatory Conditioned Reflexes to Simple and Composite Stimuli in Children of School Age. Collection "Experimental Research on the Higher Nervous Activity of the Child).
26. KRASNOGORSKII, N. I., (1939). Razvitiye ucheniya o fiziol. deyatel'nosti mozga u detei (Development of the Study of the Physiological Activity of the Brain in Children). Leningrad.
27. KRASNOGORSKII, N. I., (1953). *Zh. vyssh. nervn. deyat.* 3: No. 2.

28. KRUTETSKII, V. A. and EL'KONIN, D. B., (1956). *Vopr. psikhol.* No. 4.
29. KUPALOV, P. S., (1952). *Zh. vyssh. nervn. deyat.* 2: No. 4.
30. KUPALOV, P. S., (1954). *Zh. vyssh. nervn. deyat.* 4: No. 1.
31. LANG-BELONOGOVA, N. S. and KOK, E. P., (1952). *Trud. Inst. fiziol. im.* Pavlova 1.
32. LEVITOV, N. D., (1952-6). Voprosy psikhologii kharaktera (The Psychology of Character). 1st Ed., 1952; 2nd Ed. 1956.
33. LEITES, N. S., (1956). Opyt psikhologicheskoi kharakteristiki temperamentov, sb. "Tipologicheskiye osobennosti vyssh. nervn. deyat. cheloveka (Attempt at the Psychological Definition of Temperaments. In Collection: Typological Features of the Higher Nervous Activity of Man). Moscow.
34. MAIZEL', N. I., (1956). Issledovaniye tipologicheskikh razlichii po uravnoveshennosti protsessov vozbuzhdeniya i tormozheniya metodikoi fotokhimicheskogo uslovnogo refleksa (Investigation of the Typological Differences in Balance of the Processes of Excitation and Inhibition by a Photochemical Conditioned Reflex Method).
35. MAKOGONOVA, A. A., (1954). Raspredeleniye vnimaniya v svyazi s osobennosti nervnoi deyatel'nosti (Division of the Attention in Relation to the Features of Nervous Activity). Moscow.
36. MAKOGONOVA, A. A., (1951). Division of Attention in Radio Operators in Connexion with Typological Features of Higher Nervous Activity (Papers at a Congress on Psychology, 1-6 July 1955). Moscow.
37. MEIMAN, E., (1917). Intelligence and Will. Russian translation.
38. MYASISHCHEV, V. N., (1954). *Uch. zap. L.G.U.* No. 184.
39. MYASISHCHEV, V. N., (1955). *Uch. zap. L.G.U.* No. 203.
40. NEBYLITSYN, V. D., (1956). The Relationship between Sensitivity and the Strength of the Nervous System. In the Collection Typological Features of the Higher Nervous Activity of Man. Moscow.
41. NEBYLITSYN, V. D., (1957). Individual Differences as Revealed by the Strength-Sensitivity Parameter in the Visual and Auditory Analysers. Vopr. psikhologii No. 4.
42. NOVIKOVA, A. A., (1930). Conditioned Inhibition and its Typological Features in Children of School Age. In Collection: The Systematic Investigation of Conditioned Reflex Activity in Children. Moscow-Leningrad.
43. PAVLOV, I. P., (1951-2). *Poln. sobr. soch.* (Complete Works).
44. PAVLOV'S Wednesdays, 1949.
45. PALEI, I. M. and PSHENICHNOV, V. V., (1955). *Vopr. psikhol.* No. 5.
47. POPESKU-NEVIANU, P. G., (1954). *Uch. zap. L.G.U.* No. 185.
48. SMIRNOV, A. A., LEONT'EV, A. N., RUBINSTEIN, S. L. and TEPLOV, B. M., (1956). Psychology. A Textbook for Paedagogic Institutes.
49. PEN, R. M., (1933). Typological Features of Reflex Activity in Children. In Collection: Experimental Investigation of the Higher Nervous Activity of Children.
50. RAVICH-SHCHERBO, I. V., (1956). Investigation of Typological Differences in Mobility of Nervous Processes in the Visual Analyser. In Collection: Typological Features of the Higher Nervous Activity of Man. Moscow.
51. ROZHDESTVENSKAYA, V. I., (1957). Ergographic Method of Determining the Strength of Excitation Processes in Man. Scientific Papers of R.S.F.S.R. Acad. Paed. Sciences No. 1.
52. ROZHDESTVENSKAYA, V. I., (1957). Determination of the Strength of the Cortical Cells from their Capacity for Prolonged Maintenance of Concentrated Excitation. Scientific Papers of R.S.F.S.R. Acad. Paed. Sciences. No. 3.

53. ROKOTOVA, N. A., (1954). *Fiziol. Zh.* SSSR 40: No. 6.
54. RUBINSTEIN, S. L., (1946). Principles of General Psychology. Moscow.
55. RUBINSTEIN, S. L., (1952). The Pavlov doctrine and Problems of Psychology. In the Collection: The Pavlov Doctrine and Philosophical Problems of Psychology. Moscow.
56. RUBINSTEIN, S. L., (1955). *Vopr. psikholog.* No. 1.
57. RUBINSTEIN, S. L., (1957). *Vopr. psikholog.* No. 3.
58. SAMARIN, Y. A., (1954). *Izv. Akad. Ped. Nauk R.S.F.S.R.* No. 52.
59. TEPLOV, B. M., (1946–1954). Psychology. A Textbook for Middle Schools. Editions 1–8.
60. TEPLOV, B. M., (1954). An Attempt at the Development of Methods for the Investigation of Typological Differences in the Higher Nervous Activity of Man. Papers at Congress on Psychology (3–8 July 1953). Moscow.
61. TEPLOV, B. M., (1955). *Vopr. psikholog.* No. 1.
62. TEPLOV, B. M., (1955). *Vopr. psikholog.* No. 6.
63. TEPLOV, B. M., (1956). Some Problems in the Investigation of General Types of Higher Nervous Activity in Man and Animals. In Collection: Typological Features of the Higher Nervous Activity of Man. Moscow.
64. TEPLOV, B. M., and LEITES, N. S. (1956). On Individual Psychological Differences. Papers at a Congress on the Psychology of Personality. Moscow.
65. CHERNORUTSKII, M. V., (1933). *Zh. vyssh. nervn deyat.* 3: No. 1.
66. YAKOVLEVA, V. V., (1944). *Trud. fiziol. labor. im. Pavlova.* 11: a
67. YAKUSHEVA, T. G., (1956). *Vopr. psikholog.* No. 4,.
68. ACH, N., (1910). Über den Willensakt und das Temperament.
69. SIEBECK, H., (1884). Geschichte der Psychologie. Pt. 1, Section 2,.
70. SPEARMAN, C., (1927). The Abilities of Man. London,.
71. STERN, W., (1911). Die differenzielle Psychologie.
72. TEPLOV, B. M, (1957). Les différences psychologiques individuelles et les propriétés typologiques du système nerveux. *J. de Psychologie* No. 2.
73. UMANSKII, L. I., (1958). An Experimental Study of the Typological Features of the Nervous System in Children (as Revealed in Games). Vopr. psikholog. No. 1.
74. ZEIDENBERG-SOLOMONIDIS, D., (1956). *La Raison,* 14.

INDIVIDUAL DIFFERENCES IN THE STRENGTH AND SENSITIVITY OF BOTH VISUAL AND AUDITORY ANALYSERS *

V. D. NEBYLITSYN

Institute of Psychology, Academy of Paedagogical Sciences of the R.S.F.S.R., Moscow.

THE problem of functional differences between analysers (or, in another rather narrower śense, this particular typological property) is among those problems which have had least work devoted to them, either on the physiological or the psychological side. Questions in both these sciences can probably not be satisfactorily solved without proper account being taken of this factor. In general form these questions may be formulated as the problem of the success of different ways of adjusting to environment, or as the problem of special abilities, types of ideas, and so on. In addition, there is the question of the interaction of the sense organs.

The theoretical and practical importance of the problem of differences between analysers is beyond doubt. The attention accorded it by both physiologists and psychologists, however, is quite insufficient.

Worthy of particular attention are the works of E. G. Vatsuro and his fellow-workers, who were concerned with the fact that different levels of the typological parameter of the mobility of perception may be present in different analysers of one and the same animal. Thus it was found [5] that in the chimpanzee nervous processes in the kinaesthetic analyser are much more mobile than in the visual, evidence of this being provided by the considerably greater speed of formation of a temporary connection in the kinaesthetic analyser as against one in the optic analyser. In an investigation carried out with dogs E. G. Vatsuro and M. S. Kolesnikov [5,8] reach the conclusion that there is a greater ability for processes taking place in the acoustic analyser of these animals than for those in the visual analyser. In an analogous investigation made with monkeys [6] a reverse relationship was shown: the lability of processes in the visual analyser in monkeys proved to be lower than that for the auditory analyser.

* *Voprosy psikhologii*, No. 4, pp. 53–69, 1957.

On the basis of all these observations E. G. Vatsuro [7] formulated a thesis of "leading afferentation", to the effect that the different analysers play a varying role in the organisation of an animal's behaviour, depending upon the perfecting of their functional properties.

Differences between the analysers in respect of the mobility of the nervous processes is thus a well established fact in the case of certain animals. It should be noted, however, that these differences which are common to the whole species, represent peculiarities of the species as a whole. They are apparently determined in their phylogenesis by the nature of the role assumed by each analyser in the adaptation of the organism to the environment. Despite this uniformity one must still suppose that individual deviations are possible, and that in man, because of the boundless variety of his spheres of activity, such deviations become the norm. B. M. Teplov especially stresses this qualitative difference between man and the animals: "What in animals was the characteristic of a species became in man the characteristic of an individual. Herein lies one of the features peculiar to man. "Leading afferentation" must come out especially sharply in those people whose main occupation favours the development of a comparative dominance of the first signalling system—musicians, painters, sportsmen, etc." [23; 101].

The possibility of just such individual differences between the general-motor and speech-motor analysers is mentioned in a paper by P. G. Popescu-Nevianu [16]. The investigation was carried out with human beings and the results yielded by various methods were considered in terms of individual differences. So far as the question of partial differences on other typological parameters is concerned, the data in the literature are too insignificant for any definite conclusions to be drawn.

Only in one paper by E. G. Vatsuro [7], was leading afferentation observed. In lower apes an imbalance in the direction of dominance of excititation in the acoustic analyser as compared to the visual was noted. E. G. Vatsuro and M. S. Kolesnikov [8] elsewhere comment, on differences which they discovered in the working capacity of cortical elements of the optic and acoustic analyser (the latter having the advantage), and on a correspondingly different tolerance to caffeine in these analysers.

These data speak for the possibility of differences between analysers in the level of the strength of the cortical cells.

While being extremely limited in quantity, the physiological material just adduced does nevertheless provide evidence of the possibility of variation in typological parameters when different analysers are compared.

The different analyser systems of one and the same individual may possess different degrees of perfection of the same physiological properties.

What data are there on the question of differences between analysers in studies made in the psychophysiology of the sensory organs. that is with the basic characteristics of the analyser as a mechanism for the reception of external effects, its sensitivity and excitability?

There can be at least two approaches to the study of this problem of differences between the analysers in their sensitivity. One of these approaches is as follows.

It is known that the threshold sensitivity of any sensory system is not a strictly constant quantity. Being subjected to the action of a number of external and internal factors, it varies continually and for the most part without any definite rhythm, around some mean figure [12, 21, 30]. Is the direction and the quantity of these variations common to, and identical for, all the analysers at any given moment, or is the character of the changes individual for each of the afferent systems? Does the nervous system here function as one single formation, or does each analyser represent to some degree a separate system *in this respect*? The problem of the correlation in the fluctuations of thresholds was subjected to detailéd study in a work by M. Wertheimer [30] which compared the results of change in auditory and visual sensitivity over the same periods of time. The author, while taking the stand that the changes in sensitivity ought to coincide, inasmuch as "the organism functions as a whole", finds an absence of any clear correlation between the fluctuations in the sensitivity of these two sensory organs. This conclusion finds confirmation in the data of other authors also to whom Wertheimer refers, e.g. Crozier's work on the relationship between keenness of vision and absolute visual sensitivity or Goodfellow's on the relationship of auditory and vibratory sensations; and Wertheimer and Ward on the relationship of pain and sound thresholds.

The conclusion which may be drawn from all this is that the different analysers can, it would appear, function "separately" to some extent. They can have functional characteristics which are to a certain degree independent. What remains open is only the question of what gives rise to the fluctuations in the thresholds—variations in excitability of the periphery of the analyser, i.e. of its receptor section, or variations in excitability of its cortical terminal. Wertheimer, on the ground of this same fact of non-coincidence of changes in sensitivity in the different modalities, sees as the cause of these changes the processes taking place in the receptor. He considers that the cortex of the large hemispheres, if not the entire organism, "acts as a whole". We shall however adduce data below which in our view provide evidence of the possibility of qualitative differentiation of reaction being proper to the cortical sections of the analysers also.

Another possible approach to study of the problem of differences between analysers in sensitivity level finds its basis in the following considerations.

It is known that the visual and auditory analysers, considering these two analysers only, have approximately identical threshold characteristics. Thus, on the data of P. Rives [29], the threshold energy for a point of white light is 1.95×10^{-9} erg/sec, and on the data of N. I. Pinegin [15], for blue rays the threshold energy is 3.22×10^{-9} erg/sec. Very much the same figures are characteristic of the threshold excitability of the auditory analyser: for a frequency of 1000 c/s the amount of the threshold is expressed by a figure of 2.45×10^{-9} erg/sec. These figures, however, are only averages, which do not take into account the individual variations in one or the other direction which are present in actuality. And these individual differences in the thresholds of excitability of any analyser are exceedingly wide. Within the limits of normality the excitability of an analyser can be scores of times greater or less in different people. Thus according to S. I. Vavilov [4] the absolute sensitivity of the visual analyser varies for different persons between two and some tens of quanta. This is confirmed in the experiments of N. I. Pinegin [15], who with 8 subjects obtained limits of variation from 3.05×10^{-10} erg/sec to 6.71×10^{-9} erg/sec, the upper figure thus being approximately 22 times greater than the lower limit. On the data of B. Ye. Sheivekhman and others [27, 28]—data obtained by examination of 2000 persons—the extent of individual variations on a frequency of 1000 c/s is about 30 db, the upper figure here being about 30 times greater than the lower.

The question naturally arises: if great individual differences in thresholds are a fact, do they then march parallel for the various analysers, or can they, like the variously directed fluctuations of absolute thresholds, move in opposite directions? Here we have the very question of differences in sensitivity between analysers of these differences we are attempting to elucidate.

Unfortunately, we found no clear answer to this question in the literature. There are only isolated remarks by some authors which would seem to admit the possibility of variations in the level of the basic analyser function. At the same time, the solution of the problem does not in fact call for complicated facilities for registering the amounts of thresholds in objective physical units. It is sufficient to obtain from a certain number of subjects a series of values—even though these may be quite relative—for the sensitivity of one analyser, and another series for another analyser, and then to calculate the coefficient of correlation even if this is only a rank correlation between the two series. The sign and amount of the coefficient will show the degree of uniformity between the functional indices of the two analysers.

This work has been done by us, and we shall consider its results below.

To sum up all that has been said on the question of differences between analysers in the amount of absolute thresholds, it may be noted that: although the mean group figures for sensitivity of hearing and rod vision in general coincide, there are considerable individual differences in this respect. There are grounds for thinking that these differences may take different directions and consequently create the possibility of individual differences between analysers. We have not, however, got experimental data on this question at our disposal.

There is one more aspect of the problem of differences between analysers—the psychological aspect—which does not require detailed analysis inasmuch as the relevant facts are sufficiently well known. We have in mind the existence, constantly remarked on in works on psychology, of individual peculiarities of memory, in particular the memory types—visual, aural, motor, and mixed which in many ways determine peculiarities in memorising—we have also some differences in the character of ideas (their type, structure, stability etc.); peculiarities of creative imagination, and so on; in a word, much of what in practice is described, with some justification, by the word "abilities". The problem of "special gifts" too, understood as meaning primarily the question of innate peculiarities in the structure and functioning of the nervous system, clearly stands in direct relationship to the problem of differences between analysers, or at least between different functional systems of the cortex. "If general typological properties" writes B. M. Teplov, "determine a man's temperament, then particular properties are of the greatest importance in the study of special abilities" [23, 102]. All these and many other psychological phenomena still remain enigmatic so far as what conditions them physiologically. All the more important and interesting, then, appears the task of approaching, even if in an exploratory and crude way, the study of their possible physiological foundations.

The present paper gives an exposition of materials obtained in the course of an experimental check of the hypothesis advanced by B. M. Teplov on the mutual connection of sensitivity and strength of the nervous system [23, 13]. As soon as the presence of a two-way dependence between these two relative constants of the nervous system was established in work with stimuli affecting the visual analyser, an analogous work was started on the study of this relationship in the auditory analyser. Here we encountered facts which cannot be assessed other than as evidence of the possibility of a "divorce" between analysers in respect of their basic functional characteristics.

TECHNIQUE USED IN THE INVESTIGATION

Determination of Sensitivity

Visual sensitivity was measured by us by means of an adaptometer working on S. V. Kravkov's system, after dark adaption for 45 min. At the signal "Attention!" the subject fixed his eyes (binocular vision) on a shining red point and noted the appearance and disappearance of a round white patch lying 10 deg to the right of the fixation point. Measurements were made at two minute intervals and continued for 20–40 min, depending upon the speed with which the subject attained uniformity and stability or recorded reaction.

The experiments for determination of aural sensitivity were made with the help of a ZG–10 sound generator in a room relatively insulated from external noise. Sound at a frequency of 1000 c/s was transmitted (binaurally) through the headphones of a flying helmet worn by the subject. By smoothly turning the alternating resistance handle the tension at the output end of the generator was regulated and this regulated the level of sound pressure in the auditory canal. The subject noted the moments of appearance and disappearance of the sound, and the mean between these values was taken as the figure for sensitivity.

25 persons, mainly students, took part in the experiments for determination of sensitivity and in those now to be described for the determination of the strength of the cortical cells.

DETERMINATION OF STRENGTH OF CORTICAL CELLS

In order to judge the strength of the cortical cells of an analyser we used three main experimental techniques.

The first of these is as follows.

By means of an adaptometer system slightly different from that usually used (a white light point stimulus, the "test point", being below the fixation point) a preliminary measurement was made of the light sensitivity of binocular peripheric vision. In the course of the succeeding 3–4 experiments

measurement of thresholds was made in the presence of an additional
stimulus — a further point of white light lying below the second, at an
angular distance from it of 45′. The minimum brightness of this third
point was 0·6 of the threshold brightness, and its maximum brightness
160 times that of the threshold. The presence of this point even as a subliminal stimulus, led, owing to the rules governing induction which have
been demonstrated by B. M. Teplov [22], to a change in sensitivity in
relation to the "test point". The change in the thresholds dependent upon
the intensity of the additional point stimulus is recorded in Figs. 1–3 (1a)
as a continuous curve.

In the course of the succeeding three experiments the subjects were
given caffeine in doses of 0·05 g, 0·1 g and 0·3 g, administered in solution
15 min before the beginning of the measurements. The effect of the caffeine
is a function of the dose administered and of the degree of weakness of the
nervous system. General cortical excitation evoked by the caffeine is summated with excitation from the third (or "further") stimulus point, this
latter acting as an "induction stimulus". Variations in this summated
excitation lead to variations in change in sensitivity to the second (or
"test") point. The curves of change in the thresholds thus obtained are
indicated in Figs. 1–3 (1a). The variations in the form of these "caffeine
curves" are here the main index of the strength of the cortical cells.

In some subjects the form of the curve under the influence of caffeine
does not change; we can therefore postulate an absence of influence of
caffeine upon the cortex, and therefore assume a high degree of strength
of the cortical cells. In this case all four curves (the original one and three
"caffeine" curves) approximately coincide (Fig. 2a).

In other subjects caffeine even in small doses (0·05 g) evokes a diminu-
tion in the irradiation effect and a heightening of the concentration effect
of the stimulation process, apparently by reason of the summation of
excitations. This is expressed in a lowering of sensitivity to the test point
owing to increased negative induction. The curve, dotted in the figure,
shifts downwards.

The effect of a medium dose (0·1 g) proves even more considerable
in the case of these subjects. Following such a dose, strong secondary
stimuli evoke not negative induction but irradiation of the excitation
process. Apparently under the influence of this dose the summated excitation at the focus of the additional stimulus (in the case of this being
of great intensity) becomes too strong and therefore irradiates. This is expressed on the graphs in a characteristic upward bend of the appropriate
curve to the zero line or even above it (Fig. 1a).

A particularly striking effect is produced with subjects of this group when they are given the maximum dose (0·3 g) of caffeine, which appears to evoke so great a tension of the stimulation process in the cortex that the foci of excitation from all additional stimuli even subliminal ones, combining with it, become too strong and lead to irradiation alone and consequently to a heightening of sensitivity. For this reason the curve for this experiment is flattened out in a singular manner and lies completely above zero (Fig. 1a).

The subjects in whose case the form of the curve exhibits these characteristic changes under the influence of caffeine, are said to have weak cells in the visual sector of the cortex of the large hemispheres.

The results of the caffeine test are thus a basic index of strength when this technique is employed.

Besides the influence of caffeine, an index of strength can here be provided by the original curve, whose form varies with different subjects. With persons possessing strong cells in the visual analyser very little irradiation action of weak secondary stimuli—or even none at all—is observed. On the other hand negative induction from strong stimuli is very marked in these cases; almost the whole, or sometimes the whole, curve lies below the zero ordinate (Fig. 2a). In the case of persons having weak cells of the visual sector there is marked irradiation from weak secondary stimuli, whereas the action of negative induction is not very marked and is only present when the secondary stimuli are sufficiently strong. The curve of the experiment, or that part of it which expresses the action of weak additional stimuli, is usually above the abscissa* in the case of these subjects (see Fig. 1).

"Extinction with reinforcement"—the second of the techniques employed by us—was also elaborated by V. I. Rozhdestvenskaya in relation to the photochemical reflex in man [20]. By means of combining a sound stimulus (pure tone) and a reinforcement (general illumination of both eyes, evoking a lowering of sensitivity by 40–80 per cent) a conditioned reflex is elaborated in the subject, the reflex being shown in the fact that application of the sound stimulus alone will of itself evoke a lowering of sensitivity (by 20–40 per cent). After the reflex is stabilized there follows a test for "extinction with reinforcement". The conditioned reflex is tested, then ten combinations of the conditional and unconditional stimuli are given with a two-minute interval between them. The length of the interval

* This technique for determining the strength of the cortical cells of the visual analyser was first described in detail by V. I. Rozhdestvenskaya (19).

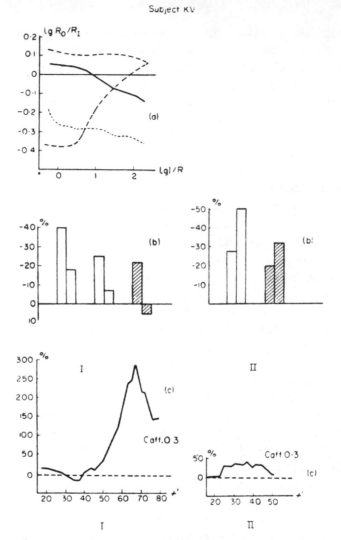

FIG. 1. Results of investigation of strength of cortical cells of one of the subjects showing differences in strength between the auditory and visual analysers:

I—visual analyser; II—auditory analyser:

(a) Results of testing by "induction" technique. Abscissae—intensity of secondary stimulus in threshold units; ordinates—relation of sensitivity when secondary stimulus present to sensitivity when the latter absent. _____ original curve; .... dose 0·05 g; — — — dose 0·1 g; —.—.—.—. dose 0·3 g;

(b) Results of testing by "extinguishing with reinforcement" technique. Ordinates — amount of conditioned reflex as a percentage; left column—after extinguishing; shaded columns—results of experiment using caffeine;

(c) Influence of caffeine on absolute thresholds. Abscissae—time in min; ordinates—change in sensitivity as a percentage of the background.

in ordinary experiments is 4–6 min. After restoration of sensitivity to the background level, or if this is not arrived at, after some stable figure is reached, the conditioned reflex is again tested. The fall-off in the conditioned reflex effect as compared with the amount of the conditioned reaction as measured before the start of the extinguishing process, serves as an index of the weakness of the cortical cells, and preservation or even heightening of the reflex as an index of a greater or lesser degree of their strength.

In additional experiments the subjects were given caffeine in 0·2 g doses. This helped to bring out even more sharply the differences in the strength of the cells.

The results of comparing data obtained by this method with data from other techniques gave grounds for believing that the variant of the technique in which a conditional sound stimulus is used gives a characteristic of the strength of the auditory analyser, which we shall deal with in detail later. For this reason we altered this technique for the purpose of determining the strength of the cortical cells of the visual analyser, using as a conditional stimulus not sound, but a light stimulus, of red light (which does not disadapt the rods of the retina)*. Otherwise the method remained exactly as described above.

A third method of testing the strength of the cortical cells, one which had yielded satisfactory results in a preceding work [13], is very simple; it consists simply of registration of changes in absolute sensitivity of the analyser under the influence of varying doses of caffeine.

The experiments using this technique were organised as follows. After one or two training experiments for determination and stabilisation of thresholds, experiments were begun in which the subjects were given caffeine in the same doses as in the experiments using the first, "induction", technique (0·05 g, 0·1 g, 0·3 g). In each of these experiments, after determination of "background" sensitivity, the subject was given the appropriate dose of caffeine. After a 20-minute interval the experiment was continued for 30–50 minutes. The figures characterising sensitivity after taking caffeine were then compared with the original background figures.

In the first stages of the work the index of strength under this method was provided by the individual variations in the amounts of changes in absolute sensitivity after ingestion of caffeine. In subjects with strong analyser cells sensitivity changes by not more than 30–40 per cent, and

* The possibility of elaborating a conditioned photochemical reflex to a visual stimulus was first demonstrated by I. V. Ravich-Shcherbo (17), and later used in the work of E. A. Golubeva (9).

often does not change at all, whereas in subjects with weak cells sensitivity may increase by 200–300 per cent above the background level. Subsequently it transpired that one may take as an index of weakness of the cells not only the amount of the changes in the absolute thresholds, but their direction also, whether an increase of sensitivity, or a decrease.

The latter is frequently observed in subjects with weak analyser cells, and never in the case of subjects "strong" in the visual analyser. It also appeared that in the auditory analyser no cases of considerable increase in sensitivity under the influence of caffeine were observed. Instead of this, persons "weak" in the auditory analyser react to caffeine most often by a lowering of auditory sensitivity, whereas subjects "strong" in the auditory analyser show a reaction consisting of a slight heightening in sensitivity of the order of 40 per cent. This is similar to the case of those "strong" in the visual analyser.

Thus the index of strength under this technique is provided by the individual variations in the value and direction of changes in sensitivity under the influence of varying doses of caffeine.

We have described three methods of investigating the strength of the cortical cells; they all refer to different aspects of the activity of the sensory sectors of the cortex. In each case what is being tested is some specific quality of the work of the cortical cells. Nevertheless all three techniques have at least one feature in common. When they are applied, the cells receiving an impulse are working under exceptional conditions—conditions of overloading or overstrain. It is owing to this common feature in the methods described that comparison of their results shows, with isolated exceptions, a coincidence of results when these refer to one and the same analyser. This, we believe, is evidence of their comparability of value for the purpose for which they were used.

RESULTS OF THE INVESTIGATIONS

The study of differences in strength and sensitivity between analysers was not the original object of our work. We were obliged to concern ourselves with it only when, having established experimentally the existence of a two-way dependence between sensitivity and strength in the visual analyser, we proceeded to study the working out of this interconnection in the field of auditory function. The first fact to emerge here was the complete lack of coincidence between the rankings of the subjects for visual sensitivity and for auditory acuity. This means that low thresholds of rod vision may be associated with high auditory thresholds, and high auditory sensitivity with low absolute sensitivity of the eye. This is the case. Calculation shows that the Spearman rank correlation coefficient for 25 subjects is no higher than 0·263. We see that there is a practical absence of correlation between the ranks of indices of sensitivity of the two analysers, as will be confirmed by a glance at Table 1.

But if we take as established the thesis of the existence of differences between analysers in level of sensitivity, we must, in accordance with our basic hypothesis, also admit the possibility of corresponding differences between analysers in their degree of strength, i.e. admit the existence of strength as a partial typological property, characterising the functional stability or working capacity, not of the cortex of the large hemispheres as a whole, but of separate regions of it, in the given case—of separate analysers.

TABLE 1. *Comparison of ranks on visual and auditory sensitivity*

Subjects	Visual analysers		Auditory analyser	
	Grading	sensitivity	sensitivity	grading
S. T.	1	24·5	129·4	8·5
K. V.	2	22·1	63·0	24
K. N.	3	15·9	201·2	2
K. L.	4·5	15·0	116·7	11
P. R.	4·5	15·0	107·4	12·5
Y. Y.	6	13·4	179·9	5·5
K. G.	7	12·7	184·5	4
L. R.	8	11·5	102·6	14·5
M. S.	9	10·9	82·2	19
R. Zh.	11	8·9	70·2	21
S.M.	11	8·9	197·6	3
Sh. B.	11	8·9	167·2	7
B. T.	13	8·5	82·2	19
V. T.	14	8·1	92·6	17
M. A.	15·5	6·7	179·9	5·5
A. V.	15·5	6·7	102·6	14·5
K. Y.	18	6·3	61·8	25
K. A.	18	6·3	107·4	12·5
Ch. I.	18	6·3	270·0	1
Z. A.	20·5	5·6	97·1	16
R. Z.	20·5	5·6	121·4	10
K. O.	22	5·3	64·3	23
B. L.	23	4·8	82·2	19
G. Y.	24	4·4	65·4	22
B. S.	25	3·0	129·4	8·5

The possibility of differences in degree of strength between analysers in the individual has, so far as we know, not been experimentally demonstrated elsewhere. We believe that our work has provided facts which definitely indicate such a possibility.

True, in the majority of cases it is possible to state a coincidence of the characteristics for the visual and auditory analysers. Of 25 subjects, such a coincidence was found in 18 cases, that is 72 per cent. But against this background of identical numerical data stand out three cases of quite unambiguous difference between the strength characteristics, and four further cases in which it would appear possible to speak of partial differences in manifestation of strength. Let us consider in more detail the three cases of most clearly defined differences.

Subject K. V. Occupies second place for visual sensitivity. All three methods of determining strength of the visual analyser clearly showed the weakness of the cortical cells of this region (see Fig. 1). Investigation by the inductional influences technique yielded curves characteristic for weak subjects i.e. concentration of excitation at the focus of the supplementary stimulus and marked changes in concentration under the influence of all the three doses of caffeine. Extinction with reinforcement in the visual analyser led to a fall-off of the reflex and to its complete disappearance in the experiment using caffeine. The direct influence of caffeine (dose 0·3 g) on the visual thresholds was expressed in a lowering of sensitivity to start with, followed by a heightening of it by 270 per cent. At the same time, this subject occupies 24th place for auditory acuity. The test for extinction in the auditory analyser leads to an increase in the reflex. The influence of caffeine on auditory sensitivity is 8 per cent for the small dose, zero for the medium dose, and 35 per cent for the maximum dose. These last data would appear to be evidence of the strength of the cortical cells of the given region.

Subject R. Z. In absolute visual sensitivity, shares 20–21st place (5·6 in the conventional units). The test on the induction technique yielded curves characteristic of strong subjects, i.e. great concentration of excitation at the focus of supplementary stimulus and absence of influence of caffeine upon this. Extinguishing with reinforcement hardly changes the amount of the reflex. The influence of caffeine upon the visual thresholds is expressed by the Figures 0, 0, and 24 per cent, in a downward direction (see Fig. 2). In auditory acuity R. Z. occupies a place in the upper half of the list—the 10th, (twice as high as K. V.). The extinction test leads to a lowering of the reflex, particularly in the experiment where caffeine is used—a sign of weakness of the nerve cells; the direct action of caffeine on auditory sensitivity is 18·40 and 40 per cent in a downwards direction, which is also very typical for subjects with weak cells.

For subject R. Z., then, the partial variance runs in an opposite direction to that for subject K. V.; the latter has a strong auditory and a weak visual analyser, and R. Z., on the other hand, a weak auditory and strong visual analyser.

Subject Ch. I. is distinguished by a low light sensitivity 19th place, which does not change under the influence of caffeine. The test on the inductional technique gave results typical for subjects having strong cells

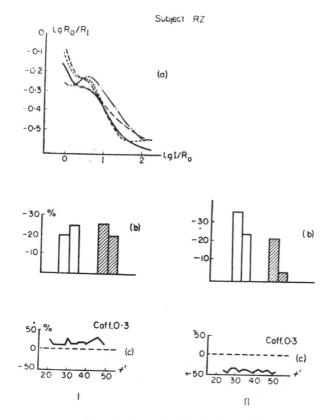

FIG. 2. Key as for Fig. 1 (page 60).

in the visual analyser. The photochemical conditioned reflex to light had not been elaborated in this subject after 40 combinations, and the test for extinction could therefore not be made. So far as the auditory analyser is concerned, here Ch. I. possesses very high sensitivity 1st place. The test for the extinction of a conditioned reflex elaborated to sound led to a deep fall-off of the reflex, so that the conditioned stimulus evoked, instead of a decrease an increase of sensitivity. Auditory sensitivity changes under the influence of caffeine in a manner characteristic for weak cells, i.e. a lowering by 20–30 per cent when large doses are given (see Fig. 3). All these data speak of the weakness of the auditory sector of the cortex and of the strength of the visual sector. The strength characteristic for subject Ch. I. is thus analogous to that for R. Z.

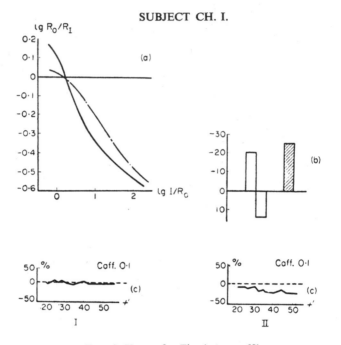

FIG. 3. Key as for Fig. 1 (page 60).

The experimental material adduced, we feel, is sufficiently convincing evidence of the possibility of partial typological characteristics for strength with reference to different analysers. Such cases are not rare, perhaps amounting to one-quarter of our material if all 7 cases are counted. We may conclude from this that individuals do exist about whom the term "strength of the nervous system" should be used only with an indication of what analysers it characterises.

Our experiments also revealed an absence of any significant correlation between the thresholds of the visual and auditory analysers. From this we drew the conclusion that there are also differences between analysers in level of absolute sensitivity.

It is important to note that both these functional indices—strength and sensitivity—are united by an inner mutual connection. In particular, in the three cases of most sharply defined variations between analysers in level of strength there are similarly sharp variations in level of sensitivity. It follows that the two-way relationship previously established as existing between sensitivity and strength holds good even for those persons concerning whom one ought not to speak of "the strength of the nervous system" as a whole, but only to compare the level of strength of the cortical cells of the different analysers.

This means that we now can and should speak of differences between analysers on the strength sensitivity parameter, thus linking the sensitivity and the strength of the nerve cells into one typological property.

As will be obvious from the text of this paper, our main method for revealing differences between analysers in level of strength was the use of caffeine. The facts bear witness that the influence of this chemical stimulant upon the activity of the various analysers of one and the same person may be of varying character. Caffeine can prove, as has been described above, an indifferent agent in relation to one analyser, and can cause a marked increase or decrease of sensitivity in another analyser, i.e. it can cause reactions of opposite type in neighbouring sectors of the cortex, right up to the moment of protective inhibition (which is clearly the basis for the decrease in sensitivity) occurring alongside a zero effect.

The question may arise: inasmuch as the experiments using the effect of caffeine on absolute sensitivity of the two analysers were for technical reasons made separately, are not the differences recorded in the reactions of the analysers to be considered as differences in the functional state of the subject? In order to obtain an answer to this question, special experiments were made with the three "chief" subjects (K. V., R. Z. and Ch. I.), and in these measurement of auditory and visual sensitivity was made in the course of the same period of time, one being measured alternately with the other, at 1–2 min intervals. The results of these control experiments, as may be seen from Fig. 4, accord with those obtained earlier: it was possible to observe a "strong" reaction of one analyser and a simultaneous "weak" reaction of the other, the same direction being maintained in the partial differences in strength as had been noted in the preceding experiments.

For a first approach to an explanation of this phenomenon one may adduce the facts, well known in pharmacology, of the selective action of some substances upon different sectors of the nervous system. V. V. Zakusov writes "Although the action of any chemical substance upon

protoplasm is in principle uniform, it is manifested differently in each
separate case, depending upon the sensitivity to it of the protoplasm of
different cells" [10; 46]. It is probable that the cortex of the large hemispheres may in some cases consist of cells with varying sensitivity to and
resistance to the action of chemical stimulants. It might be thought that
it is just such cases which we have encountered in this work.

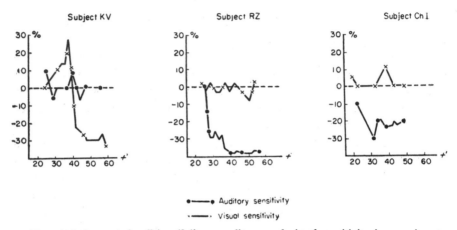

FIG. 4. Influence of caffeine (0·1) on auditory and visual sensitivity in experiments
with simultaneous measurement of thresholds. Abscissae—time in min; ordinates—
changes in sensitivity as a percentage of background.

It would appear that the same differences in sensitivity and resistance
of cells governs the effect of the action of the physiological conditioned-
reflex-stimulus in "extinction with reinforcement"—an effect which so
strikingly coincides with the effect of the action of caffeine. The intimate
nature of these differences, however, and consequently the causes of variance between analysers on the strength-sensitivity parameter, remains
unclear.

Let us now turn to a question which is directly linked with the problem
of differences between analysers. Strength data have been obtained by the
extinction with reinforcement of a photo-chemical related to stimulation
of different sensory systems. What is the cortical structure to which this
data relate? Do they characterise the strength of the cortical cells of the
analyser to which the reinforcement—the light stimulus—is addressed, or
do they perhaps characterise it for that analyser which receives the energy
of the conditioned-reflex signal?

The role of the unconditional stimulus in typological characterization
has been taken into account in some works, and has even been specially

studied [25; 1]. On the basis of this A. G. Ivanov-Smolenskii [11] formulated the thesis of the partial type in dependence upon the kind of reinforcement.

The role of the different cortical regions, however, and in particular that of the analysers, in individual-typological characterisation, has hardly been studied at all. The data available in the literature permit one to think that the individual differences between animals in this respect are insignificant [2]. In man, however, as has been noted previously, it would seem that one should presuppose great possibilities for such differences. In the opinion of B. M. Teplov, it is in just this sense that one must understand the variations which are shown when types of nervous system are analysed by different techniques: "This fact is not indicative of shortcomings in the techniques, not in the least, but is of much deeper significance" [24, 292]. And indeed, in those cases where the results of "extinction with reinforcement" (conditioned reflex to pure tone) do not coincide with the results of the "induction" technique, it is natural to suppose that the absence of agreement between the techniques may be put down to the differences in strength between the analysers. This is likely inasmuch as the conditioned reflex was elaborated to a sound stimulus, while the induction relationships were studied using light stimuli. The facts described above concerning the differentiated reaction of the analysers to caffeine also speak in favour of this reading of the difference between the data.

In order to check this supposition, and to provide a counter-check on the data concerning the direct action of caffeine on absolute sensitivity, either one had to create for the auditory analyser a technique analogous to the "visual" induction technique, or invent a variant of "extinguishing with reinforcement" which would be deliberately addressed to the cells of the visual analyser only. We chose the second of these alternatives, seeing that it was simpler to achieve. By elaborating a conditioned photochemical reflex to red light (instead of to sound) and then carrying out extinction with reinforcement, we obtained a technique which referred entirely to the sphere of the visual analyser because both the conditioned and the unconditioned stimuli were light signals.

It was interesting to compare the results of the application of these two variants of the technique, and to look at both sets in conjuction with the results of the tests using other techniques.

This comparison showed that among the subjects in whom we succeeded in elaborating both conditioned reflexes—to sound and to red light—we find the three people in whose case attempts to cause extinction in the two analysers had produced opposite effects. These are the two subjects described above, M. A. and R. Z., as having on the "extinction" data, strong cells in the visual analyser and weak ones in the auditory, and subject K. V., whose strength characteristic is the other way round.

Comparison with the indices obtained by the other techniques shows that these variations coincide with similar ones brought out by the other methods of revealing strength, especially in the cases of K. V. and R. Z.

Since the two variants of the "extinction with reinforcement" technique are distinguished from one another by one feature only, that is the modality of the conditional stimulus, we came to the conclusion that the differences observed in the effect of the extinction with reinforcement depend upon just this varying feature. Consequently, extinguishing with reinforcement gives the characteristic of strength (functional stability) of that analyser which is the receptor of the energy of the conditional signal. Its cells are forced to withstand a "frontal attack" in the form of the continued repetition of different combinations with a very short interval in between.

This conclusion finds an indirect confirmation in some works devoted to the study of excitation and inhibition and in certain remarks made by I. P. Pavlov. For instance, Pavlov in his "Lectures on the work of the large hemispheres" says that " the cortical cell *under the influence of conditioned stimuli* inevitably passes sooner or later, very quickly if they (stimuli) are repeated frequently, into a state of inhibition" [14; 263] (authors italics). Again, "If one relates the effect of the beats of a metronome to the state of the cortical cell, one must in consequence conclude that the latter, given frequent stimulation, exhausting itself functionally and not having the time to restore itself, passes into a state of complete inhibition . . ." [14; 261]. I. P. Pavlov, then, connects the processes of inhibition in the cortical cell with the application of a conditioned stimulus. In the text quoted, what is under discussion is not only extinguishing inhibition itself, but that form of inhibition which was later given the name "protective inhibition": "The cell passes into a state of inhibition under reinforcement also. The development in it of an inhibitory state without reinforcement is a particular case of a more general relation" [*ibid.*, 246].

Some experimental investigations made in recent times also provide indirect evidence in favour of our hypothesis. Z. A. Barsukova, [3] for example, considers that protective inhibition under the action of a strong tone arises in the analyser cells of the cortex and then spreads to the cortical representation of the corresponding unconditional reflex. The consequence of this is a falling-off of the reflex effect. In a paper by I. I. Chinka [26] a fall-off of unconditional reflex is again noted (actually a considerable heightening of the threshold of motor reaction to electrical stimulation) when a sound conditioned-reflex stimulus is stepped up in such a way as to give rise to protective inhibition in the cortex of the large hemispheres.

But if extinguishing with reinforcement is an index of the strength of the analyser to whose cells the conditioned signal is addressed, what then is the role of the unconditional stimulus or reinforcement?

One may suppose that the unconditional stimulus, by virtue of the connection established between its focus and the focus of the conditioned signal, is a kind of "purveyor" of energy to the focus of conditioned stimulation. This is a source of supply for it which creates a specific conditioned-reflex excitation as distinct from, say, the excitation evoked by the action of an ordinary indifferent stimulus. This is why extinction with reinforcement can characterise the strength of the cortical cells. The extinguishing of a reflex without reinforcement is not an index of strength, just as the simple application of an indifferent stimulus, one which has not yet become the signal of a temporary connection, is not an index of strength. The continued repetition of combinations of signals and responses with a minimal interval between them leads to the accumulation of excitation in the cells of the conditioned signal. This is as it were "borrowed" from the focus of the unconditional reflex, and leads to the development—in weak cells—of protective inhibition, such as we do not observe, naturally, upon repetition of an indifferent stimulus or upon isolated application of a conditioned—reflex signal.

Such, in our opinion, is the role of the unconditional stimulus in extinction with reinforcement, and the mechanism of this method of testing the strength of the cortical cells.

CONCLUSIONS

1. In the investigation a coincidence was found between the strength characteristics of the visual and auditory analysers in the majority of subjects.

2. At the same time the possibility was demonstrated of the existence of differences in individuals, on the strength-sensitivity parameter, between the visual and auditory analysers.

3. It may be supposed that extinction with reinforcement provides a measure of the strength characteristic of the cortical cells of the analyser which is the receiver of the energy of the conditioned signal.

Translated by RUTH KISCH

REFERENCES

1. ALEKSEYEVA, M. S., (1953). Opredeleniye tipa nervnoi sistemy u sobak na baze razlichnykh podkreplenii (pishchevogo i kislotno-oboronitel'nogo) (Definition of type of nervous system in dogs, on basis of different reinforcements (food and acid-defence). *Trudy instituta fiziologii imeni Pavlova* (Proceedings of *Pavlov Institute of Physiology*), II.

2. ALEKSEYEVA, M. S., Sravnitel'naya otsenka tipa nervnoi sistemy po dvigatel'noi i sekretornoi pishchevym metodikam (Comparative assessment of type of nervous system by motor and secretory food techniques). *Ibid.*

3. BARSUKOVA, Z. A., (1956). Razvitiye zapredel'nogo tormozheniya pri usilenii chistogo tona, primenyayemogo v kachestve uslovnogo razdrazhitelya (Development of prohibitive inhibition upon stepping-up of a pure tone used as a conditioned stimulus). *Zh. vyssh. nervn. deyat.* im. I. P. Pavlova, No. 2.

4. VAVILOV, S. I., (1956). Glaz i solntse (The eye and the sun). 7th ed., Acad. Sci. U.S.S.R., Moscow.

5. VATSURO, E. G., (1945). Issledovaniye po sravnitel'noi labil'nosti protsessov vysshei nervnoi deyatel'nosti primenitel'no k funktsionirovaniyu otdel'nykh analizatorov (Investigation into comparative lability of processes of higher nervous activity, in relation to functioning of separate analysers). *Trudy fiziologicheskoi laboratorii* I. P. Pavlova, 12, 2.

6. VATSURO, E. G., (1947). K voprosu o mekhanizme povedeniya cheloveko-obraznoi obez'yany (shimpanze) (On the question of the behaviour mechanism of an anthropoid ape (chimpanzee)). *Trudy Instituta evolyutsionnoi fiziologii i patologii vysshei nervnoi deyatel'nosti im.* I. P. Pavlova, *I.*

7. VATSURO, E. G., (1944). Printsip vedushchei afferentatsii v uchenii o vysshei nervnoi deyatel'nosti (Principle of leading afferentation in the theory of higher nervous activity). *Fiziol. zh. SSSR, 35, 5.*

8. VATSURO, E. G., and KOLESNIKOV. M. S. (1948). O razlichii funktsional'nykh svoistv otdel'nykh analizatorov (On difference between functional properties of separate analysers). *13-oye soveshchaniye po fiziologicheskim problemam. Tezisy dokladov* (13th conference on physiological problems. Abstracts of papers), Acad. Sci., U.S.S.R. Moscow.

9. GOLUBEVA, E. A., (1957). K voprosu o nekotorykh reflektornykh mekhanizmakh deistviya sveta na zritel'nyi analizator cheloveka (On the question of some mechanisms of the action of light on the visual analyser of man). *Materialy soveshchaniya po psikhologii* (1–6 iyulya 1955 g.) (Materials of conference on psychology, 1–6 July 1955), Acad. Sci., of R.S.F.S.R. Moscow.

10. ZAKUSOV, V. V., (1953). Farmakologiya nervnoi sistemy (Pharmacology of nervous system). Medgiz, Moscow.

11. IVANOV-SMOLENSKII, A. G., (1935). Eksperimental'noye issledovaniye vysshei nervnoi deyatel'nosti rebënka (Experimental investigation of higher nervous activity of child). *Fiziol. zh. SSSR, 19, 1.*

12. KLAAS, Y. A. and CHISTOVICH, L. A., (1950). O vliyanii neoshchushchayemykh zvukovykh razdrazhitelei v usloviyakh binaural'novo vzaimodeistviya (On the influence of unsensed sound stimuli under conditions of binaural interaction). *Problemy fizio-*

logicheskoi akustiki (Problems of physiological acoustics), Coll. papers II, Acad. Sci. U.S.S.R. Moscow-Leningrad.

13. NEBYLITSYN, V. D., (1956). O sootnoshenii mezhdu chuvstvitel'nost'yu i siloi nervnoi sistemy (On relationship between sensitivity and strength of nervous system). "Tipologicheskiye osobennosti vysshei nervnoi deyatel'nosti cheloveka" (Typological peculiarities of higher nervous activity in man), Coll. papers ed. B. M. Teplov, Acad. Sci., R.S.F.S.R. Moscow.

14. PAVLOV, I. P., (1951). Poln. sobr. soch. (Complete Works), Vol. 4.

15. PINEGIN, N. I., (1946). Minimum energii, neobkhodimoi dlya poyavleniya zritel'-nogo effekta (The minimum energy needed for appearance of visual effect). *Problemy fiziologicheskoi optiki* (Problems of physiological optics), Coll. papers 3, Acad. Sci., U.S.S.R. Moscow-Leningrad.

16. POPESCU-NEVIANU, P. G., (1954). Opyt issledovaniya tipovykh osobennostei cheloveka (Essay in investigation of typological peculiarities of man), *Uch. zap. LGU*, No. 185.

17. RAVICH-SHCHERBO, I. V., (1956). Issledovaniye tipologicheskykh razlichii po podvizhnosti nervnykh protsesov v zritel'nom analizatore (Investigation of typological differences in mobility of nervous processes in the visual analyser). *Tipologi-cheskiye osobennosti vysshei nervnoi deyatel'nosti cheloveka* (Typological peculiarities of higher nervous activity in man), Coll. papers ed. B. M. Teplov, Acad. Paed. Sci., of R.S.F.S.R. Moscow.

18. RZHEVKIN, S. N., (1936). Slukh i rech' v svete sovremennykh fizicheskykh issledo-vanii (Hearing and speech in light of modern physical research), 2nd ed., United Sci. and Tech. Publ. Houses, Moscow–Leningrad.

19. ROZHDESTVENSKAYA, V. I., (1955). Opyt opredeleniya sily protsessa vozbuzh-deniya po osobennostyam yego irradiatsii i kontsentratsii v zritel'nom analizatore (An attempt to define strength of the process of excitation by the peculiarities of its irradiation and concentration in the visual analyser). *Vop. Psikhol.*, 3.

20. ROZHDESTVENSKAYA, V. I., (1957). Opredeleniye sily korkovykh kletok po sposobnosti ikh dlitel'no vyderzhivat' kontsentrirovannoye vozbuzhdeniye (Deter-mination of strength of cortical cells by their ability to withstand concentrated excita-tion for a prolonged period). Dokl. Akad. Paed. Sci. of R.S.F.S.R., 3.

21. SNYAKIN, P. G., (1953). Nekotorye voprosy problemy eksteroanalizatorov v svete uchenii I. P. Pavlova (Some questions of problem of exteroanalysers in light of I. P. Pavlov's teaching). *Ucheniye I. P. Pavlova v teoritecheskoii prakticheskoi medit-syny* (Teaching of I. P. Pavlov in theoretical and practical medicine), Coll. papers, No. 2, Moscow.

22. TEPLOV, B. M., (1937). Induktivnye izmeneniya absolyutnoi i razlichitel'noi chuv-stvitel'nosti glaza (Inductive changes in absolute and differentiating sensitivity of the eye). *Vest. oftal'molog.*, XI 1.

23. TEPLOV, B. M., (1956). Nekotorye voprosy izucheniya obshchikh tipov vysshei nervnoi deyatel'nosti cheloveka i zhivotnykh (Some questions of study of general types of higher nervous activity in man and animals). "Tipologicheskiye osobennosti vysshei nervnoi deyatel'nosti cheloveka i zhivotnykh" (Typological peculiarities of higher nervous activity in man and animals), Coll. papers ed. B. M. Teplov, of R.S.F.S.R. Acad. Paed. Sci., Moscow.

24. TEPLOV, B. M., (1954). Opyt razrabotki metodik izucheniya tipologicheskykh razlichii vysshei nervnoi deyatel'nosti cheloveka (An attempt to elaborate techniques

for study of differences in higher nervous activity in man). "Doklady na soveshchanii po voprosam psikhologii, (3–8 iyulya, 1953 g.)" (Papers read at conference on questions of psychology, 3–8 July, 1953), Acad. Paed. Sci., R.S.F.S.R. Moscow.

25. KHOZAK, L. Y., (1953). Issledovaniye orientirovochno-issledovatel'skikh, pishchedobyvatel'nykh i passivno-oboronitel'nykh uslovnykh refleksov u detei shkol'novo vozrasta (Investigation of orientative-exploratory, food-acquisition and passive-defensory conditioned reflexes in children of school age). *Eksperimental'noye issledovaniye vysshei nervnoi deyatel'nosti rebönka* (Experimental investigation of higher nervous activity of child), Coll. papers.

26. CHINKA, I. I., (1956). O razvitii zapredel'novo tormozheniya pri postepennom usilenii fizicheskoi intensivnosti uslovnovo razdrazhitelya (On the development of prohibitive inhibition upon gradual stepping-up of physical intensity of a conditioned stimulus). *Trudy instituta fiziologii im. I. P. Pavlova*, V.

27. SHEIVEKHMAN, B. YE., BABKIN, V. P. and GLEKIN, G. V., (1956). Opredeleniye srednikh porogovykh velichin intensivnosti zvukov, vosprinimayemykh zroslym chelovekom (Determination of average threshold amounts for intensity of sounds perceived by an adult human being) *Problemy fiziologicheskoi akustiki* (Problems of physiological acoustics), 3, Acad. Sci. U.S.S.R., Moscow–Leningrad.

28. SHEIVEKHMAN, B. YE., GLEKIN G. V. and MEIZEROV, YE S., (1956). Individual'niye predely razbrosov velichin maksimal'noi intensivnosti zvukov, vosprinimayemykh chelovekom v tishine (Individual limits to range of amounts for maximum intensity of sounds perceived by man under conditions of quiet). "Vospriyatiye zvukovykh signalov v razlichnykh akusticheskykh usloviyakh" (Perception of sound signals under differing acoustic conditions), Acad. Sci. U.S.S.R., Moscow.

29. RIVES, P., (1950). "The minimum radiation visually perceptible ..." (quoted by S. V. Kravkov in Glaz i yego rabota (The eye and its work)).

30. WERTHEIMER, M., (1955). The variation of auditory and visual absolute thresholds in time, *J. Gen. Psychol.*, 52.

FEATURES OF THE AFFERENT APPARATUS OF THE CONDITIONED REFLEX AND THEIR IMPORTANCE FOR PSYCHOLOGY *

P. K. ANOKHIN

Department of Physiology of Moscow University ('An address to the Conference on Psychology, 1–6 July 1955)

IT is a well-known fact that the Pavlov school manifested an unfailing interest in psychological problems, particularly when these problems bordered on, and were significant in, relation to the physiology of higher nervous activity.

Throughout the entire developmental period of the conditioned reflex doctrine, Pavlov delivered many addresses to congresses of psychologists in which he pointed out how great a part the new branch of physiology which he had developed played in the materialistic understanding and interpretation of complex phenomena in the psychical life of man. Naturally, he laid particular emphasis on the importance of the conditioned reflex, of which he was the discoverer, for a physiological understanding of the association theory in psychology. His undelivered address to the International Psychological Congress at Madrid in 1936 would have dealt with this specific subject.

The doctrine of higher nervous activity, supplemented by the theory of interaction between the first and second signal systems, has enabled us to penetrate more and more deeply into the complex processes of the higher nervous activity which is specific to man—higher nervous activity as manifested through speech and thought. Yet, the more and more minutely the higher nervous activity physiologist analyses the phenomena of man's psychical activity, the more he becomes convinced that the conception of the conditioned reflex, as a universal physiological conception, must be enriched and amplified even further by new facts, bringing it into even closer relationship with purely psychological conceptions. For his part, the psychologist, with all the achievements of modern brain physiology and particularly those in the field of higher nervous activity at his disposal, must re-examine his basic conceptions in the light of these

* Voprosy psikhologii, No. 6, pp. 16–38, 1955.

achievements. In other words, true succes in the building of a materialistic psychology can only be attained if the physiologist and the psychologist
direct their research in accordance with common, jointly formulated aims.

We are still a long way from such organized and combined work on
the fundamental conceptions in psychology. There is, however, one form
of combined effort of which we can avail ourselves with advantage for
the solving of this problem, important in the methodological aspect, namely
joint meetings and congresses of psychologists and physiologists.

Even though this is but the first stage in the solution of the problems
which trouble the physiologist and psychologist yet, as the case of Pavlov's
own addresses to similar congresses has shown, it undoubtedly leads to
positive results. It is as a result of these addresses that, today, the main
problems in physiology and psychology are so clearly outlined, and that
the doctrine of higher nervous activity has become the basis for the development of a materialistic psychology.

Having accepted the honour of delivering a scientific address to the
Conference of Psychologists, I asked myself which of the many important
problems concerning both physiologist and psychologist should, as likely
to justify this aim of close linkage between physiology and psychology,
be the subject of my communication.

THE DECISIVE ROLE OF THE AFFERENT SYSTEMS
IN NERVOUS ACTIVITY

The experience of myself and my fellow-workers in the study of the
behavioural acts of animals, extending over many years, has convinced
me that a suitable subject for this purpose is *the universal and decisive
role of the afferent function of the organism in the formation of its higher
adaptations, up to and including mental acts.*

In actual fact, it is almost impossible to find any adaptational act
of animal or man in which afferent impulses caused by stimuli in the outside world do not play a prominent part. Becoming linked in a great variety
of combinations, afferent impulses effect constant control over what the
central nervous system should do at a given moment and what pattern
of operative excitations should be built up in relation to a given external
situation to ensure that the animal becomes adapted to it in an advantageous way.

This general role of afferent function was clearly formulated by Pavlov
on many occasions, as far back as 1911, when he expounded his views
on the alimentary centre.

Even then there was clear indication of his view on the decisive role of the afferent part of the central nervous system, and subsequently, throughout the entire period of his productive activity, he frequently returned to this idea. He wrote in 1911: "I am of the opinion that main centre of gravity of nervous activity lies specifically in the receiving part of the central station; the basis for the advance of the central nervous system, which is effected by the cerebrum, by the cerebral hemispheres, lies in this part; here is situated the main organ for that very perfect equilibration with the external world which typifies the higher animal organism. As for the centrifugal part, it is simply executive [1]",

Subsequently, he held to this view invariably and analysed all factual material on higher nervous activity in accordance therewith. One can therefore omit his numerous pronouncements on this subject. His last formulation of the conception must, however, be quoted as it expresses the ultimate profundity and extension of this idea and as it serves us as a starting point for further discoveries in this field.

Analysing the individual problems of higher nervous activity, Pavlov said:

"If we were to divide the entire central nervous system simply into two halves—an afferent and an efferent half, then it seems to me that the cerebral cortex would represent the isolated afferent part. The higher analysis and synthesis of incoming stimulations are effected exclusively in this division, and from this division already *prepared combinations of stimulations and inhibitions* (author's italics) are directed to the efferent division. In other words, only the afferent part is the "active" creative division, and the efferent part is merely the "passive" executive division" (2).

Somewhat later, Pavlov made the still more definite pronouncement that afferent inpulses constituted an "essential condition" for the regulating influence of the central nervous system on the peripheral organs.

We see, therefore, that the afferent part of the nervous system, that is, the occurrence of constant afferent impulses from the periphery, occupied the central place in Pavlov's conception of the integrated activity of the organism. An interesting point is that comparative anatomical investigations on the numbers of nerve fibres in the posterior and anterior roots have shown that sensory fibres are three to five times more numerous than motor fibres. This fact affords one more proof of the universal importance of afferent fibre function.

Recognition of the universal importance of the afferent division of the central nervous system gives rise, however, to several problems.

The first thing that strikes one is the obvious disagreement between this conception and the reflex theory of Descartes. What role did, in fact, Descartes assign to the afferent division of the central nervous system? The generally accepted schema of the reflex arc makes it clear that the afferent impulses always plays the part merely of an initiating impulse, an "inciter". This stimulus may be more or less complex but, in the actual concept of the "reflex arc", it is invariably merely the initial impetus for the development of some reflex effect. Thus, in Descartes' conception, only an afferent stimulus is necessary for the development of a reflex effect, which always serves to adapt the organism purposefully to the surrounding conditions and, according to Descartes, the role of the afferent system in the formation of adaptational acts of animals and man is, in essence, limited to this.

This is obviously very different from Pavlov's pronouncements quoted above, whereby the afferent system was assigned a decisive role in the creation of "combinations of excitations and inhibitions".

What is the essential nature of this difference? It is, first of all, that the original reflex schema suggested by Descartes ("the reflex arc") has proved clearly inadequate for explanation of all the varied factual material derived from investigations on the adaptational behaviour of the intact animal, particularly in the Pavlov school.

By being the first to introduce the conception of the *external stimulus*, as a factor determining the adaptation of the animal to the external world, Descartes made a great contribution to the advance of materialistic conceptions on man. In place of all kinds of "spontaneous" and "primordial" causes, he gave primary importance to the material effect of external agents on the nervous system of animals and man. In this way he established a *deterministic* relationship between the behaviour of animals and changes in the environment.

It was this aspect of Descartes' reflex theory that Pavlov adopted, considering it "scientific", in that it answered in all respects to the requirements of the law of causality in the life of animal organisms.

Yet, having established the importance of the initial external stimulus for the reflex responses of the animal, Descartes said nothing whatever on the question of why the response was purposeful. Why should the stimulus lead to the excitation of just those combinations of central nerve elements which infallibly manifest themselves at the periphery in work-performing efforts of one particular form and no other? Descartes never discussed these questions, nor did be consider how the organism corrected the mistake in the event of a reflex response not giving the adaptational effect at once.

Dualist in his outlook, Descartes relegated the question of the purposefulness of the reflex response to the sphere of "higher reason" and thereby determined for many years the entire course of research on the complex adaptational acts of animal and man.

It is no exaggeration to say that, although intensive and detailed analysis of processes constituting "reflex arcs" was going on throughout the pre-Pavlov period in the development of nervous system physiology, no attempt was ever made to give a physiological interpretation of the *purposefulness* of the reflex response. By introducing the *factor of reinforcement* into the process of acquiring new reflex acts—conditioned reflexes, Pavlov produced a radical change in the entire course of research on the complex adaptational acts of the animal.

This fact also affords an explanation of the apparent contradiction which arises in connection with Pavlov's high evaluation of afferent impulses as playing a decisive part in the formation of complex behavioural acts.

The considerable number of investigations which have been carried out by my fellow-workers over a period of twenty-five years has convinced us that the explanation of this apparent contradiction must be sought, not in the initial part of the "reflex arc"—in connection with its exciting stimulus, but at the other end of the reflex, in relation to the *reflex effect* itself. It was to this that all that Pavlov said about the decisive role of the afferent part of the central nervous system referred, and it is here that the complex adjustment of the reflex effect to the interests of the organism as a whole takes place—something which, in its essential nature, also merits the epithet "creative".

The reflex theory of Descartes assumes that the reflex response of the organism is purposeful from the very beginning, and its adaptation to the particular environmental conditions is taken to be a matter of course.

In consequence, the entire attention of the physiologist was for many years directed to "finished" reflex acts, built up earlier. But the incongruity of the old conceptions of the entire complex of the adaptational behaviour of the animal became very obvious the moment a study was made of *the actual process of formation of elaboration of new reflex responses. These invariably required the encouragement of the reflex by the method of reinforcement* which, as we know, is the very essence of the conditioned reflex. In exactly the same way, the inadequacy of the "classical" reflex theory again became particularly obvious in the experiments in which the animal had, by way *of compensation for disturbed functions*, to create, under the eyes of the experimenter, completely new reflex acts, adapting itself adequately to the new conditions affecting its life. This will be the subject of discussion in the next part.

THEORY OF RETURN AFFERENTATION

Since 1930 our laboratory has been continuously engaged in research on compensation mechanisms for disturbed functions in the organism. In addition to its enormous theoretical importance, this absorbing problem will also enable us to understand all the adaptations taking place in the sick animal which constitute a "physiological measure" against disease and bring its functional features into line with the new conditions. With these points in mind, we have made wide investigations on the compensatory adaptations that arise when the animal's motor functions are disturbed as a result of special operations of various types, and particularly as a result of cross-anastomosis of nerve trunks [3].

We know that disturbances of motor activity finally become compensated after a series of stages in which the animal resorts to various measures which replace the lost function and enable it to attain the appropriate adaptational effect. If the disturbance is not too extensive, the function is restored in more or less perfect form. The whole process of restoration usually involves an enormous variety of attempts to rectify the defect, these attempts involving all groups of the animal's muscles.

We have shown by direct experiments that the process of compensation advances more slowly when the extremity, the function of which had been disturbed by cross-anastomosis of nerves, was subjected to prior deafferentation, or when the corresponding cortical zone was removed after the establishment of compensation [4]. This decisive role of afferent impulses from the periphery in the compensation process was seen with particular clarity in an experiment of E. A. Asratyan in which he removed the cerebral cortex completely. The compensation process was then quite impossible or extremely limited [5].

I do not intend to discuss the entire problem of function compensation here; it would mean too great a digression. The important point for me now is to point out that it was the work on this problem that first brought to our attention the inadequacy of any explanation of the process of compensation based solely on the Descartes schema of the "reflex arc". This work demanded from us the formulation of an additional link in the reflex, in the form of *continuously operating* return afferentation.

In order to render the pattern of our research on the actual mechanisms which led gradually to the compensation of disturbed functions more penetrating, we postulated three questions, without answers to which it would be impossible to discover the intimate mechanisms concerned in compensatory adaptations. These were:

(1) Can the central nervous system *begin* a compensatory process without signalisation from the periphery on the existence of a defect of function, and if so, through what actual afferent impulses is this signalization effected?

(2) Inasmuch as all the animal's attempts to compensate the defect are directed to *compensation for that specific defect*, what are the actual physiological mechanisms which determine the *direction* of the entire chain of compensatory adaptations specifically to compensation of the defect?

(3) On the basis of what information does the central nervous system determine the *end* of adaptational reactions, that is, that the disturbed functions have been restored; through what mechanisms does it *stop* further attempts at restoration and consolidate the newly laid down system of central relationships?

A careful analysis of these three questions will suffice to show that there cannot be a complete theory for the compensation of functions without reasonably satisfactory answers thereto. Once we have the answers to these questions we shall be in a position to construct a deterministically connected chain of physiological processes, directed to compensation, from the moment the defect is produced until the moment of function restoration.

For more detailed information on the work on these three questions on models of disturbed functions I refer the reader to our latest publication on this subject (6).

For the present I shall confine myself to the general patterns that emerged inevitably from our investigations of many years on this subject.

First and foremost, it must be stated that no reflex activity which developed in response to signalisation on a loss of function could lead to any positive effect without immediate return afferentation indicating the adequacy or inadequacy of the completed reflex activity.

There could be no restoration of the disturbed functions without this return signalization of the degree of success of the first reflex responses to the central nervous system.

I should like first of all to discuss the term "return afferentation" itself, which has been suggested by us to explain the continuous correction of the compensation process from the periphery. The term implies that afferent signalisation which develops as a result of reflex activity is directed specifically to that particular complex of processes in the central nervous system which determined the given activity at the periphery. This is, in the true sense of the word, "return" afferentation, in that it is directed in the opposite direction to the earlier effector exictation, and it proceeds to the initial station for the dispatch of this excitation. This relationship can be depicted diagrammatically in the following form (Fig. 1).

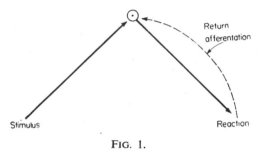

FIG. 1.

A natural question at this point is how widespread are these relationship in the normal reflex activity of animals and man.

By way of example, I would first of all draw attention to the significance of the fact of *reinforcement* in the elaboration of conditioned reflexes with different biological import. It is quite obvious that, in introducing the actual conception of *reinforcement*, Pavlov appreciated the return direction of the afferent impulses that developed from the action of the unconditioned stimulus on various combinations of receptor formations.

In actual fact, as the very meaning of the term would indicate, it is only possible to "reinforce" something that is already occurring, something that exists and is the addressee of the reinforcement itself. As we shall see later, this prior formation is the conditioned excitation in the cortex or, more accurately, the excitation in the cortical representation of the unconditioned centre, caused by the conditioned stimulus.

Thus, both the elaboration and the subsequent existence of the conditioned reflex are only conceivable in the presence of its constant reinforcement by the unconditioned reflex or when there is continual return afferentation. The reinforcement of the conditioned reflex is known to be the biological factor which determines the purposefulness of the organism's adaptation to the given external conditions. The reinforcement is the factor which corrects this adaptation and, consequently, it is as much an inalienable part of the conditioned reflex as any return afferentation in the case of successive compensatory adaptations is an inalienable part of the reflex activity performed.

From this standpoint, it would be correct to say that, by introducing the *factor of reinforcement* into the process for the elaboration of new reflex responses in the organism, Pavlov was reflecting the universal pattern in the life of all organisms which directs any reflex activity under any conditions in the natural existence of the animals. This pattern we have termed return afferentation and have ascribed to it a correcting and reinforcing action. It is difficult at the present time to conceive of any reflex act in the intact animal which would be terminated simply by the effector link in the "reflex arc", in accordance with the traditional Descartes schema.

Let us assume, however, that such a reflex act does exist or that its existence is pointed out to us. According to the conception of reflex activity, this act must either give or fail to give a successful adaptational effect. In the former case the given reflex action *ends* and the animal should proceed to its next behavioural link, while in the latter case the animal undertakes a series of new attempts to achieve the positive effect not attained by the first action.

It will be asked: how can the animal's nervous system detect the difference between these two possible effects of the reflex action?

It might be answered that it is not necessary for the animal to detect this difference. But such animals would very soon be doomed to extinction. It can hardly be doubted, therefore, that in relation to every reflex act the animal immediately receives return signalisation of whether the action achieved an adaptational effect or not. It is only under these conditions, that is, when there is constant return afferentation accompanying every reflex act like an echo, that the natural behavioural acts of the intact animal can develop, come to an end and be followed by other acts, together constituting an organised chain of purposeful adaptations to surrounding conditions*.

Several points requiring more detailed consideration arise in connection with the above representations on the need for return afferentation.

First of all the *composition* of return afferent signalisation has to be determined. Initially we did not attempt to determine the detailed composition of return afferentation but limited ourselves to the more general demonstration that it arose from the *organs in action*. As so general a state-

---

* Here as elsewhere the conception "purposefulness" is used by us in its broad biological sense, as understood by Pavlov.

ment may fail to give investigators an altogether correctly oriented conception on this important matter, I shall now take the liberty of formulating the question in greater detail.

By its very meaning, return afferentation must reflect very completely the degree of success attending the given reflex action and, consequently, its composition must depend directly on the complexity of the particular action and on the receptor surfaces by which the *result* of the action can be determined. All our acts usually have very varied afferentation. Figuratively speaking, each reflex act gives the central nervous system a whole volley of afferentations varying in strength, in localisation, in time of development and rapidity of spread through the central nervous system. In other words, we have an afferent integral, peculiar to each individual case, which reflects the adaptational effect of the reflex action concerned, down to the finest detail.

For example, the act of picking up a fork or knife is completed at once by a complex of tactile, thermal, visual and kinaesthetic afferent stimuli signalising the end and the success of the particular reflex action.

It should, however, be remembered that, with a great number of different return afferentations in relation to any reflex action, some of them are eliminated and the main afferentation—those afferent impulses which acquire decisive indicator significance—comes into prominence. Should the main afferentation be eliminated, other receptor surfaces, the afferent impulses from which had not previously had a decisive role, come into action.

In more complex acts (e.g. entry into a room) the return afferentation signalling the correctness of the particular act may include many afferent impulses such as visual ones from the room and its contents as well as thermal, olfactory and kinaesthetic afferentations.

The question of how widely the term "reinforcement" can be applied to reflex acts of various kinds also arises in connection with the assessment of the composition of return afferentations. Essentially, all our actions are of a continuous or chain character. Each link in the chain, having ended with the return afferentation peculiar to it, is followed by the next link.

A correct sequence of the links can, however, only be guaranteed if each link receives, in the form of "reinforcement", return afferentation which is adequate for that link.

Consequently, the concept of "reinforcement" can with complete justification be applied to any fractional stage in adaptation which has received appropriate return afferentation.

The final stage in all compensatory adaptations or in any long series of reflex acts is the attainment of the main adaptational effect. Like all the other stages of adaptation, the final stage also has its return afferentation, but this is distinguished by several special features. It does not stimulate the nervous system to the continued formation of new reflex actions, but quite the contrary; it checks further attempts at the organisation of new reflex acts and *reinforces* the last combination of excitations in the brain centres which gave the successful adaptational effect at the periphery.

This last return afferentation we have termed *sanctioning afferentation*, as it actually "sanctions" the last formed system of relationships in the nerve centres [3].

Returning, then, to all that has been stated earlier in this section of the paper, we can conclude that the afferent phenomena which come into play at the end of the reflex action are so varied and so important for the development of the animal's purposeful adaptation and more particularly for the compensation of functional defects that they rightly merit separation into the special category of *return afferentations*.

Return afferentations, as universal phenomena in animal behaviour, constitute a property of the *intact* animal, a phenomenon of its natural behaviour. Naturally, they cannot occur or lead to any adaptational effect when there is mutilation. This must be the explanation for the paradoxical fact that the continuous correcting effect of return afferentations has never once been mentioned, despite the fact that the history of the development of Descartes' reflex theory extends to three hundred years. The vivisection which has yielded rich *analytical* results meant the deliberate removal of any possibility of discovering return afferentations and consequently also of the possibility of describing the complete architecture of the nervous processes in the adaptational act.

At the same time, since our elucidation of the various forms of return afferentation, it has now become perfectly clear that the generally accepted conception of the *chain reflex*, as at present constituted, is inadequate and requires serious change.

According to existing conceptions, a chain reflex is, in fact, one in which "the end of one action serves as the start for another". We have seen, however, that the end of an action can never serve as the start for another action. The end of the action in one link is the source of return afferentation which is directed to the centres of the reflex that has just developed, and only thereafter, and *depending on what consequences this return afferentation will have in the nerve centres, does the next stage in the chain reflex begin to develop* (Fig. 2).

Figure 2 gives comparative schemas for the chain reflex according to the usual conceptions (A) and a chain of return afferentations as seen by us in relation to an extension of Descartes' reflex schema (B). As soon as one assumes that inaccuracy of the reflex act might occur in any link during the development of a chain reflex in accordance with old conceptions, it becomes perfectly clear that this schema cannot be applied to the actual conditions of the animal's life. *No correction of this inaccuracy would be possible.*

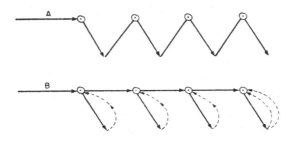

FIG. 2. Comparison of a chain reflex with a chain of return afferentations.

Development of the theory of return afferentation must inevitably raise the question of the relationship of return afferentation to the "classical" reflex arc, the extent to which it amplifies the latter and the possibility of return afferentation being a *fourth link* in the reflex. The fact is that return afferentation can be made one of the links in the reflex arc on as good grounds as the links already known. As we see it, it is absolutely essential for the realization of purposeful adaptation and, indeed, it corrects imperfection in the activity of the three first links, while it is just as constant a feature of every reflex action as its other links and has quite a definite physiological and structural content. In view of all these points, I cannot see any serious objection to the theory that return afferentation constitutes an additional or fourth link in the reflex. Transformation of the Descartes schema of the reflex in this way removes a long list of contradictions which have accumulated in the past and, at the same time, it opens up great possibilities for the investigation and explanation of complex forms of behaviour in animals and man in the natural conditions of their existence.

Here, it will not be superfluous to mention that foreign thought in recent years has come very close to the conceptions just described, often using very similar expressions.

It will suffice to draw attention to the statements of Adrian who, in one of his last public lectures (in memory of Jackson), made an attempt to understand the plastic adaptation of the animal to surrounding conditions. In his survey of recent achievements in the field of brain physiology he dwelt on the indecision of animals when faced with complex forms of adaptation. In a cautious approach to the subject he wrote: "A purposive movement certainly appears to be guided by its effects" [7].

Individual investigators made conjectures in this direction at the International Congress on the "Principles of the Complex Organization of the Nervous System" [8]. Wagner also came close to these questions in his monograph, "Problems and Examples of Biological Regulation", in which he developed the "Servotheorie" and attempted to explain the nature of adaptational behaviour by means of the theory [9]. Cybernetics, which employs conceptions of "return connections" for control of the correctness and purposefulness of the work both of machines and of the human organisms comes particularly close to this problem. All these statements appeared many years after our original publications on this problem and, while they expressed general conjectures, they were very far from revealing the physiological mechanisms. Nevertheless, these circumstances afford yet another confirmation of the need for further development of the above conceptions which have been produced and developed in Soviet laboratories.

So far I have not touched on the second of the questions we raised earlier, namely, how the attempts to find adaptational acts for the compensation of disturbed functions are directed. This question is very closely connected with the further development of our conceptions of the physiological basis for the purposeful nature of reflex acts and will therefore be the subject of special analysis in the next section of this paper.

THEORY OF THE ACCEPTOR OF EFFECT

Even in the earliest stages in the development of sanctioning afferentation as the final form of return afferentation we conceived of certain aspects of the problem which led us gradually to the discovery of a special central afferent apparatus, of the existence of which we had previously no conception.

The fact that a whole series of return afferentations inevitably accompanies the entire series of compensatory adaptations up to and including the restoration of function must inevitably raise the question of why the central nervous system stops the whole series of compensatory adaptations and the organism is held at its last attempt at compensation. Or, more graphically expressed, how and from what signs does the organism decide that this last—the sanctioning—afferentation is actually of such a nature that it corresponds to the essential demands of its adaptation to the external world?

As this problem is one of extreme importance for an understanding of the features of the afferent apparatus of reflex activity discovered by us, I shall take the liberty of discussing it in greater detail. Let us represent the complexes of return afferentations accompanying a series of successive adaptations by corresponding symbols. Let the first inadequate afferentation be $(a+b+k)$, the second $(a+k+1)$, the third $(a+k+r)$ and, finally, the sanctioning afferentation $(a+k+m+t)$. Holding to deterministic physiological conceptions, we must ask ourselves by what means, at the disposal of the central nervous system, does it determine the differences between the separate links in this chain of return afferentations or, in other words, *how does the animal "recognize" that the last afferent complex $(a+k+m+t)$ constitutes information of a finally restored effect or generally of the adequacy of the adaptational effect.* If we adhere strictly to deterministic attitudes, then actually the entire material contained at present in our neurophysiological arsenal cannot give us the answer to this question. Indeed, all return afferentations, including sanctioning afferentation are, for the animal's central nervous system, merely complexes of afferent impulses and there are no obvious reasons, from the usual point of view, why one complex should *stimulate* the central nervous system to further mobilization of reflex adaptational acts while another *arrests* the adaptational actions.

Let us assume that we intend to pick up a glass standing on the table among a large number of vessels. In stretching out our hand we carelessly grasp the handle of a jug. As we all know from experience, the mistake is immediately corrected. The jug is left where it is and the hand finds the glass we require.

What is the physiological basis on which we noticed the mistake and corrected it?

The shape of the jug and the contact of the hand with it, like the shape of the glass and contact of the hand, merely constitute aggregates of return afferent impulses, differing only in some of their components. Why then should we have selected the last return afferentation as the final one, as the sanctioning afferentation?

Our lives are filled with similar events, evident in our every step, in every act in our much varied behaviour.

This last example makes it clear that only that return afferentation which corresponds to the intention giving rise to the reflex act itself arrests further reflex actions or, expressed physiologically, the return afferentation must correspond to *some kind of stored complex of excitations which developed before the actual reflex act took shape.*

As a result of such arguments we came inevitably to the conclusion that this stored complex of excitations, which preceded reflex activity, must be something in the nature of an afferent "control" apparatus, which determined *how far a particular return afferentation reaching the central nervous system corresponded to the complex.*

We gave particular attention to the development of this problem on the model of an alimentary conditioned reflex and its return afferentation—the reinforcement by food.

It had long been noted that the conditioned excitation developing in the cerebral cortex in response to the use of this particular conditioned stimulus was not of a type which, in its quality, would be the same for any conditioned signals. On the contrary, the aggregate of external behavioural signs indicated that the nature of this conditioned excitation was directly dependent on the nature of the reinforcing factor. A very illuminating example of this relationship was afforded by the biological quality of the conditioned reactions in response to conditioned stimuli reinforced by food and by electric current.

This relationship is also seen in demonstrative form within the limits of the same unconditioned reinforcement. It was demonstrated long ago in Pavlov's laboratory that the chemical composition of conditioned reflex saliva was in close correspondence with the quality of the food reinforcement and, consequently, with its salivogenic effect [10].

It is from this accurate coincidence of the quality of the unconditioned and conditioned excitation that the "substitution", "anticipation" and other theories sprang, but these are merely verbal designations for this well-known phenomenon and do not bring us even one step nearer to the discovery of its physiological nature [11].

The question still remained unanswered as before. What were the actual physiological mechanisms whereby the conditioned effector excitation, in the form of secretion and general alimentary excitation, arising in response to the given conditioned stimulus corresponded more or less closely to the effector excitations which could be expected to develop later also from the reinforcing factor itself? Framed in even more specific terms, the question can be put in this form: does the conditioned excitation caused by the conditioned stimulus in the corresponding analyser travel directly to the *effector paths* of the unconditioned stimulus or does it reproduce all over again its afferent part which we know is concentrated in the cortical representation of the unconditioned reflex? [12].

This second question can be illustrated by the following simple schema (Fig. 3).

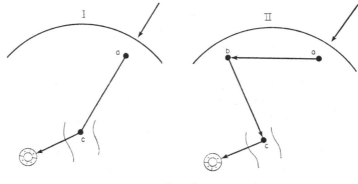

FIG. 3.

It will be seen from the diagram that, if we assume that the conditioned stimulation spreads directly from the region of the corresponding analyser to the centre for the unconditioned reflex, we are thereby returning to Pavlov's very first proposition on the closure mechanism for the arc of the conditioned reflex (Fig. 3, I). It is well known that his many subsequent experimental findings inclined Pavlov to recognition of the cortical localization of both links closing the conditioned connection. It was accepted that the latter became established between cells in the corresponding analyser and cells in the cortical representation of the unconditioned stimulus. This position was completely consistent with all factual material both from Pavlov's own laboratory and from those of his pupils, and is, therefore, now generally accepted. But it follows from this position that the conditioned excitation in the corresponding analyser can spread to the unconditioned alimentary centre *only through its cortical representation* (Fig. 3, II, b).

Notwithstanding that this hypothesis satisfied our conceptions on the physiological architecture of the conditioned reflex completely and is now current opinion, no special attention has hitherto been given to the physiological consequences which inevitably follow acceptance of that view.

Indeed, what is the exact physiological nature of this "cortical representation of the unconditioned centre"? It follows from the very meaning of unconditioned reinforcement, as afferent stimulation, that this "representation" must be *afferent in character*, and this is wholly in agreement with Pavlov's view on the cortex as an "isolated afferent part" of the central nervous system (*v. supra*).

Oscillographic experiments by our fellow-worker, I. I. Laptev, have shown that the unconditioned stimulus itself causes a fairly complex afferent discharge.

Tactile, thermal and chemical receptors in the tongue were stimulated in a definite order. The specific streams of impulses travelled at different speeds to the various parts of the cortex.

It became clear from this that the cortical representation of the unconditioned stimulus was in no way a definite "focus" or "point" in the cerebral cortex but a system of afferent cells integrated into a single complete unit [13].

Correlation of all these findings then led us inevitably to the following position, which is of great importance for us: *each conditioned excitation is directed through the corresponding analyser to the system of afferent connections in the cortical representation of the unconditioned centre, which has been excited many times in the past by the unconditioned stimulus, and which will again be stimulated by the same unconditioned stimulus several seconds after the arrival in it of the given conditioned excitation.* In other words, whenever the conditioned stimulus is tested, the group or system of cortical cells, reproducing through the action of the conditioned stimulus the appetizing qualities of the unconditioned stimulus *becomes excited several seconds before the fresh unconditioned excitation reaches it* ("reinforcement").

Let us look for a moment at the peculiar relationship established between the nerve excitations in the cortical apparatus of the conditioned reaction at the point in time when, as a result of unconditioned reinforcement, streams of various, but always specific, afferent excitations (return afferentation) also arrive there. It must be remembered here that the quality of these excitations is in direct relationship to the particular stimulating effect of the given reinforcing agent on the visual, olfactory and taste receptors.

This sequence in the development of cortical processes during the fifteen seconds of action of the conditioned stimulus alone can be depicted in phases, as is shown in Figure 4.

Let us assume that, in the case of the particular experimental animal concerned, all conditioned stimuli delivered in the course of a year had been reinforced with 20 g rusk powder. Passing along all sensory paths, this stimulation excites certain afferent cells *B* in the cerebral cortex (tactile, thermal, chemical). The system of interconnections between these cells will thereafter constitute the afferent cortical representation of the unconditioned centre.

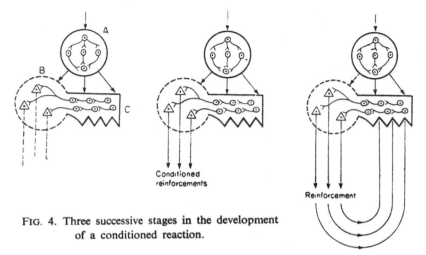

FIG. 4. Three successive stages in the development of a conditioned reaction.

As a result of prolonged training of the conditioned reflex, relationships are created in the cerebral cortex or, more accurately, in the cortical representation of the unconditioned centre, whereby, with each new application of the conditioned stimulus, *that additional afferent apparatus which reproduces accurately the qualitative features of the food reinforcement constantly employed is brought into a state of excitation* simultaneously with the effector apparatuses of the conditioned reaction (secretion, movement, respiration etc.). As also in the case of compensation, this cortical afferent apparatus of the conditioned excitation is of the nature of a "control apparatus", which manifests its effect several seconds after the commencement of the conditioned stimulus, that is, *when the action of the alimentary unconditioned stimulus has already started.*

When return afferent impulses from the unconditioned stimulus reach the cortex, the animal's behaviour will only be usual and stable if the unconditioned excitation is in its visual, olfactory and taste qualities in exact correspondence with the *already prepared afferent excitation* which was brought into activity by the conditioned stimulus several seconds before reinforcement. The final relationships in the afferent apparatus are in the form depicted in Figure 4 (third phase).

We suggest that this schema is a fundamental one and will explain any form of elaborated adaptational behaviour satisfactorily.

The schema shows that the return afferentation arising from the effect of the unconditioned stimulus must correspond accurately to the supplementary complex of afferent excitations, which forms part of the conditioned excitation. If there is complete correspondence between these two excitations, the behaviour of the animal remains normal, which means that the animal's alimentary excitation has been "satisfied", and is in complete accord with the earlier elaborated signal relationships between the conditioned stimulus and the reinforcement. From this standpoint, the supplementary afferent apparatus of the conditioned reflex must be regarded as the apparatus producing the final assessment of the *adequacy or inadequacy of the particular reinforcement or of the adaptational effect*, which followed the signal stimulus.

We first had thought of the existence of such a physiological apparatus in the cerebral cortex (of "sanctioning afferentation") some twenty-five years ago [3, 14], but special experiments were necessary before one could be sure of the actual physiological properties of this apparatus. We therefore undertook a series of experiments to that end.

In the setting up of these experiments we reasoned in the following way. If the already prepared conditioned excitation of the afferent cells in the cortical representation of the unconditioned centre does reflect accurately the properties of the future return unconditioned excitation and if the normal elaborated behaviour of the animal is based on the adequacy of this relationship, then the behaviour must inevitably change if something quite different is substituted for the unconditioned stimulus. In consequence of such substitution, the now outdated conditioned excitation in the supplementary afferent apparatus would be of one quality (on the basis of previous reinforcements) and the unconditioned stimulus would *suddenly* be of a different quality and, consequently, the return afferentation from the latter, reaching the cerebral cortex, would not correspond in the composition of its nervous impulses with the conditioned excitation stored there. What will the actual behaviour of the animal be under these circumstances?

This plan was methodically carried out in our laboratory [15], on the basis of bilateral reinforcement and we were able to discover these features of higher nervous activity.

The experiment took the following form. In all, two secretory-motor conditioned reflexes were elaborated in an animal—to the tone "la" with reinforcement on the right side and to the tone "fa" with reinforcement on the left side of the stand. Both reflexes were reinforced with 20 g rusk and were consolidated reasonably well. After a short latent period the animal jumped to the appropriate side of the stand and stood there until the unconditioned stimulus was delivered. The animal made no wrong motor reactions at the stage of the experiments described.

At the start of an experimental day dried meat was placed on the plate on the left side and so, after being accustomed to rusk reinforcement, the animal was bound to receive meat reinforcement to one of the regular applications of the tone "fa". From our analysis (above) of the features of the afferent apparatus of conditioned excitation, we had to assume that, at some moment, the new unconditioned stimuli, *no longer coinciding in their visual, olfactory and taste qualities with the already aroused conditioned excitation*, would lead first to inconsistency between the two excitations and then to the development of an orientation-investigatory reaction. The greater the discordancy between the stored conditioned afferent excitations and the actual afferent excitations from the new unconditioned stimulus, the more pronounced the orientation-investigatory reaction should be.

Indeed, when a change of this nature was made in the unconditioned stimulus there was generally an orientation-investigatory reaction which, depending on the strength of the stimulating effect from the suddenly changed unconditioned stimulus, passed into either an active alimentary reaction (on substitution of meat for bread) or arrest of the alimentary reaction and even refusal of food (transfer from meat to bread).

The experiment described made it possible for us to observe both forms of reaction, the second very clearly, and this we shall describe here in more detail, in view of its importance.

When the animal unexpectedly received meat there was a brief orientation-investigatory reaction and then it ate the meat avidly, its usual stereotypic behaviour being sharply changed under these experimental conditions.

First of all, it did not leave the food-box and return to the middle of the stand as usual, but continued to sit near the food-box, from which it had just received the unexpected meat reinforcement. For several days subsequently the animal's behaviour had a quite definite physiological content. Having arrived in the experimental room and having leapt on to the stand, it turned immediately to the food-box on the left side—*that from which it had on one occasion received meat*. Here it displayed an accentuated investigatory reaction, persistently sniffing at the food-box.

The subsequent behaviour of the animal made it possible to understand the physiological content of this behaviour fairly completely.

As soon as the conditioned stimulus was delivered, *irrespective of the side of the stand with which this stimulus was conditionally associated*, the animal immediately jumped to the left-hand food-box and stood there until food was delivered. This reaction developed in relation to both the tone "fa" (left side) and the tone "la" (right side). There was accentuated dominance of the whole system of excitations which determined the animal's reaction to the left and which was intensified by the meat reinforcement. The eating of the meat created clear dominance of the whole "left reaction". The fact that this persistent dominant was created from one exceptional feeding with meat is of very great importance for an understanding of the exact relationship between the conditioned and unconditioned reflexes, but what interests us at the moment is not this, but another feature.

We have already stated that during this period in the work the animal ran to the *left side* and stood there until food was delivered when the "la" tone (for the right side) was used. As soon as the bowl with the usual rusks was delivered, *the animal turned away and refused to eat.*

Subsequently, the dog's initially increased alimentary excitation declined, and the conditioned secretion was reduced and at times disappeared completely. The dog meanwhile lapsed into a clearly neurotic state.

Let us try to imagine the entire aggregate of the physiological relationships through which such a reaction could develop.

The very fact of a motor reaction to the left, the "meat" side, occurring twenty days after a single reinforcement with meat indicates that one exceptional reinforcement with meat created a dominant state in a certain system of relationships which lasted twenty days. This circumstance alone would be sufficient to enable us to draw conclusions as to the nature of the acceptor of effect prepared with the particular conditioned excitation: in its afferent properties it should correspond exactly with the stimulation of the animal's analysers by the meat rolls. Direct confirmation of this view was afforded by the animal's refusal to eat bread rolls. Thus, the occurrence of a motor reaction with clear dominance to the "meat side" and the subsequent refusal to eat the bread rolls all indicates that the lack of correspondence between the supplementary afferent complex of the conditioned excitation and the return afferentation from the true unconditioned reinforcement was an important factor determining the animal's behaviour and state.

In effect, all forms of elaborated conditioned reflex acts are accomplished with obligatory interaction between the afferent apparatus of the conditioned reflex and the return excitations from the reinforcing agents. If this encounter reveals the adequacy of the two excitations for each other, the behavioural act of the animal is sanctioned, is reinforced. If the return excitation is inadequate for the excitations of this afferent apparatus, there is immediate development of an orientation-investigatory reaction which, *by mobilizing the afferent function of the cerebral cortex to a maximum extent* (the inclusion and intensification of excitations in all analysers), leads to the organization of new complexes of afferent excitations. As a result thereof there is continuous application of increasingly perfected peripheral efforts. These "trials" go on as long as the return afferentation from any of the successive effects does not prove completely adequate for the complex of afferent excitations which developed at the very beginning of the particular behavioural act.

Reverting to the experiments with unconditioned reinforcement substitution, we must add that the need for *agreement* between these two excitations was made particularly obvious when the animal exhibited an accentuated orientation-investigatory reaction and even refused to eat meat so long as it was exceptionally substituted for the usual bread reinforcement (observations of I. A. Zachiniaeva).

One may legitimately ask what there was to prevent the animal simply and promptly eating the meat as it had previously eaten the bread rolls. It is clear that the animal's reaction could only have developed in the way it did *because meat was not in agreement with something or other.* There is then the question—not in agreement with what? But we already know the mechanism of this non-agreement: the ensemble of the signs of meat—its sight and smell, as signs of the unconditioned stimulus, reaching the cortex in the form of specific nerve impulses, proved inadequate for the stored afferent excitation which developed at the very beginning of the action of the conditioned stimulus and corresponded completely to all the afferent signs of the bread previously used. It follows, therefore that, in the form of experiment described, we disturbed those adequate relationships which had been established after many reinforcements between the supplementary afferent complex of conditioned excitation and the return afferentation which always developed from the eating of bread.

It was definitely established in these experiments that a supplementary complex of afferent traces from the preceding reinforcements was already developing in the dog's cerebral cortex during the period of action of the well learnt conditioned stimulus alone, along with the processes determining the effector processes of the conditioned reaction (secretion, respiration, movement etc.). *All the animal's subsequent behaviour is directly dependent on the degree of coincidence achieved between this supplementary afferent complex of the conditioned reflex and the stream of afferent impulses from the periphery, produced by the reinforcing agent.*

When, however, there was any substitution in or removal of the unconditioned reinforcement, that is whenever there was dissociation between
the supplementary afferent complex of the conditioned excitation and the
return afferent impulse from the unconditioned stimulus, there was, first
of all, development of an orientation-investigatory reaction (Fig. 5). There
are grounds for believing that the frontal regions of the cortex play a considerable part in the determination of the coincidence or non-coincidence
of the two excitations (Shumilina, 1949).

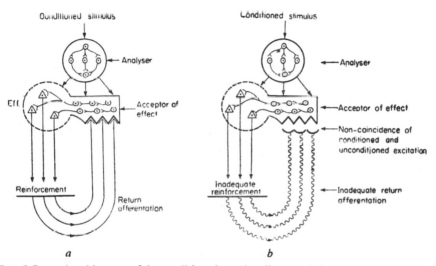

FIG. 5 General architecture of the conditioned reaction diagrammatic representation of the
effect of inadequate reinforcement Conditioned stimulus, Conditioned stimulus Analyser,
Analyser Acceptor of effect, Acceptor of effect, Non-coincidence of conditioned and
unconditioned excitation, Reinforcement Return afferentation, Inadequate reinforcement,
Inadequate return afferentation.

Inasmuch as a hitherto unknown feature of higher nervous activity
had been revealed by these experiments, we were compelled to give it
some sort of designation.

The specially typical physiological feature of the supplementary afferent
complex of the conditioned excitation was its reception of the return
afferent impulses arising from the results of the reflex effect and determination of the agreement or otherwise of these return afferentations with
the stored excitation, that is, with the animal's past experience. We therefore
recognized that the expression "acceptor of effect" was the most fitting
term to denote this cortical apparatus. This apparatus could more correctly

and more exactly be designated the "acceptor of the afferent results of the perfected reflex effect" but, for simplicity of reference, we retain the contracted expression, the "acceptor of effect". The "acceptor" conception affords the most accurate reflection of the meaning of all the experimental results obtained by ourselves and our fellow-workers since 1930, as the Latin word *"acceptare"* implies the two meanings of to receive and to approve.

We shall now digress a little to discuss how successful the term suggested by us has been. At the present moment it is important for us to note that we use this term to designate the very real physiological mechanism which fulfils *the cortical function of assessing the results of any reflex act or any adaptational effect on the part of the intact animal.* Formed as a result of past external effects and constituting part of every conditioned excitation and behavioural act, the acceptor of effect fulfils a function which is decisive for adaptational behaviour: *from the various impulses received from the periphery it determines the degree of accuracy and adequacy of the acts performed in relation to the original initiating stimulus.*

When, for example, a conditioned stimulus, which had always been reinforced with meat, acts on the animal's nervous system, the acceptor of effect, which is already formulated in the commencing part of the action of the conditioned stimulus (Fig. 4), that is, long before the actual reinforcement, then determines *to what extent the reinforcement received corresponds to the earlier afferent experience of the animal.*

Reference can also be made to an example from our daily lives. If an individual, sitting in his study, thinks of going into the dining room for some reason then, at that moment, a complete afferent complex of all the signs and stimulations received in the past from the dining room (acceptor of effect) is reproduced in his cerebral cortex. Having entered the dining room and receiving from it a certain aggregate of stimulations in the form of return afferentations which are *completely coincident with the earlier formed acceptor of effect*, the individual then proceeds to the next link in his behavioural chain.

Let us assume, however, that, abstractedly, the man entered the kitchen or bathroom instead of the dining room. The aggregate of all the external stimulations from the kitchen or bathroom setting is such that, these stimuli, reaching the cerebral cortex, *immediately exhibit lack of agreement with the acceptor of effect which was specific for the dining room and which was already developing in the cortex at a time when the man was still in the study.* In consequence of this dissociation between the stored supplementary afferent complex and the return afferentations from the end of the incorrect action, an orientation-investigatory reaction develops immediately in the individual and he *corrects his mistake*, that is, he brings the stored afferent excitation and the reinforcing effect of the dining room setting into complete agreement.

This last example shows that, in relation to any of our actions, the presence of the additional afferent complex is the sole and universal factor preventing us from making errors and enabling us to correct mistakes once made. And so far we have not been able to see any other possible ways of explaining on a physiological basis how the individual, when he wished to go to the dining room but went to the bathroom by mistake, *detected* the error in his behaviour.

This pattern is so universal and of such decisive significance for an understanding of the behaviour of animals and men that it, naturally, has not escaped the attention of investigators who, at different times and in different forms, have been confronted with the need for its elucidation.

First of all, let it be said once more that the very fact of "reinforcement" which is of universal importance for the doctrine of higher nervous activity, is itself an expression of this pattern. It was by virtue of the amplification of the reflex by reinforcement that radical transformation of the Descartes reflex theory in the doctrine of conditioned reflexes was brought about.

In exactly the same way the "law of effect" suggested in his time by Thorndike (1935) for the phenomenological assessment of the behaviour of animals is essentially the outward expression of the physiological pattern we have just been analysing. Vexkhüll's statement (1929) on "conceptions" in animals, which he used as the basis for idealistic theories, must be regarded in the same light here. Adrian's conjecture that an act "certainly appears to be guided by its effects" (7), undoubtedly refers to the same problem. Cybernetics makes wide use of the idea of return controls both in calculating machines and in other automatic apparatus. It is perhaps unnecessary to say that the so-called "Charpentier illusion" is a direct result of this pattern.

Here in the Soviet Union very close approaches have been made to this problem first, by the psychologists in their investigation of so-called "adjustments" (D. N. Uznadze *et al.*), and again, by I. S. Beritov's physiological laboratory in the investigation of "representations" as a factor guiding the behaviour of animals (16). No attempt was, however, made in any of these trends of thought to give a physiological interpretation to this phenomenon.

Right from the start of the work in our laboratory on this subject (1932), we refused to apply psychological terms to these features of higher nervous activity, designating this regulating factor "sanctioning afferenta-tion" and, as will be evident from what has been explained above, this pattern has submitted to completely physiological treatment without loss of its synthetic importance in the adaptational behaviour of animals.

P. S. Kupalov has recently come very close to our conception of con-ditioned excitation, although he did not discover physiological mechanisms of this supplementary apparatus which regulates the purposeful adaptations of animals to external conditions (17).

THE IMPORTANCE OF THE THEORY EXPOUNDED IN THE EXPLANATION OF SOME PHYSIOLOGICAL AND PSYCHOLOGICAL PHENOMENA

The most effective aspect of the theoretical conceptions on the archi-tecture of the supplementary afferent apparatus in all reflex reactions that have been described is that they enable us to introduce clarity and physiological content into processes which have hitherto remained unex-plained.

For example, we have already directed attention to the question of *why the whole series of compensatory adaptations for disturbance of function always proceeds in one certain direction, namely, towards restoration of function.* What mechanisms guide the selection of reflex acts approaching

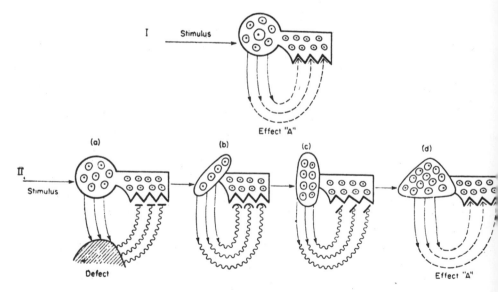

FIG. 6.

more and more closely to the restoration of function? Recognition of the conception of the acceptor of effect clarifies the entire process. It is shown diagrammatically in the individual stages of adaptation in Figure 6.

The diagram labelled *I* gives the architecture of the normal reflex act as it has been presented in all the preceding exposition. The external stimulus causes excitation of all the parts of the cortical apparatus for the particular act. The acceptor of effect is depicted, as in the preceding figures, in the form of a supplementary apparatus with adequate connections for the completely defined return afferentation ("complementary connection")

The several stages depicted under *II* represent the gradual evolution of adaptational behaviour after production of a defect in function "*A*". The first stage *(a)* indicates that, when the former external stimulus acts, the former complex of excitations—both effector excitations and excitations of the acceptor of effect—develop in the central nervous system. By virtue of the defect in the peripheral effect, however, the reflex effect that develops is not adaptational and, in consequence, a new form of return afferentation develops which does not agree with the stored acceptor of effect. This lack of agreement is represented symbolically by the horizontal lines which do not fit into the acceptor of effect. A very important result of this non-coincidence is that the central nervous system, mobilizing all its resources, constructs a new system of central excitations of efferent nature *(b)*, while leaving the acceptor of effect in exactly the same form as before, in that the given stimulus can still be the stimulus for the completely determined adaptational act. Even this second effect does not, however, yield the adaptational effect "*A*" and consequently, the picture of central excitations is again reconstructed and a new adaptational effect is produced, with a new form of return afferentation *(c)*. Figure 6 II depicts a series of such successive adaptations, each associated with the formation of a new picture of central effector excitations. As the diagram shows, only the last system of central excitations *(d)* gave the adaptational effect "*A*" and this also led to coincidence of the return afferentations with the excitations of the acceptor of effect.

Two points in this diagram deserve particular attention. (1) The final adaptational effect in the case of functional defect is generally effected by another system of central effector excitations which differs from the normal system *(I)*, and (2) the acceptor of effect, connected with the features of the adaptational effect, "*A*", *remains the same throughout the entire course of the compensatory adaptations.* This latter circumstance is that which guides the entire series of compensatory adaptations. The effect becomes "sanctioning" only when the return afferentation from it proves adequate for the excitations of the acceptor of effect.

All and every compensatory process can thus be completely explained on a physiological basis.

The phenomenon of the dynamic stereotype can also be interpreted completely on the same basis.

The conceptions expounded by us are of special interest in relation to the physiological analysis of specifically psychological conceptions.

The conception of "meaning" in education and in perception of the outside world, for example, is obviously a variant of coincidence between the stored conditioned excitation and return afferentations, which are "meaningful" in relation to this stored excitation.

All education proceeds with return afferentations playing an obligatory correcting role, and indeed it is only on this basis that education is possible. Every correction of mistakes is invariably the result of non-coincidence between the excitations of the acceptor of effect and return afferentations from the incorrect action. Without this mechanism, both the *detection of the error and its correction* are impossible. It can hardly be disputed that practically any acquisition of habits (speech, labour, athletic etc.) proceeds in the same way as was indicated in the schema for continuous compensatory adaptation (Fig. 6). All forms of searching for objects are based on the features of the apparatus of the acceptor of effect. It would be impossible to "find" anything if the object sought did not not agree in all its qualities with the qualities of the excitations in the stored acceptor of effect.

It is also interesting to note that very familiar and automatized conditioned reflex acts, although their occurrence takes place with the participation of all the components of the return afferentations described above, often do not reach consciousness and develop "unconsciously". As soon, however, as the return afferentation fails to coincide with the stored excitations of the acceptor of effect, the whole process immediately becomes a conscious one.

On the same basis, any automatic action encountering an obstacle in its execution immediately becomes the subject of all-round conscious treatment, as a result of which a way out of the complex situation is found.

Our conceptions on supplementary afferent apparatuses of the conditioned reflex are being reported for the first time in their present complete form to the Conference on Psychology. It is, therefore, naturally difficult at the moment to foresee how widely they will be applied for the physiological analysis of specifically psychological problems.

Yet the material already in existence gives me grounds for hoping that working contact between the physiologist and the psychologist will be even more complete and even more successful than it has been in the past.

Translated by DR. R. CRAWFORD

REFERENCES

1. PAVLOV, I. P. Poln. sobr. soch. (Complete Works), Vol. 3, Bk. 1, p. 156.
2. PAVLOV, I. P. Poln. sobr. soch. (Complete Works), Vol. 3, Bk. 2, pp. 104–105.
3. The Problem of the Centre and the Periphery (Problema tsentra i periferii), coll. papers edited by P. K. Anokhin, Gor'kii, 1935.
4. ANOKHIN, P. K. and IVANOV, A. G., (1935). in "The Problem of the Centre and the Periphery" (Problema tsentra i periferii), coll. papers edited by P. K. Anokhin, p. 72, Gor'kii.
5. ASRATYAN, E. A., (1954). The Physiology of the Central Nervous System (Fiziologiya tsentral'noi nervnoi sistemy), U.S.S.R. Acad. Med. Sci.
6. ANOKHIN, P. K., (1954). *Khirurgiya*, Nos. 10 and 12.
7. ADRIAN, E. D., (1947). *Brain*, 70, No. 1.
8. ADRIAN, E. D., (1955). *J. of E.E.G. and Clin. Neurophysiol*, 17, No. 2, p. 318.
9. WAGNER. (1955). Problems and Samples of Biological Regulation.
10. YEGOROV, YA. YE., (1911). Dissertation. St. Petersburg.
11. HILGARD and MARQUIS. (1940). Conditioning and Learning.
12. PAVLOV, I. P., Poln. sobr. soch. (Complete Works), Vol. 3, Bk. 2, p. 92.
13. LAPTEV, I. I., (1949). in "Problems of Higher Nervous Activity" (Problemy vysshei nervnoi deyatel'nosti), coll. papers edited by P. K. Anokhin. U.S.S.R. Acad. Med. Sci.
14. Uch. zap. MGU—Conference on Compensation, 1945.
15. ANOKHIN, P. K. and STREZH, YE. G., (1933). *Fiziol. zh. SSSR*, No. 5.
16. BERITOV, I. S., (1947). The Basic Forms of Nervous and Psychic Activity (Ob osnovnykh formakh nervnoi i psikhonervnoi deyatel'nosti), Acad. Sci. U.S.S.R., Moscow-Leningrad.
17. KUPALOV, P. S., (1955). *Zh. nervn. deyat.*, 5, No. 2.

THE DYNAMICS OF "TRANSFER"
OF CONDITIONED REFLEX CONNECTIONS
FROM ONE SIGNAL SYSTEM TO THE OTHER*

V. S. MERLIN

Paedagogic Institute, Molotov

A. G. IVANOV-SMOLENSKII was the first to submit the phenomenon which he termed the "projection" of conditioned reflex processes from one signal system to the other to experimental investigation. This "projection", according to Ivanov-Smolenskii, manifested itself in two ways. First, conditioned reflexes to stimuli in one signal system were retained when these stimuli were suddenly replaced by the corresponding stimuli in the other signal system; light stimuli, for example, could be replaced by the corresponding verbal equivalents or vice versa. Secondly, "projection" manifested itself in the fact; that the subject gave correct verbal accounts of the stimuli used, their relationship to one another and of their own reactions to these stimuli.

Ivanov-Smolenskii explained both forms of manifestation of the "projection" of conditioned reflex processes from one signal system to the other in the same way. His explanation was based on the principle of selective irradiation, whereby a nervous process arising in any centres in one signal system spreads selectively to the corresponding centres in the other signal system. It is implied here that, having spread, the nerve process (excitation or inhibition) is firmly retained in the parts of the cortex it has invaded. This type of irradiation is therefore termed "static", as distinct from the usual type of irradiation in the cortex and subcortex, which is dynamic in character. In this conception the first and second signal systems are obviously pictured as being spatially discrete. It should be mentioned that, in his last work, Ivanov-Smolenskii again stressed that selective static irradiation was the fundamental element in elective generalization, but that signs of selective dynamic irradiation and selective induction were also observed (1).

* *Voprosy psikhologii*, No. 2, pp. 53–67, 1957.

The main difficulty confronting the theory of selective static irradiation is the unusually dynamic character of functional relationships in speech and thought activity. The same object or phenomenon can have different names, depending on the thought context. The reaction to the word concept may sometimes be the exact opposite of the reaction to the isolated object or phenomenon designated by this concept (e.g. the reactions to the mathematical concept and actual plurality of objects). This dynamic character of functional relationships is difficult to reconcile with the conception of spatial seperation of the first and second signal systems or with the static type of nerve process irradiation. It can be assumed that it was difficulty of this nature that compelled Pavlov to reject the conception of topographically separate first and second signal systems, which was the view he originally held. In the last year of his life Pavlov expressed himself thus: "When one is discussing the separateness of these systems, one must think in terms mainly of functional, and not anatomical, localization, and of the training of these systems" (2).

Again, doubts are raised by the actual method used for the investigation of "projection" of conditioned reflex processes from one signal system to the other, namely, the exceptional or sudden replacement of the conditioned stimuli in one signal system by stimuli in the other. It is generally impossible by this method to trace the dynamics of "projection". Naturally, therefore, the conception of "projection" acquires a purely static character. An attempt was made in the present work to trace the *dynamics* of this process which Ivanov-Smolenskii termed "projection". The main problem was to determine whether the dynamics of "projection" was consistent with the conception of selective and static irradiation from one signal system to the other.

We employed two new methodological principles in the investigation.

First, "projection" was studied by the method of sudden replacement of conditioned stimuli in one signal system by stimuli in the other. system and by alternation of the stimuli in the two signal systems throughout an entire experiment.

Secondly, the two main indices of projection—replacement of the conditioned stimuli and the verbal response—were studied independently and were then systematically compared. We suggest that difference between or identity of the two mechanisms can only be established in this way.

METHOD

The skin-galvanic reaction was used as the conditioned reflex index. Speech and motor reinforcement (in accordance with preliminary instructions) was employed. On the order "Pull!", the subject had to pull on a spring handle with previously prescribed force. The force of the movement was recorded through transmission mechanism on a scale which was on the experimenter's table. After the subject had completed the movement the experimenter told him the reading on the scale and encouraged him, saying "Correct". The muscular contraction served as the unconditioned stimulus for the skin-galvanic reaction. The strength of the reinforcement (in consequence of the reports made by the experimenter) remained almost uniform throughout an experiment. The encouragement given by the experimenter maintained optimum tone in the cortex. The differential stimuli were not accompanied by an order from the experimenter ("Pull!"). The conditioned stimuli acted alone for 10 seconds and, jointly with reinforcement, for a further 20 seconds. The movement was executed with the right hand and the galvanometer electrodes were fastened to the dorsal aspect and the palm of the left hand. The recording of the skin-galvanic reaction was visual. The conditioned stimuli were delivered in stereotype. The stereotype consisted of two pairs of coloured lamps and two verbal equivalents corresponding to the colours. The lamps in each pair were lit simultaneously but at different points in the visual field 5–10 cm apart. Direct and verbal stimuli alternated. In the first series of experiments positive conditioned reflexes and the corresponding differentiations were elaborated to stimuli in the first signal system and the formation of conditioned reflexes to the corresponding but unreinforced verbal equivalents was investigated. In the second series (with the same subjects) conditioned reflex connections were elaborated to the verbal equivalents and the formation of conditioned reflexes to the corresponding but unreinforced stimuli in the first signal system was examined. The speech reinforcement of the movement in the second series of experiments was effected either by word of mouth or by illuminating a screen bearing the appropriate inscription.

Two orders of alternation of the conditioned stimuli were used within each series of experiments. The first order was (1) the main positive reinforced stimulus (A); (2) the differential stimulus in the same signal system (B); (3) the stimulus in the other signal system corresponding to differentiation (b); and (4) the stimulus in the other signal system corresponding to the positive stimulus (a). This order will be referred to hereafter as I $ABba$ (for the first series of experiments) and II $ABba$ (for the second series). The other sequence was (1) the main positive reinforced stimulus (A); (2) the corresponding unreinforced stimulus in the other signal system (a); (3) the stimulus, differential in relation to the reinforced stimulus A, in the same signal system (B); and (4) the stimulus in the other signal system corresponding to the differential stimulus (*b*). This sequence will be referred to hereafter as I *AaBb* (for the first series) and II *AaBb* (for the second series). The time interval between the first two conditioned stimuli was changed from 1·5 to 1·0 minute and the intervals between the remaining conditioned stimuli were always one minute.

In each of the two main series, after stable transfer of the conditioned connections from one signal system to the other had been effected, the positive, previously reinforced conditioned reflex was extinguished and parallel changes occurring in the previously unreinforced conditioned reflex (to the corresponding stimuli in the other signal system) were observed.

Adaptation of the skin-galvanic reaction to all the direct and verbal stimuli used in an experiment was effected before each series of experiments, that is, the orientation reactions to all these stimuli were extinguished to 0. In the adaptation experiments the stimuli were delivered at random, in no definite sequence. The subject gave his verbal account after each experiment.

The subjects were nine first-year students of the Pedagogic Institute, aged 17–18, drawn from the academic groups in which the author taught. They had only a very general and elementary knowledge of conditioned reflex theory. The total number of experiments was 72.

RESULTS

In our experiments the reinforced stimulus in one signal system alternated with the unreinforced stimuli in the other signal system. This procedure is exactly similar to the procedure for differentation of a conditioned reflex. We thus simultaneously created conditions for two opposite processes—transfer of conditioned reflex connexions from one signal system to the other and differentation of reinforced and unreinforced conditioned stimuli. What relationship exists between these processes? Which of them will actually take place? Consideration must be given to the fact that the occurrence or non-occurrence of transfer of conditioned reflex connexions will depend both on the general patterns of higher nervous activity and on the individual's individual and typological features.

There was none among our subjects in whom transfer from one signal system to the other could be said to be absent. In 6 of the 9 subjects we observed complete transfer of both positive and inhibitory conditioned reflex connections from the first to the second signal system and from the second to the first. In the case of 2 subjects there was complete transfer only from the first signal system to the second and in one subject, only from the second to the first.

The main fact established in the experiments was that *the rapidity of formation, the persistence and the strength of "projection" or differentiation depended on the relative positions in the stereotype of the reinforced conditioned stimulus in one signal system and the corresponding but unreinforced (projected) stimulus in the other signal system.* When the corresponding unreinforced (projected) stimulus in the other signal system was used directly after the reinforced stimulus (order *AaBb*), the "transfer" of the conditioned connections was most rapid, most enduring and most stable. When the reinforced stimulus in one signal system was followed first by the two inhibitory stimuli and only thereafter by the unreinforced projected stimulus in the other signal system (order *ABba*), then either transfer of the conditioned connection was completely absent or, having developed, it disappeared rapidly.

We give some records of the experiments. In Record No. 3 (subject B.) the positive conditioned stimulus in the first signal system—blue and green colours—and the corresponding unreinforced conditioned stimulus in the second signal system—the words "blue" and "green"—were separated by the two inhibitory stimuli—white and orange colours and the corresponding words (*ABba*).

The Record shows that at first (conditioned stimulus "B. G." No. 4) there was projection of the positive conditioned reflex from the first to the second signal system. This "projection" was, however, unstable. The reactions to the stimuli "B. G." No. 5 and No. 7 were 0. Subsequently, after a single appearance in response to stimulus No. 8, it again declined and reached values of 0 and 1 (No. 9 and No. 10).

Let us compare Record No. 4, made immediately afterwards with Record No. 3. In this experiment the conditioned positive stimulus in the first signal system was followed immediately by the corresponding verbal stimulus (*AaBb*).

In this case a positive conditioned reflex to the words "blue, green" was formed from the very beginning of the experiment (stimulus No.11) and remained present to the end. The results in the cases of the other 5 subjects were completely similar. Changing the time interval between the direct stimuli (blue and green lights) and the corresponding words from 1·5 to 1·0 minute did not make any lasting difference. The position then was that, with the stimuli in one order—*ABba*—transfer of the positive conditioned reflex from the first to the second signal system either was absent altogether or, if it did form, was unstable and ultimately disap-

Record No. 3. Subject B. Experiment of 24 March 1955

Experiment commenced 18°01'; ended 18°54'30''

Notation. B.G.: blue and green colours. "B.G.": verbal stimulus—the words "blue, green". W.O.: white and orange colours. "W.O.": verbal stimulus—the words "white, orange"

Serial No. of the presentation of the given stimulus	Time	Conditioned stimulus	Reinforcement	Motor reaction Unconditioned	Skin-galvanic reaction		Background	Speech reaction
					Conditioned	Unconditioned		
5	14'00''	B.G.	+	180	+10	+15	—	—
4	15'30''	W.O.	—	—	+35	—	—	—
4	17'30''	"W.O."	—	—	+35	—	—	—
4	18'30''	"B.G."	—	—	+ 8	—	—	—
6	19'30''	B.G.	+	185	+30	+75	—	—
5	21'00''	W.O.	—	—	+30	—	—	—
5	22'00''	"W.O."	—	—	+11	—	—	—
5	23'00''	"B.G."			0	—	—	—
7	24'00''	B.G.	+	175	+35	+95	—	—
6	25'30''	W.O.	—	—	+10	—	—	—
6	27'00''	"W.O."	—	—	+20	—	—	—
6	28'00''	"B.G."	—	—	+ 2	—	—	—
8	29'00''	B.G.	+	160	+20	+60	—	—
7	30'30''	W.O.	—	—	+20	—	—	—
7	31'30''	"W.O."	—	—	0	—	—	—
7	32'30''	"B.G."	—	—	0	—	—	—
8	33'30''	B.G.	+	170	+ 3	+53	—	—
8	35'30''	W.O.	—	—	0	—	—	—
8	36'30''	"W.O."	—	—	+ 3	—	Noise	—
8	37'30''	"B.G."	—	—	+ 3	—	—	—
10	46'40''	B.G.	+	170	+18	+95	—	—
9	48'00''	W.O.	—	—	0	—	—	—
9	49'00''	"W.O."	—	—	0	—	—	—
9	50'00''	"B.G."	—	—	0	—	—	—
11	51'00''	B.G.	+	170	+5	+97	—	—
10	52'30''	W.O.	—	—	0	—	—	—
10	53'30''	"W.O."	—	—	+ 6	—	—	—
10	54'30''	"B.G."	—	—	+ 1	—	—	—

peared; with the stimuli in the other order—*AaBb*—transfer took place and was seen in relation to at least three successive applications of the sequence—an indication of its stable character. We suggest that this last fact is of fundamental importance.

Record No. 4

Experiment commenced 18.00 hr; ended 18.27 hr

Serial No. of presentation of the given stimulus	Time	Conditioned stimulus	Reinforce-ment	Motor reaction	Skin-galvanic reaction		Background	Remarks
					Conditioned	Unconditioned		
12	0′30″	B.G.	+	170	+ 5	+125	—	—
11	2′00″	"B.G."	—		+15		—	—
11	3′00″	W.O.	—		+ 2		—	—
11	4′00″	"W.O."	—		+ 8		—	—
13	5′00″	B.G.	+	170	+10	+250	—	—
12	6′30″	"B.G."	—		+ 5		—	—
12	7′30″	W.O.	—		0		—	—
12	8′30″	"W.O."	—		+ 6		—	—
14	9′30″	B.G.	+	170	+12	+160	—	—
13	11′30″	"B.G."	—		+10		—	—
13	12′00″	W.O.	—		0		—	—
13	13′00″	"W.O."	—		0		—	—

In addition, these experiments showed that the order *ABba* was the most favourable for differentation of the conditioned stimuli *belonging to the same signal system*. When the positive and differential stimuli were separated from each other by an intervening speech stimulus, differentiation was either absent or was achieved with difficulty and was unstable. Instead, generalization of the conditioned reflex took place. When the differential stimulus followed the positive directly, the best conditions were created for differential inhibition. We give the following Records to illustrate these points.

In Record No. 3 for subject Zh. the positive (B. G.) and differential (W. O.) stimuli in the first signal system were separated by one intervening verbal conditioned stimulus "B. G.". Right to the end of the experiment there was no differentation. In Record No. 4 for the same subject the arrangement of the experiment up to the seventh presentation of the stimuli was the same, and differentiation was likewise absent. From the seventh presentation the differential unreinforced stimulus W. O. followed directly after the positive reinforced stimulus B. G.; with the stimuli in this order there was subsequent gradual development of differentation, a nil reaction was already being observed at the end of the experiment (stimulus No. 10), and it was found that differentation had been transferred from the first

Record No. 3. Subject Zh. Experiment of 26 February 1955

Experiment commenced 18.05 hr; ended 18.38 hr

Serial No. of presentation of the given stimulus	Time	Conditioned stimulus	Reinforcement	Motor reaction	Skin-galvanic reaction		Background	Speech reaction
					Conditioned	Unconditioned		
1	8′30″	G.B.	+	65	− 5+20	+25	+25	29″
1	11′30″	"G.B."	−	−	+15	−	−	−
1	13′20″	W.O.	−	−	+27	−	−	−
1	15′20″	"W.O."	−	−	+31	−	−	−
2	17′20″	G.B.	+	80	+25	+35	−	20″
2	19′20″	"G.B."	−	−	+25	−	−	−
2	21′20″	W.O.	−	−	+12	−	−	−
2	23′20″	"W.O."	−		+10−10	−	−	−
3	25′20″	G.B.	+	75	+ 5−30	−35	−	20″
3	27′20″	"G.B."	−	−	⊢ 5−15	−	−	−
3	29′20″	W.O.	−	−	+ 2	−	−	−
3	31′20″	"W.O."	−		+ 5−35	−	−	−
4	33′20″	G.B.	+	75	−23	−63	−	20″
4	34′20″	"G.B."	−	−	+ 5−19	−	−	−
4	36′20″	W.O.	−	−	−35	−	−	−
4	38′20″	"W.O."	−	−	+ 5−15	−	−	−

to the second signal system, although in unstable form ("W. O." No. 8 and No. 10).

The results were the same with the other subjects. Change of the intervals between the conditioned stimuli from 1·5 to 1·0 minute produced no lasting differences.

The series of experiments II *ABba* and II *AaBb* showed that transfer of the conditioned connections in the reverse direction, from the second signal system to the first, proceeded in exactly the same way and under exactly the same conditions. Lack of space prevents us from giving Records.

Certain questions arise. Is this transfer absolutely stable and enduring? Will the projected conditioned reflex be retained for an indefinite time, despite the absence of reinforcement, so long as we reinforce the main reflex? Special experiments, which we have not undertaken, will be necessary for answers to these questions. The dependence of the transferred conditioned reflex on the reinforced main reflex is seen, however, in another fact: the transferred conditioned reflex was extinguished when the main conditioned reflex was extinguished.

Record No. 4. Subject Zh. Experiment of 1 March 1955

Experiment commenced 19.00 hr; ended 19.49 hr

Serial No. of presentation of given conditioned stimulus	Time	Conditioned stimulus	Reinforcement	Motor reaction	Skin-galvanic reaction		Background	Remarks
					Conditioned	Unconditioned		
5	5′00″	B.G.	+	85	−10	−22	—	—
5	7′00″	"B.G."	—	—	−14	—	—	—
5	9′00″	W.O.	—	—	−8	—	—	—
5	11′04″	"W.O."	—	—	−14	—	—	—
6	13′00″	B.G.	+	45	−14	−22	—	—
6	15′00″	"B.G."	—		−8	—	—	—
6	17′00″	W.O.	—		−15	—	—	—
6	19′00″	"W.O."	—		−15	—	—	—
7	21′00″	B.G.	+	40	−15	−25	—	—
7	23′00″	W.O.	—		−5	—	—	—
7	25′00″	"W.O."	—		−15	−25	—	—
7	27′00″	"B.G."	—		−14	—	—	—
8	29′00″	B.G.	+	40	−24	−30	—	—
8	31′00″	W.O.	—		−9	—	—	—
8	33′00″	"W.O."	—		−7	—	—	—
8	35′00″	"B.G."	—		−4	—	—	—
9	37′00″	B.G.	+	40	−15	−15	—	—
9	39′00″	W.O.	—		−12	—	—	—
9	41′00″	"W.O."	—		−15	—	—	—
9	43′00″	"B.G."	—		−3	—	—	—
10	45′00″	B.G.	+	39	−7	−12	—	—
10	47′00″	W.O.	—		−0	—	—	—
10	49′00″	"W.O."	—		−0	—	—	—
10	51′00″	"B.G."	—		−2	—	—	—

We reproduce a continuation of the Record of subject B. Comparison of this Record with that given earlier (Record on p. 109) reveals the following. So long as we reinforced the main stimulus (blue and green colours) the transferred conditioned reflex to the words "blue, green" was not inhibited despite the fact that we did not reinforce it on 13 occasions. When later we began to extinguish the main reflex to the blue and green colours, the conditioned reflex to the words "blue, green" began to decline gradually, which meant that extinctive inhibition was starting. As often happens, the extinction here proceeded in an undulant manner. From

Record No. 4. Subject B. Experiment of 25 March 1955

Experiment commenced 18.00 hr; ended 18.27 hr

Serial No. of presentation of the given stimulus	Time	Conditioned stimulus	Reinforcement	Motor-reaction	Skin-galvanic reaction	Background	Remarks
15	14′00″	B.G.	—	—	+ 1		
14	15′00″	"B.G."		—	+17	—	
16	16′00″	B.G.	--	—	+ 4	—	
15	17′00″	"B.G."	-	—	+10	—	
17	18′00″	B.G.	—	—	0	—	
18	19′00″	"B.G."	—	—	+17	—	
18	20′00″	B.G.	—	—	+17	—	
17	21′00″	"B.G."	--	—	+ 1	—	
19	22′00″	B.G.	—	—	0	—	
18	23′00″	"B.G."	—	—	+ 6	—	
20	24′00″	B.G.	—	—	0	—	
19	25′00″	"B.G."		—	+15	—	
21	26′00″	B.G.	—	—	0	—	
20	27′00″	"B.G."	—	—	0	—	

time to time the conditioned reflex to the words "blue, green" increased, sometimes even fairly considerably (stimulus No. 19). Ultimately, however, after 7 non-reinforcements of the reaction to the verbal stimulus, the reaction was nil (stimulus No. 20). We therefore have grounds for assuming that in this case we were actually dealing with dependence of the conditioned reflex connections in one signal system on their formation in the other.

Our experiments have thus demonstrated that whichever of the two opposite phenomena develops—differentiation of the stimuli within the same signal system or transfer of the conditioned reflex from one signal system to the other—depends on the character of the alternation of the reinforced and unreinforced stimuli. If the reinforced stimulus is followed immediately by the unreinforced stimulus in the same signal system, differentation of these two stimuli develops. If the reinforced stimulus is followed by the corresponding unreinforced stimulus in the other signal system, there is transfer of the conditioned reflex from the one system to the other.

The second main fact established in our experiments is the following. The theory of selective irradiation implies that the nervous process develops originally at the points in the cortex on which the main stimuli act, and then spreads to the corresponding cortical points of the other signal system. This in fact is the origin of the term "projection" of conditioned reflex connections. This view is not supported by the findings in our experiments. In no experiment was it the case that the conditioned reflex connections were *first* formed in the foci of the main stimuli and were then transferred to the other signal system. On the contrary, in the case of some subjects, despite the fact that we reinforced the direct stimulus (blue and green colours), elaboration of the conditioned skin-galvanic reaction to the corresponding words ("blue, green") outstripped elaboration of the reaction to the direct stimulus. We give a Record of an experiment.

Record No. 2. Subject S. Experiment of 10 March 1955

Experiment commenced 18.08 hr; ended 18.45 hr

Serial No. of presentation of given stimulus	Time	Conditioned stimulus	Reinforcement	Motor reaction	Skin-galvanic reaction		Background	Remarks
					Conditioned	Unconditioned		
1	10'00"	B.G.	+	85	0	+39	—	
1	11'30"	W.O.	—	—	+ 1	—	—	
1	12'30"	"W.O."	—	—	+ 1	—	—	
1	13'30"	"B.G."	—	—	+ 5	—	—	
2	14'30"	B.G.	+	85	+ 5	+30	—	
2	16'00"	W.O.	—	—	+ 1	—	—	
2	17'00"	"W.O."	—	—	0	—	—	
2	18'00"	"B.G."	—	-	+ 4	—	—	
3	19'00"	B.G.	+	90	+12	+80	—	
3	21'00"	W.O.	—	—	+ 6	—	·—	
3	22'00"	"W.O."	—	—	+28	—	—	
3	23'00"	"B.G."	—	—	+22	—	—	

In the first application of the reinforced direct stimulus B. G. the reaction was nil, while the first application of the corresponding verbal stimulus "B. G." (unreinforced) was attended by a reaction equal to +5. Similar phenomena were seen in three other subjects. In all the other subjects in whom projection of conditioned connections from one signal system to the other was observed the conditioned skin-galvanic reactions to the main, reinforced stimulus and to the corresponding projected stimulus developed simultaneously.

This fact might also be explained on the grounds that every application of a new stimulus or of a new order of the stimuli might evoke an orientation reaction. The fact that the *inhibitory reactions* in the different signal systems also developed simultaneously acquires, therefore, special importance. Differentiation to the projected stimulus developed simultaneously with differentiation to the main stimulus, and sometimes even before it (see Record No. 3, subject B, experiment of 24 March 1955, stimulus No. 5 and No. 7, on p. 109). It was the same with extinction. We give the record of an experiment on subject G. of 5 May 1955. In this experiment the conditioned reflex to the basic stimulus in the first signal system, the blue and green colours, was extinguished. Prior to extinction this reflex, after 30 reinforcements, was equivalent to a galvanometer beam deviation of 10 mm on the scale.

Record No. 4. Subject G. Experiment of 25 March 1955

Experiment commenced 19.05 hr; ended 20.01 hr

Serial No. of presentation of the given stimulus	Time	Conditioned stimulus	Reinforcement	Motor reaction	Skin-galvanic reaction		Background	Remarks
					Conditioned	Unconditioned		
31	53′00″	B.G.	—	—	−5	—	—	
30	54′00″	"B.G."	—	—	+2	—	—	
32	55′00″	B.G.	—	—	+2−2	—	—	
31	56′00″	"B.G."	—	—	0	—	—	
33	57′00″	B.G.	—	—	+3	—	—	
32	58′00″	"B.G."	—	—	0	—	—	
34	59′00″	B.G.	—	—	0	—	—	
33	00′00″	"B.G."	—	—	0	—	—	
35	01′00″	B.G.	—	—	0	—	—	

It will be seen that, during extinction, absolute inhibition developed first in response to the projected stimulus, the words "blue, green" (stimuli No. 31 and 32), and only thereafter in response to the basic stimulus, the blue and green colours (stimulus 34).

The same phenomenon was seen in three more subjects, and it occurred in both the first and second series of experiments in each of them.

8*

In this connection there was also another characteristic feature. In some cases a conditioned reflex appeared sometimes in response to the basic stimulus and sometimes in response to the corresponding projected stimulus. *It was as if the excitation or inhibition fluctuated (oscillated) between the first and second signal systems.* It is of particular importance that this fluctuation was seen in relation to both the positive conditioned reaction and the inhibitory conditioned reaction (differentiation), which again excludes any explanation of this phenomenon by the effect of an orientation reaction. To illustrate this we give an extract from the Record of subject G. for 25 March 1955.

Record No. 3. Subject G. Experiment of 25 March 1955
Experiment began 19.09 hr; ended 19.59 hr

Serial No. of presentation of the given stimulus	Time	Conditioned stimulus	Reinforcement	Motor reaction	Skin-galvanic reaction		Background	Remarks
					Conditioned	Unconditioned		
11	42'30"	B.G.	+	115	+4	+15	—	
11	43'00"	W.O.	—	—	+3	—	—	
11	44'00"	"W.O."	—	—	+1	—	—	
11	45'00"	"B.G."	—	—	0	—	—	
12	46'00"	B.G.	+	115	+4	+24	—	
12	47'30"	W.O.	—	—	0	—	—	
12	48'30"	"W.O."	—	—	+3	—	—	
12	49'30"	"B.G."	—	—	+6	—	—	
13	50'30"	B.G.	+	105	+5	—	—	
13	51'30"	W.O.	—	—	+5	—	—	
13	52'30"	"W.O."	—	—	+2	—	—	
13	53'30"	"B.G."	—	—	+7	—	—	

The Record shows that differentiation developed sometimes in response to the projected stimulus, the words "white, orange" (reduction of the reactions to stimuli No. 11 and No. 13) and sometimes in response to the main stimulus, white and orange colours (stimulus No. 12).

Thus the actual term "projection" or "transfer" is not in accordance with the facts observed. The phenomenon discovered and investigated by Ivanov-Smolenskii would be more correctly termed *dependence* of the conditioned reflex connections in one signal system on the elaboration of connections to stimuli in the other signal system with corresponding significance. This terminology does not contain any implied explanation of the physiological mechanism, as does the term "projection".

Finally, we present the third main fact emerging from our experiments. The notion of selective irradiation of nerve processes contained in Ivanov-Smolenskii's conception is linked with one tacitly implied but experimentally unconfirmed assumption. It is suggested that "transfer" of conditioned reflex connections from the first signal system to the second and adequate verbal accounting by the subject are physiologically identical processes. But the participation in speech activity of specialized parts of the cortex, the speech "centres", distinct from the centres for the first signal system is not a matter of any doubt. This, of course, does not in any way mean that speech activity depends solely on these specialized and localized areas. How then, if not by selective irradiation, can the transfer of conditioned reflex connections from one signal system to the other be effected? In order to answer this question it is necessary, first of all, to determine experimentally whether transfer of conditioned reflex connections from the first to the second signal system does in fact depend on the same nervous processes as adequate verbal accounting. For this we compared the degree of adequacy in the verbal accounts given by our subjects with the presence or absence of transfer of conditioned connections from the first to the second signal system.

Comparison of the verbal accounts given by our subjects with the projection of conditioned reflex connections from the first to the second signal system revealed that there was no correspondence between the two. In the case of some subjects, despite definite and stable projection, the verbal account was generally very inaccurate. Subject S., for example, had correct projection of the positive and inhibitory conditioned reflex connections from the first signal system to the second, yet his verbal account was like this: "The first time you said "blue, green" I started a bit, but afterwards, when I became accustomed to the routine, I was no longer straining, and when you said "Pull!", I pulled. When you said "White, orange" I also tried to . . . ., but afterwards when I was accustomed to the routine, I did not begin to pull. (What was the order of the signals?) First "white, orange" then "blue, green". Later "pull" and then let go, and again the same, and later the little lamps lit—in the same order. (In what order did the lamps light?) First the blue and green, then the white and orange. (In what order did the names of the colours alternate?) When you said the names the lamps did not light. The colours were named first, then the lamps lit. (Were the names of the colours the same as those of the lamps or not?) On the contrary, I think that when you said "blue, green" the white and orange lamps lit and when you said "white, orange", the blue and green lamps lit".

Thus, the subject perceived the words "white, orange", not as following the corresponding colours but as a signal preceding the delivery of the opposite colours, blue and green. In the same way she perceived the words "blue, green", not as following the corresponding colours but as a preliminary signal for the opposite colours, white and orange. It follows, therefore, that the subject's verbal account contained no recognition of the correspondence between the colour signals and the words that followed. At the same time there was complete correspondence between the two in the skin-galvanic reactions. The subject reacted in exactly the same way to the words "blue, green" as to the colours, blue and green, that is, by a positive skin-galvanic reaction, and the words "white, orange" caused inhibition of the skin-galvanic reaction, just as the corresponding colours. Thus, the verbal account in this case was not in agreement with the projection of the conditioned connections from the first to the second signal system. The same inversion of the connection between the verbal and the direct colour stimuli was present in the verbal accounts given by subjects B. and G., while the projection of the conditioned reflex connections from the first to the second signal system in these subjects was correct.

The following feature, observed, it is true, in only one subject, was still more convincing. In the experiments on this subject (because she was found to be suffering from partial colour blindness) we used a higher and a lower tone (Galton's whistle) of 1200 and 1220 c/s as conditioned stimuli in the first signal system and the corresponding verbal equivalents as stimuli in the second signal system. In the first experimental session (transfer of conditioned connections from the second to the first signal system) the subject made it evident that she distinguished the two tones badly: "Sometimes they are the same and sometimes they seem different. I cannot tell which is the higher and which the lower tone". At the same time, after four non-reinforcements of the differential stimulus, the words "low tone", which gave absolute inhibition, the inhibition was at once transferred to the first signal system and was retained to the end of the experiment. The positive conditioned reflex was likewise transferred to the first signal system, but it was inconstant and unstable (in the series II *ABba*).

All these facts indicate that, physiologically, adequate verbal accounting is not identical with transfer.

Further, it is quite important to remember that the verbal account is inadequate only in the first or the first two experiments. After several experiments even those subjects whose verbal accounts were at first incorrect then gave completely correct accounts.

This is apparently explained by the fact that, as a result of previous interrogation by the experimenter, there was a certain direction of the subject's interest to the phenomena which were likely to be discussed in the subsequent experiments. Consequently, the degree of adequacy of the verbal account depended on the presence of a special task confronting the subject. Physiologically, this task could be regarded as completely specific verbal reinforcement in the form of implied instructions.

DISCUSSION

The facts ascertained are opposed to the conception of selective and static irradiation in the following respects. This conception implies that the nervous process, having spread from one signal system to the other, is firmly maintained in the parts of the cortex it invades. Hence the term static irradiation. At the same time the phenomenon of "transfer" of conditioned reflex connections from one signal system to the other is unusually variable. Transfer having taken place, it may then prove unstable or disappear completely. Again, unstable initially, transfer may later become stable. It follows, therefore, that the excitation or inhibition developing in the cortical elements of the second signal system during "transfer" is itself unstable by virtue of the specific function of the second signal system. It becomes stable or, conversely, unstable, depending on definite objective conditions. The principal conditions on which the occurrence or non-occurrence of transfer from one signal system to the other and the stability or instability of the transfer depended were the time relationships between the direct conditioned stimuli in the first signal system and the verbal stimuli of corresponding significance in the second signal system. These time relationships are expressed in the order of alternation of the direct and verbal stimuli and in the different intervals between the stimuli determined by a given sequence. Consequently, the nervous processes developing in connection with transfer to the second signal system are dynamic in the same degree and in the same sense as nervous processes in the cortex generally are dynamic. They are determined by the time relationships between the stimuli. Thus, if it is assumed that transfer is explained by irradiation, then irradiation too must be dynamic and not static in character. Observed facts are not, however, consistent with selective irradiation of dynamic type.

The principal law governing the dynamics of nervous processes in the cerebral cortex is that, after irradiation, there is subsequent concentration of the nervous process. It is natural, therefore, that more time should be required for the development of concentration than for the development of irradiation. In our experiments, however, both transfer of the positive conditioned reflex from one signal system to the other and differentiation within the same signal system proceeded most favourably when the main reinforced stimulus was followed immediately by the corresponding stimulus in the other signal system in the case of transfer, and by the similar stimulus in the same signal system in the case of differentiation. Change of the interval from 1·5 to 1·0 minute was of no material importance in either case. Consequently, quite paradoxically and against all we know about irradiation and concentration, the same or even a lesser interval of time was required for irradiation of the nervous processes from one signal system to the other in comparison with the time required for concentration of the nervous process in one signal system and for differentiation derived therefrom.

Further, in experiments with irradiation and concentration the time interval is always the indicator of the distance between the corresponding points in the cortex. More time is required for irradiation to more distant points in the cortex and, conversely, the irradiating process reaches the nearer points earlier. In our experiments the most favourable conditions both for transfer and for generalization of the conditioned stimuli in the same signal system were created in the *AaBb* series. In this series, however, the interval between the main and the projected stimulus was from 1·0 to 1·5 minutes and the interval between the reinforced and the unreinforced stimulus in the same signal system was from 2·0 to 2·5 minutes. Consequently, irradiation of the nervous process between the cortical points referable to the same signal system and to the same analyser required a considerably greater time interval than irradiation between cortical points referable to different signal systems and different analysers (auditory analyser for the second signal system stimulus and visual for the stimulus in the first signal system).

The irradiation cannot even be explained by the fact that not infrequently a conditioned reflex—positive or inhibitory—to a projected stimulus develops before that to the basic stimulus.

It cannot therefore be asserted that the nervous process developed initially in the focus of the main stimulus and then spread to the focus of the projected stimulus. Consequently the actual term "projection" or "transfer" is not consistent with the observed facts. Finally, the fact that we sometimes observed alternation of the conditioned reflex—positive or inhibitory—in response sometimes to the main and sometimes to the projected stimulus is not consistent with the conception of selective irradiation. Nor can the occurrence of selective irradiation be based on the fact that the nerve process in projection must spread to those localized parts of the cortex which participate in speech activity. We have seen that speech activity, as manifested in the verbal account, was determined by other objective conditions than "transfer" of the conditioned reflex connections from the first signal system to the second. There are therefore no grounds for asserting that the physiological mechanism of transfer is identical with the mechanism for any speech activity.

Thus, none of the facts observed is consistent with the conception of selective irradiation.

In what direction should a positive answer to the question of transfer of conditioned reflex connections be sought?

First of all, it seems obvious that an answer should be sought on the assumption of *different functional levels in the same cortical elements*, and not of topographically discrete first and second signal systems.

Secondly, the facts described above concerning the fluctuation (oscillation) of conditioned reflexes between the first and second signal systems create the impression that this phenomenon is dependent on assimilation of rhythm by the cortical cells subject thereto, in the sense of the Vvedenskii–Ukhtomskii doctrine. The testing of both these hypotheses will, of course, require special investigations.

CONCLUSIONS

(1) The occurrence or non-occurrence of transfer of conditioned connections from one signal system to the other depended on the order of alternation of the conditioned stimuli.

(2) The order of the conditioned stimuli most favourable for transfer was one in which the main stimulus in one signal system was followed immediately by the corresponding (projected) stimulus in the other signal system (*AaBb*). In the same way, the order in which the reinforced stimulus was directly followed by the unreinforced stimulus in the same signal system was the most favourable for differentiation (*ABba*).

(3) The most unfavourable order for "transfer" was that in which the inhibitory stimuli were used between the main reinforced stimulus in one signal system and the corresponding projected stimulus (*ABba*). In the same way the order in which the reinforced and unreinforced stimuli in

the same signal system were separated by a stimulus in the other signal system was the least favourable for differentiation.

(4) A positive or inhibitory reaction to the projected stimulus sometimes developed earlier than that to the corresponding basic reinforced or differential stimulus in the other signal system. In some cases alternation of the conditioned reflex, positive or inhibitory, was observed in response sometimes to the main and sometimes to the projected stimulus.

(5) Rapid development of transfer of conditioned connections from one signal system to the other and persistence and stability of the transfer were sometimes observed even in cases in which the subject gave an inadequate verbal account of the nature of the link between the stimuli employed or of their differences.

(6) None of the facts established are in agreement with the conception of selective and static irradiation from one signal system to the other (A. G. Ivanov–Smolenskii).

Translated by DR. R. CRAWFORD

REFERENCES

1. Scientific Papers of the Institute of Higher Nervous Activity. Vol. 2. U.S.S.R. Academy of Sciences, Moscow, 1956.
2. Pavlov's Wednesdays. Vol. 3, p. 319.

ON THE THEORY OF THE SENSE OF TOUCH * †

B. G. ANAN'EV

Dept. of Psychology, Leningrad University, and Leningrad Educational Research Institute
(Academy of Pedagogical Sciences of the R.S.F.S.R.)

THE sense of touch is one of the most important sources of human consciousness, one which Lenin held to be on the same level of importance as sight. During the 19th and 20th centuries the problem of touch has been studied experimentally by several sciences: psychology, physiology, anatomy, clinical neurology, pedagogics, and defectology. Great contributions to the study of touch have been made by scientists abroad (Weber, von Frey, von Skramlik, Head, Kants, Revese and others).

To I. M. Sechenov, however, belongs the honour of having created a unified scientific theory of touch common to all the sciences studying this phenomenon of sensory reflection.

Using as his basic approach the materialist theory of consciousness, Sechenov showed that touch is a special form of reflection in the brain of the mechanical, physical and spatial properties of material bodies. He was the first to reveal the reflex nature of touch, having made a meticulous study of the inter-relation of tactile sensations and voluntary movements. The latter were in their turn reflected in the brain in the form of kinaesthesia signalling the correspondence of these movements to the external cause evoking them. The integrated character of the reflex act of touch in the process of handling an object was taken by Sechenov to be a pattern of the reflex nature of any process of perception. By the genetic method Sechenov discovered the community of sight and touch in the reflection of spatial characteristics and relationships, formulating this in the well-known thesis that touch is "a sense parallel to sight".

Sechenov's reflex theory of touch was creatively developed by A. A. Ukhtomskii. Before the October Socialist Revolution, Ukhtomskii in de-

---

* This paper when originally presented was accompanied by a showing of the film *The Hand as an Organ of Perception*, demonstrating experiments made by members of the department under the author's direction, 1946–55.

† Conference on Psychology, 1–6 July, 1955 (*Materialy soveshchaniya po psikhologii*, 1–6 iyulya 1955 g.), pp. 189–194. Acad. Paed. Sci. of R.S.F.S.R., Moscow, 1957.

fending the reflex theory of mental activity showed that the highest level of nervous activity is organically linked with the development of active motor reflexes, which are just the opposite in significance to the defensive motor reflexes which his -philosophical opponent Vvedenskii took to be the one and only type of reflex, from which creative activity cannot be deduced. Developing Sechenov's teaching, Ukhtomskii demonstrated that the defensive motor reflex is based on sensitivity to pain, whereas active motor reflexes find their basis in tactile receptors. Subsequently Ukhtomskii clearly formulated the thesis that tactile impulses, their cortical integration, active movements and their kinaesthesias, are all links in the chain of a single reflex act manifesting itself in the process of handling. Like Sechenov, Ukhtomskii considered the human hand to be an important complex tool of the brain of man, being at one and the same time a natural organ of labour and an organ of cognition of the external world.

An important contribution to Sechenov's reflex theory of touch was made by I. P. Pavlov and his school, who discovered the dermal-mechanic and dermal-temperature analysers. He drew attention to the particular connection with these of the motor analyser represented by a region of the cortex that had earlier been treated as a motor region assumed to be antithetic to the sensory zones of the cortex. Using stimuli appropriate to these analysers Pavlov and his school studied conditioned reflexes and their differentiations, their peculiar characteristics and their part in the systematic activity of the cortex.

Attention was turned to the fact that conditioned reflexes from the dermal-kinaesthetic analyser cannot be elaborated without involving the dermal-mechanic analyser. But conditioned reflexes from this analyser are elaborated without bringing in the kinaesthetic analyser, which provides evidence of the biological dependence of cortical motor reactions upon the dermal-mechanic analyser. Sechenov's and Ukhtomskii's idea of the tactile-kinaesthetic structure of complex motor acts thus found precise experimental confirmation.

The reflex theory of touch provided a scientific explanation of the nature and mechanism of touch. In addition the theory of anthropogenesis, elaborated by Engels, hypothesised that the human hand is not only a natural organ of labour, but a *product of labour*, which has had an enormous influence on the development of the brain. Owing to the hand being the product of labour and its sole organ, it became also an important organ of cognition of the mechanical, physical and spatial properties of the material bodies of the external world which are worked upon by man with tools. Engels attributed great significance to touch in the process of cognition, linking with it the first origin of elementary geometrical knowledge. Engels anticipated subsequent discoveries by the natural sciences and by psychology, stressing the thesis that touch is a source of cognition specific to man, born of development through social labour.

This unity of the reflex theory of touch and the historical-materialist understanding of its origin and essential nature provides the theoretical foundation of studies of the sense of touch in Soviet psychological science. Starting with this foundation, Soviet scientists have discovered important new facts elucidating directly or indirectly the genesis and role of touch (work by Kotlyarova, Leont'ev and Zaporozhets, Kolodnaya and others).

On this same basis a series of experimental investigations begun in 1937 has been carried out in our laboratories, by Shifman, Rosenfel'd, Yarmolenko, Anan'ev, Davydova, Vekker, Idel'son, Lomov, Pantsyrnaya, Tregubova, Rykova and others. Part of these investigations has been published.

Following the theories of the founder of the reflex theory of touch, we turned especial attention to the correlation of tactile and kinaesthetic sensations in the process of handling. We also examined the dependence of the structure of movements in handling on the analysis and synthesis of tactile and kinaesthetic signals reflecting the formation and properties of the objects handled.

We have attributed special significance to the facts discovered by Vekker, who showed that upon the exclusion of kinaesthetic signals (in passive touch) not only the size but also the form of the object is reflected, if the latter is in a state of *movement*, i.e. is shifted across the unmoving hand. He has demonstrated that not only the movement of the hand itself, but the movement of the object also, forms a comparatively adequate image, if instructions indicate a point from which to calculate movements.

Yarmolenko and Pantsyrnaya dealt with another problem. It was essential to elucidate the possibility of forming knowledge of the shape of a figure by means of instrumental handling, tactile signals being excluded. It transpired that such knowledge is formed, but with great difficulty and delay, although it is almost impossible to achieve complete exclusion of tactile signals. If direct contact of the hand with the object being touched with a "tool" (a joint-pin) is excluded, tactile signals arise from the contact of the hand with the tool, consequently reproducing kinaesthetic signals. Even isolation of the skin cannot exclude tactile impulses, which evidently play a certain role in connection with the sense of touch via instruments.

Our investigations further showed that tactile and kinaesthetic analysis is carried out in a peculiar way by each finger of the hand, proceeding differently in the right and left hands. Synthesis of the multitude of tactile-kinaesthetic sensations appears in the integrated activity of the hand, which Vekker 'considers as a single coordinate system. In this system a kind of point from which to read is provided by the thumb, which performs the function of a support in the process of handling. A special signalling function in distinguishing and apprehending the form of an object is performed by the index finger in the handling system, where each finger is a sort of transmitter of movement. In the handling of three-dimensional figures the palm of the hand is also brought in, being close in its supporting functions to that of the thumb.

It is important to note that the synthesis of tactile-kinaesthetic sensations in the process of handling is determined by the structure and spatial properties of the object handled, reflecting more or less adequately both the parts and the integrated structure of the object.

Of particular significance for the development of the sense of touch, of course, is handling with both hands rather than with one. Abramovich-Lekhtman previously showed that the foundation of actions with objects in early childhood is connected with the handling of the object with both hands.

A number of demonstrations of primary bimanual touch in actions with objects have been obtained in our laboratory by Golubeva and Bush-urova. We encountered the same fact in our study of various operations tn work processes (packing cigarettes, picking cotton by hand, etc.). Simul-ianeous working of both hands together in the handling process is typical of the reading and writing of blind persons and of their apprehension of the relief contours of geographical maps (Vekker), and of their apprehension of three-dimensional depictions in sculpture (Yarmolenko).

Recently obtained experimental data provide further evidence of the importance of the problem raised by Davydova and myself as long ago as 1940, when a cycle of experiments was made studying bimanual touch. Subsequently this problem has been systematically studied in a number of investigations carried out in our laboratory, especially by Lomov.

Under the conditions of bimanual touch the analytical and synthesising activity of the brain proceeds in a peculiar manner. This relationship between the sequential and spatial aspects of touch acquires special importance. If an object felt with both hands is symmetrical, the process takes place more or less synchronously. When the figure is asymmetrical the process is usually asynchronous. Under experimental conditions of asymmetric but synchronous handling sharp contradictions are found between the tactile-kinaesthetic signals sent by the two hands, like the phenomenon of struggle between fields of vision in stereoscopic binocular vision. In blind persons, as opposed to the sighted, this phenomenon is much weaker, though it does not disappear completely.

It was found that the relation of tactile to kinaesthetic sensitivity was different for the two hands. Many experiments by our workers have shown that in the touch complex of the right hand kinaesthetic sensitivity is dominant, whereas in that of the left hand tactile sensitivity is dominant, and this exceeds the sensitivity of the right hand in differentiating power and precision.

In persons whose right hand is the leading one, kinaesthetically speaking, the left hand often leads in respect of development of tactile sensitivity.

Such a contradictory phenomenon can only be explained on the basis of the Marxist theory of anthropogenesis.

In the process of labour man acts upon the object of labour by means of a tool, i. e. he has to deal with two material bodies. In his primeval historical phylogenesis man must inevitably have used both hands, dividing their functions according to the intended use of the object and of the tool. We have assumed that the right hand was the organ operating with the tool, while the left operated with the object worked on. This assumption has been confirmed by what we have learnt of the work of the archaeologist Semënov, who has reconstructed the act of labour in the palaeological epoch.

We further supposed that in accordance with such a division between the hands in the labour process a division also took place in the analytical functions of the two hands: the right hand specialised mainly in the kinaesthetic respect, in as much as the chief impulses from tools are kinaesthetic, and the left hand specialised in tactile signals from the change produced by the working of the tool on the surfaces of the object. To a certain extent this hypothesis is confirmed by study of the formation of activity with objects on the part of the child, by study of the formation of elementary skills in handwork lessons.

What is the mechanism of the simultaneous working of both hands as observed in bimanual touch, with its contradiction of dominants in the general tactile-kinaesthetic complex? We supposed, and this has been confirmed by experimental studies, that this mechanism lies in the associated working of the cerebral hemispheres and in the inductive relationships between them. In as much as our published works have been devoted to this problem, we shall not here quote the evidence which supports this hypothesis.

It would, however, be wrong to suppose that the coupled work of the large hemispheres is the sole basis of bimanual touch. Rykova's experiments have shown that conditioned reflexes from the dermal-mechanic analyser are transferred from one hand to the other without special training. This confirms in man the well-known Krasnogorskii phenomenon. The extent of transference from the leading hand to the non-leading and vice versa, however, varies according to the stereotype of movements that has been built up.

Also very telling are Idel'son's electroencephalographic experiments, showing that during monomanual touch bioelectrical activity is observed in the occipital and frontal sections of both hemispheres, which is gradually concentrated in one of these, that opposite to the hand used.

In a series of investigations comparing the interaction of the monocular systems in binocular vision, of the monoaural systems in binaural hearing, and of monomanual touch in bimanual handling, we have demonstrated that the coupled work of the large hemispheres is the common basis of spatial distinction and of man's orientation in space.

In the process of bimanual touch the analytical and synthesising activity of both hemispheres is extremely complicated. Lomov has studied filmed material recording the establishment of a trajectory of movements in handling, and the quantitative relationship of elements of movement and rest. Evidence of the complexity of the process during the handling of even one figure is provided by the following fact. In the course of less than half a minute 56,000 points of different kinds can be distinguished during handling: 1) points of shift across the surface of the object; 2) points of rest on the surface of the object; 3) points of movement of a finger away from the surface of the object and 4) points of rest of the finger away from the surface of the object. The sum of these points represents a sort of equilibrium in the coordinate system of the two hands.

The greatest number of points is accounted for by elements of shift and rest directly upon the surface of the object. Points of these kinds are met with most frequently where the contour of the object exhibits the least curvature, thus demanding particular differentiation, and at the angles indicating the outline of the object.

Through the combination of elements of shift and rest directly upon the surface of the object an adequate image of the object handled is created. With change in the structure and properties of the object the character of the handling also changes, reproducing fairly accurately the structure of the object.

It is essential to note that the index finger of the right hand, to which belongs the greatest number of elements of shift is also characterized by the greatest number of elements of rest upon the surface of the object. It may be supposed that in this case we have not only motor inhibition, but a stepping-up of tactile signals. In the left hand a similar combination is found not in the index but in the middle finger, in connection with which the analytical function of the fourth finger of the left hand is heightened. In the common system of the two hands the fourth fingers and little fingers perform a balancing function, which is expressed in a vast quantity of elements of shift and rest away from the surface of the object. Further study of the *analytical* activity of the brain in the process of handling will enable us to deepen our scientific knowledge of the complex *synthesis* of tactile sensations and kinaesthesia represented by active touch in man.

Even the various experimental data already accumulated by us indicate that active motor reactions find their source in the dynamics of tactile sensations, with which the kinaesthesia of these movements is specifically linked. Ukhtomskii's hypothesis of the afferent and cortical opposition of motor-defensive and active motor reflexes is fully confirmed by the new data briefly indicated in this paper.

In recent years there has been a considerable increase, among those working in psychological science, in the interest aroused by the study of the kinaesthesia of working movements and the handling of objects. In posing these questions, however, account is not always taken of the organic connection between the functions of the motor and the dermal-mechanic analysers, or of the important part played by the dermal-mechanic analyser in the organisation of conscious movements.

A comparative study of direct manual handling with mediated ("instru-mental") handling shows that tactile impulses exert a considerable influence not only on the process of reflection of the object acted upon, but also on the process of reflection of the actions of the tools being used upon the object. This influence comes out especially strongly when materials and tools are being mastered for the first time, e.g. in the course of teaching children handicraft skills. In more remotely mediated forms this influence also shows itself in complex work operations.

These traditions of Sechenov's work must be developed further in our psychological science. The theory of touch must be profitably applied in the field of industrial psychology, and likewise in the field of studying man's actions with objects at different stages of his development. If this is to be done it is essential to elaborate more profoundly the theory of touch, which has still not attracted sufficient attention from Soviet research workers.

We have not yet had any scientific monographs written about the sense of touch in man, and the material devoted to the basic scientific data on touch in textbooks and other teaching aids in both psychology and physiology cannot be considered satisfactory.

Further study of the laws governing the development of touch is also essential for a more complete treatment of the problem of perception as a whole, since the influence of touch on the genesis of sight, hearing and other forms of sensitivity is indubitable, though still insufficiently studied in detail. The conditioned-reflex connections of all the analysers of the environment with the dermal-mechanic and motor analysers are the key to understanding the mechanism of this influence, which is exceedingly important for the formation of the general structure of the sensory reflection of objective reality.

Translated by RUTH KISCH

SOME THEORETICAL PROBLEMS
OF THE IMAGE IN TOUCH *

L. M. VEKKER

Department of Psychology, Pedagogical Institute, Vilnius

I. M. SECHENOV posed the problem of the image in two of its most important aspects: from the point of view of the objective content of the image, and from that of its practical significance as a regulator of movements and actions.

"The practical significance of sensation, then", wrote Sechenov, "is determined primarily by its relation to the working organs, by its ability to evoke appropriate reactions, and only secondarily by the qualitative aspect of the sensory products—the ability of sensation to change according to change in the conditions of stimulation. In the first context sensation is one of the main means of self-preservation; in the second—a means of communication with the objective world . . . . . In its first aspect sensation belongs wholly to the field of physiology, in its second it links our science with psychology" [1].

The majority of researches into sensory images—sensations and perceptions, in particular dermal sensations and tactile perceptions—have been devoted to the second of the above-mentioned aspects of the problem, i.e. to the objective content of the image and to the mechanisms of formation of sensations and perceptions. The same line has been followed by our investigations into touch, mentioned by B. G. Anan'ev. The subsequent course of these investigations of touch led us to the problem of the tactile image from the first of the two aspects described, which is extremely important and affects the basic principles of both psychology and physiology, from the point of view of the problem of movement and action and role of the image in this action.

Up to a certain stage the investigations into the movement of the hand in its different variants, and in general the problem of the correlation of movement and action with the image of the object acted upon by the movement, were seen by us from one side only—the movement of the

---

* Conference on Psychology, 1–6 July, 1955 (*Materialy soveshchaniya po psikhologii. 1–6 iyulya 1955 g*), pp. 199–205. Acad. Paed. Sci. of R.S.F.S.R., Moscow, 1957.

hand came under consideration as a most important factor in the formation of an integrated and adequate objective image. As regards the other
side of this problem of correlation of image and movement—the dependence of movement and action upon the image—here movement was to
us, as to the majority of workers concerned with touch, only a mathematical means of revealing objectively and registering the image in the drawing
made by the subject.

At a certain stage in the investigation it became clear that what had
been for us a methodological *means of investigation* was itself an independent and major *object* for special psychological and physiological
research. It appeared that the character of the movements of the hand
in depicting the object, like the character of any objective action, could
not be explained without taking into account the influence of the image
upon the development of the reflexes which result in motor responses.

We thus approached one of the most important problems posed by
I. M. Sechenov—that of the image as a regulator of movement.

"Sensation is everywhere a regulator of movement", wrote Sechenov.
From his point of view sensation serves as a means of distinguishing the
conditions of action and as a regulator by whose help the action is brought
into correspondence with the objective conditions under which it is proceeding. Herein lies the practical significance in life of the sensory image.
This general thesis on the image as a regulator of movement is made more
concrete by Sechenov in relation to touch. "But as soon as the eye ceases
to follow the work, the movements are under the sole control of tactile-
muscular feeling in the hand itself, connected with the working movements" [2].

These theses of Sechenov on the image as a regulator of movement
find their further development in I. P. Pavlov's teaching on the signalling
function of sensations, perceptions and ideas. In this way analysis of the
reflex mechanisms of action, of the sources of the adequacy of the reflex
effects of the objective situation upon which they are directed, brings us
quite objectively to the problem of the image from the point of view of
its *practical significance in life*, i.e. from its participation in the interaction
through reflexes of organism and environment. Such an analysis of the
image from the point of view of its regulating or signalling role in action
brings us in turn to an important feature of the mental representation
of the object, to what used previously to be referred to in psychology
as the projection of the image, or what Sechenov calls its *objectified nature*.

The image can serve as a regulator of action, can bring the latter into
correspondence with the spatial conditions of its occurrence, precisely

because it provides a reflection of the ōbject in its objective position in external space. It is thus ño fortuitous connection that Sechenov makes between the regulating function of the image, its practical significance, and this most important characteristic.

"Whichever way you look at it", wrote Sechenov, "it is the two properties just dealt with, articulation of impressions and their reference back to their original causes, which determine the practical significance in life of the higher sensory organs" [3].

Sechenov considers its objectified nature to be a most important feature of the tactile as well as of the visual image. The analogy between the surface of the palm of the hand and the retina comes out further in the fact that in both cases the impression is objectivised, i.e. is felt not as a change taking place in the state of our body, but as something external contingent upon the sensing surface. We are thus brought face to face with this problem of projection, with logically compelling force, by both analysis of the objective content of the image and analysis of its practical significance in life, i.e. analysis of the *mechanisms of its regulating or signalling function*. Definition of the nature and sources of projection is also essential for subsequent solution of the problem of the mechanisms of *action with objects*.

Yet this most important problem has recently failed to appear as an object of study either in psychological theory of the image in general or in the theory of touch in particular. It has likewise disappeared from the purview of physiological investigations of the laws governing the work of the analysers.

This leads, in the last resort, to the image being written off; to sensation and perception, bearers of the property of objective imagery, being reduced to no more than the dynamics of the nervous processes underlying the image and taking place in this or that part of the analyser. One of the basic theoretical reasons for such a situation in the posing and solution of this problem is the actual divorce of the process taking place in the analyser from the object, or source of stimulation which is continuously participating in that process. This means the divorce of the internal dynamics of processes within the analyser from the direct *interaction* of the analyser with the object or stimulus. This divorce is justified and necessary at certain stages of physiological study of the activity of the analyser, of the internal dynamics of stimulus and excitation, but it is most definitely inadmissible when analysis is being made of the formation of sensation and perception as *objective images*. For in this case the object is not only a source of stimulus, but the *object being depicted*.

The receptor theory cannot shed light on the process of the formation of the objective image having the property of projection, since it reduces the whole process within the analyser to a *receptor* process of *stimulation*, to the setting in motion of the receptor, a process which, although evoked by the action of the stimulating agent, is thereafter in fact divorced from it. The receptor theory thereby inevitably turns the objective image of the object into a mere sign standing for it. For the process of stimulation in itself does not contain within it an objective depiction of the object.

In opposition to the receptor theory stands the conception which sees as the final point in consideration of the whole process within the analyser the central dynamics of excitation and inhibition, and in fact reduces the image to these latter, just as the receptor theory reduces it to the process of stimulation.

It is obvious that this conception also is unable to illuminate the mechanisms of the formation of the objectivised image, for here a special mechanism is clearly called for to "carry back" from the centre to the periphery, and the "carrying back" must be more than simply a system of nervous impulses, which in themselves contain no basis for projection; it must be truly capable of ensuring the "object-in-image" character of sensation and perception. Central neurodynamics, however, do not include any such mechanism for "carrying back" or "projecting". Here the whole process of formation of the image is first "cornered" in the centre, then, consequent upon this, a special mechanism is needed to project it back again, and this is in fact not there. So the problem automatically disappears, for an objectivised image cannot be deduced from cortical neurodynamics.

From the essence of the Sechenov–Pavlov theory of reflexes, and from a large amount of experimental data (Bykov, Pshonik, Sokolov, Rozhdestvenskaya, Anan'ev and others) it follows that the analyser works on the reflex principle. This appears especially clearly in touch, where the image is obviously formed on the basis of the reflex activity of the tactile analyser. In the latter the hand is receptor and effector, its work realising not only the actually "working", practical action, but the cognitive action also, in the process of handling the object. It is therefore impossible to end an analysis of the process of formation of the image with the cortical neurodynamics of excitation and inhibition. Like every reflex process, it must have its effector link going out once more to the periphery, to the stimulating agent.

What, then, are the specific features of reflex effects formative of an image as against reflex effects which realise actions?

Limitation of the effects of reflexes taking place in the analyser (in any analyser in general, but in the given case in the tactile analyser) to motor, adaptational, tonic and other "active" components alone in fact closes the road to discovery of the mechanisms of formation of the objective image endowed with the property of, being an "object". For in themselves these motor, tonic and other active components of the effects of reflexes in the analyser do not contain any sources of objectivity. Nor is the "object" to be found in peripheral excitation or in the central neurodynamics of stimulation and inhibition.

The basic mistake of principle in all the above-mentioned conceptions is a mechanistic understanding of the causal connection between the process taking place in the analyser and the object acting as the excitant. The object-excitant is seen only as an external cause, a trigger mechanism setting off a purely internal process within the analyser. In the receptor theory it starts the peripheral-receptor process, in the opposing "central" theory it starts the internal central neurodynamic process, and in the variant of the reflex theory which we have considered, the one which limits the effect of the reflex to "active" components, what is started is again a purely internal effector process divorced from the object itself.

The object-excitant is in all cases only a cause, and the process in the analyser only an effect. The actual *state of continuous interaction* of the periphery of the analyser with the object-excitant, a two-sided state (in which the object is not only cause, but participant, the sub-stratum of any image, including the tactile image)—this is lost entirely from view.

This divorce from the thing which is the object of the image precludes discovery of the nature of sensations and perceptions in their capacity of objective images, and at the same time gives no possibility of posing correctly the problem of projection as the basic specific property of the objective image in general, or the tactile image in particular.

The experimental material of the series of investigations made by us shows that a comparatively adequate image can be formed under conditions of *passive* touch, when the active, actually motor components of the effects of reflexes of the tactile analyser are quite absent.

Here we observe movement of the object with all parts of its contour, in sequence, across the skin surface of the finger, and preservation of continuity of this state of changing interaction between the skin surface and the object. There is therefore included in the tactile image not only the reflection of the object and of its qualities (hardness, resilience, etc.), but also the reflection of the section of skin which the object touches, and the reflection, too, *of the actual process of touching, pressing and rub-*

bing. Meanwhile, during the maintained two-sided state of interaction between the skin and the object-excitant, switching-over of the time-motor
and spatial components of the reflection takes place. If the facets of a three-
dimensional object, which are separated by the third dimension, are drawn
in sequence across the surface of the skin, the time-motor components
which in sequence take in the various, spatially separated facets of the
object, are switched over to the simultaneous-spatial schema. Then the
integrated spatial tactile image includes, besides the facet which is at the
given moment in contact with the skin surface, the reflection of the opposite facet that is separated from the first-mentioned by the third dimension.
Here we already have elements not of contact projection alone, but of
true distance projection as well.

The state which is maintained during this formation process, of direct
interaction of the analyser with the excitant, goes beyond the bounds
of the excitation process, since here we observe a *centrally-mediated ana-
lytic-synthetic process of maintenance* of the continuity of the state realising
the excitiation, and, furthermore, a corresponding *re-arrangement of its
space-time components*. This state, of course, also goes beyond the bounds
of central neurodynamics, since it, though being centrally-mediated, is
also a maintained *peripheric state of interaction with the object*. What is
present here, it would seem, is a reflex *effect* of the maintenance, reproduction and space-time synthesis of the state of interaction of the analyser
and the object. This specific maintained state of interaction with the object
is the direct basis of the objective tactile image. The mutual switching
over of its time-motor compenents to the spatially-integrated state opens
up the way to solution of the problem of projection.

The *effect of reflexes* of the tactile analyser thus includes, besides
"active" components, "passive" or *truly pictorial* ones, which are the
direct "imprint" of the object in question. Their nature cannot be discovered if they are divorced from the state of direct interaction of the
object with the analyser.

When the process of taking in the whole contour of the object is accomplished on the basis not of movement of the object itself, but of active
handling, the time-motor components of the state of interaction with the
object are founded in the active, true motor components of reflexes of
the tactile analyser. But in this case also, as experiments show, the time-
motor components of the image are switched over to the simultaneous-
spatial components. *Trajectory* as a vector characteristic of *movement*
passes into *contour* as a scalar characteristic *of the object*. The motor components of the image are comparatively suppressed (as will be shown

below, this rearrangement has a direct relation to the *regulation of action*). But even in this case one observes the reflex effect of the maintenance and appropriate spatial rearrangement of the state of interaction between the analyser and the excitant.

The objective image, being a signalling, regulating component of the reflex which realises the final, "practical" achievement of equilibrium with the external object, is at the same time a product, an *effect* of the reflex *taking place in the analyser*.

If sensation and perception represent a reflex effect, then the objective image and objective action are different concrete manifestations of the common reflex principle of the working of the nervous system. This com-

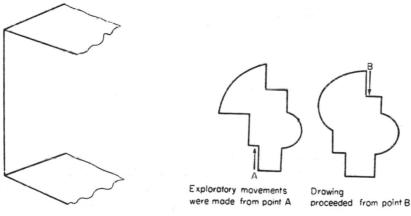

Exploratory movements
were made from point A

Drawing
proceeded from point B

FIG. 1.   FIG. 2.

munity of mechanisms of formation makes it possible to approach the problem of the signalling, regulating influence of the image upon action as a particular and highly specific case of the general problem of inter-action between different reflex effects. This is to pose the problem which in the course of our investigation actually brought us to look at the question of projection, and which is organically linked with the latter.

Taking this reading of the problem as our starting point, we carried out a special series of experiments for the comparative analysis of, and determination of the relation between, the reflex effects which realise perception and final action. In the given case this involved the action of drawing in outline the object perceived. With this aim a number of simple methodological devices were employed to vary the movements of the hand in the process of perception and action.

1. The movement of the hand along the contour of the figure during the process of perception was made from any one point of the contour, but the subject was required to start his drawing from another point (Fig. 2).

2. The exploratory movements from the given point of the contour were made in one direction, but the movements of the drawing process in the opposite direction (Fig. 3).

3. A change was made in orientation in plane for the representation as compared to the position of the object during the perception process, i.e. the subject was required to depict the figure as it would be if turned through 90 deg.

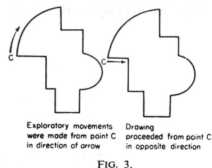

Exploratory movements   Drawing
were made from point C   proceeded from point C
in direction of arrow   in opposite direction

FIG. 3.

4. A combined method, in which the movements for perception remain the same, but variations are made in the movements for depiction—taking a different point of departure, a different direction of movement along the contour, and a different position of the contour in plane.

5. For tracing the relationship between the handling process and that of depiction when the movements of the hand were free, unrestricted by instructions, special ciné-filming of the two processes was employed, under conditions making possible subsequent comparative frame-by-frame analysis on a special projection apparatus (in the ciné-laboratory of Leningrad University) (Fig. 4, *a* and *b*).

The materials from these experiments show that the movements which realise the objective action of depicting the figure differ qualitatively in their whole structure from the movements made in the process of tactile perception. The former movements may be made from another point than the latter, in another direction, from another position in the plane. They admit of the pencil leaving the paper entirely, of breaking off to put in other parts of the contour, then coming back to what was done before. All this shows that regulation of the action is not realised on the principle of transference of true motor effects of a reflex alone, and that the transference is of a much more complex character. The structure and nature of these objective movements can be understood only if one starts from the fact that they are regulated by an integrated objective image of the object being depicted.

As has been indicated above, in the process of formation of the image time-motor components of the image pass over into· simultaneous-spatial ones. *The trajectory of a movement* as its vector characteristic passes into *the contour of the object.* Since the one contour of an object "contains" the most varied trajectories, on the basis of this switching of time-motor components to simultaneous-spatial ones movements which differ com-

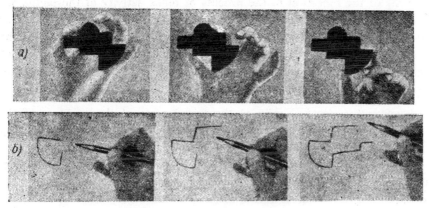

FIG. 4 [a] [b].

pletely in point of departure, direction and speed can all give an image of one and the same contour, and with it of one particular object. The data of the experiment show that in the process of regulation of action by the image a reverse phenomenon to the above is observed. With un-varying handling movements, the movements realising the drawing can vary in different respects: in point of departure, direction and speed for example. While in the process of formation of the image time-motor components pass into spatial components, different trajectories giving the same contour, in the process of regulation of action by the image there takes place an unfolding of simultaneous-spatial components of the reflection into time-motor components. *Contour* is unfolded as *trajectory.* And one and the same contour can unfold into a whole series of different trajec-tories, which are as it were contained within it in hidden form.

Such a reversible interaction between spatial and time-motor com-ponents of the reflection would seem to provide the basis of the regulating influence of the object's image upon the corresponding objective action.

It may be supposed that this variable unfolding of the spatial components of an image into time-motor components is one of the major factors in the transference of reflex effects which realises the regulation of action by the objective image. Such a character in this transference enables us to understand the thesis advanced by Sechenov to the effect that integrated objective images possessing the property of projection, or images "which we attach to external objects", "are capable of evoking, not a mechanically-unvarying reaction, but whole series of similar reactions" (*First lecture in Moscow University*).

Thus the transitions back and forth of spatial and time-motor components of the reflection in the process of reflex activity of the tactile analyser enable us to approach the problem of the "objective nature" or projection of the image as a major factor in its objective content. At the same time they give us the possibility of analysing the mechanisms of the signalling function of the image as a special single case of the general principle of transference of reflex effects.

Such is the organic unity of the two aspects of the problem of the image pointed out by Sechenov—its objective content and its "relation to the working organs", i.e. its signalling, regulating function.

The fact that dermal sensations are a primary form of objective reflection presents us with a hopeful prospect of extending the regular features already analysed in these phenomena to cover other forms of sensation and perception. This fact also sets us the task of executing such a comparative analysis and generalisation.

Translated by RUTH KISCH

REFERENCES

1. SECHENOV, I. M., PAVLOV P. I., VVDENSKII N. YE., (1952). Fiziologiya nervnoi sistemy (Physiology of the Nervous System), Coll. papers, No. 1, 389. Moscow.
2. SECHENOV, I. M., (1947). Izbrannye filosofskiye i psikhologicheskiye proizvedeniya (Selected philosophical and psychological works), 552. Moscow.
3. SECHENOV, I. M., PAVLOV I. P., VVEDENSKII N. YE., (1952). Fiziologiya nervnoi sistemy (Phsyiology of the Nervous System), Coll. papers, No. 1, 387. Moscow.

DISCRIMINATIVE SENSITIVITY AND SENSORY MEMORY *

(MATERIAL INVOLVING DISCRIMINATION AND RECOGNITION OF PITCH OF SOUNDS)

B. M. TEPLOV and M. N. BORISOVA

Institute of Psychology, Academy of Paedagogical Sciences, of the R.S.F.S.R., Moscow

DISCRIMINATIVE sensitivity may be measured in terms of a threshold of discrimination, which is determined on the basis of comparison of two stimuli differing from one another in one particular property; what is to be discovered is the smallest objective difference between stimuli which gives a barely discernible difference between sensations †. The study of discriminatory sensitivity is one of the most important questions in the physiology of the sensory organs and in the psychology of sensation.

In the physiology of higher nervous activity the main method of studying the work of the analysers is the elaboration of differentiations, the typical or "classical" case of differentiation being considered the "negative" or "inhibitory" differentiation, as a result of formation of which one stimulus evokes a conditioned reflex, whereas another stimulus more or less closely related to it does not evoke the conditioned reflex (since it is consistently presented without reinforcement).

The view is widely held that discriminatory sensitivity is to be identified with differentiation (see for instance the textbooks of B. M. Teplov [27; 38] and A. V. Zaporozhets [11; 47], a work of A. Breitburg published in 1954 [8; 131], and a number of other sources).

---

* *Voprosy psikhologii*, No. 1, pp. 61–77, 1957.

† Strictly speaking, under ordinary experimental conditions judgment is made not of difference between sensations, but of difference between stimuli. For instance, two sounds are presented which differ in frequency. The subject is answering not the question of what his sensations are, but of whether the second sound is higher or lower than the first, or the same. But judgment of difference between stimuli is of course only possible to the extent to which the difference is reflected in sensation. It may therefore be said that although the matter dealt with by the subject in his judgment is the difference between stimuli, the matter dealt with by the investigation is the difference between sensations.

Such an identification, however, cannot be considered correct. In determining thresholds of discrimination two comparable stimuli are presented either simultaneously (as is most often the practice in the field of visual sensations) or following one upon the other after a very short interval (as is usually done in the case of acoustic sensation). Here, then, a *comparison* takes place [see Anan'ev, 3; 9], which is a *reaction to a relationship* between the two stimuli, and this relationship is furthermore being directly perceived.

In the elaboration of differentiations each of the stimuli is presented in isolation, and the time interval between them is usually considerable (we have in mind the classic experiments with dogs using the salivation technique). In the "standard" experiments (both the "full" and the "small" ones) for determining the type of higher nervous activity of dogs differentiation is elaborated on the following pattern: bell, light, tone +, noise, tone − bell. The intervals between the stimuli are 5 min long. In consequence, the differentiated tones are separated one from the other by a 10 min interval, during which the "noise" stimulus is presented [15; 80–81; and 13; 741–742].

In psychological terms, in the elaboration of a differentiation what is required is recognition of the given stimulus without the possibility of comparing it directly with the one from which it is to be differentiated. Differentiation assumes *recognition without direct comparison*. It is concerned with a function of the same kind as comes into play in so-called "absolute pitch".*

The qualitative difference between the two functions under comparison lies primarily in the fact that *in differentiation reactions take place to each of the differentiated stimuli separately* (each of these stimuli may itself be either simple or complex), *whereas in comparison the two compared stimuli form one complex stimulus, and the reaction* (usually a verbal one) *is a reaction to the relationship of stimuli within this complex.*

Another essential difference lies in the fact that in differentiation not only the act of distinguishing is required, but also "the stable retention of this act of distinguishing" [the works of I. P. Pavlov; 22; vol. III, book 1, 122], whereas in the comparison of similar stimuli the difference is directly perceived (or not) and there would seem to be no need to "retain" it. In other words, *the distinguishing of simple stimuli by means of comparison depends mainly upon sensory function* (the function of sensitivity) *whereas*

* "Absolute pitch" is the term used to describe the ability to recognise or reproduce the pitch of separate sounds without comparing them with others whose pitch is known (26; 120).

differentiation means recognition, i.e. depends also upon the function of memory (the mnemonic function).* This general thesis will be developed in rather more precise detail below. In any case, it makes quite clear the fact that distinguishing through comparison is an easier task for a human being than "absolute" recognition of sensory qualities.

There is a view which has become quite widely held in recent times, to the effect that investigation of the work of the analysers in man — investigation based upon the study of sensations — does not measure up to the requirements of an objective method and is incompatible with the teachings of I. P. Pavlov. It is therefore assumed that investigation of the distinguishing capacity of the analysers must be made, not by means of the usual definition of thresholds of distinction, but exclusively by the elaboration of differentiations. As will be clear from the foregoing, the investigation of differentiations cannot replace investigation of differentiatory sensitivity by means of defining thresholds, since the two processes are essentially different. It is unreasonable, to say the least, to approach the study of sensory function only via the memory function.

It is supposed, however, that the view mentioned above is based upon actual utterances by I. P. Pavlov, mainly upon what Pavlov says at the beginning of the seventh lecture on the work of the large hemispheres. Let us consider this passage (although this has already been done fairly exhaustively by P. O. Makarov; 17; 10 *et seq.*).

"In modern physiology" writes Pavlov, "the study of the analysers" activity forms a very important section of what is known as the physiology of the sensory organs. This section is of immense interest and is significant in the highest degree, partly it may be because it has had the honour of attracting the attention of some of the greatest physiologists, with Helmholtz the genius at their head. Within this sector of knowledge sound foundations have been laid for the theory of the activity both of the peripheric constructions of the analysers and of their termini in the brain; many limits to the work of the analysers (in man) have been indicated; some complicated cases of their work have been elucidated, and many particular rules relating to it have been established. But all this vast material, subjective material for the most part, is built up on our sensations, those very simple subjective signals indicating the objective relationships of the organism with the external world. And this is a considerable shortcoming in this sector. From it is thus excluded all that must be won for physiology

* We use the term "function" in a similar sense to that given to it by S. L. Rubinshtein in the latest edition of *Osnovy obshchei psikhologii* (Bases of general psychology); 24; 178–179.

through the study of the variety and development of the analysers' activity in the animal kingdom" [22; vol. IV; 123].

What follows from this formulation by Pavlov?

Firstly, that the one and only shortcoming noted by Pavlov as belonging to the ordinary physiology of the sensory organs, that based upon the study of our sensations, is that study of the work of the analysers in animals is not attainable by its methods.

Secondly, that it is (in relation to man) "significant to the highest degree" and "of immense interest"—not that it is false in principle or subjective and idealistic in method, as some physiologists and even some psychologists think.

Thirdly, that it has "laid the foundations of the theory of the activity" not only of the receptors, but of the analysers' "termini in the brain" also; this does not accord with the idea, often repeated these days, that Helmholtz and other representatives of the "physiology of the sensory organs "never rose above" the study of the receptors, i.e. of the peripheric termini of the analysers.

And, most important of all, it can in no way follow from Pavlov's words that in studying the analysers *in man* one should henceforward renounce the use of material based on sensation. This point has been well argued by P. O. Makarov, who quite correctly asserted that "this brilliant naturalist and materialist had not the least intention of denying to physiology the right to study sensations in man" [17; 11]. It would surely be quite absurd for psychologists to renounce a particular method of studying the work of the analysers, on the grounds that the method is based on sensations, "those very simple subjective signals indicating the objective relationships of the organism with the external world"!

The technique of defining thresholds of distinction, then, remains the most direct method of studying the distinguishing capacity of the analysers in man.

So far as animals are concerned, Pavlov once put the following question—"How is it possible to study objectively, from visible reactions, the work of the analysers in animals?"

In Pavlov's opinion, this may be done in two ways. The first way, the most direct, is based on "the orienting reaction, the investigatory reflex". "It, this reflex, can first of all serve to establish to what degree the given animal's nervous system can distinguish one thing from another. If, let us suppose, there is in the normal environment, among other things, a particular sound-tone, then even a small alteration in its pitch should evoke and does evoke an orienting reaction, i.e. a particular set of the aural apparatus by the animal in relation to the sound". But, Pavlov points out, the orientating reflex is not suitable for use as a constant technique for study of the activity of an analyser, owing to the fact that in response to weak stimuli it is "very transitory" and, which is especially important, is extinguished when the stimulus is repeated [22; vol. IV, 124]. For this reason Pavlov introduced as a regular practice in investigations the second means—differentiation between stimuli by means of conditioned reflexes. The immense and multiple significance of this remarkable discovery of Pavlov's requires no more proof today. It should not be forgotten, however, that Pavlov himself stressed repeatedly that the elaboration of a differentiation requires something more of the nervous system than simple "distinction" between the differentiated agents, and that there is therefore "an essential difference between the establishment by the nervous system of a difference between external agents in general, and differentiation between those agents by means of conditioned reflexes" [22; vol. IV; 142]. See also the stenogram recording the "Wednesday" of November 21, 1934 [23; vol. II, 547–548].

The "more" that is required in the elaboration of a differentiation, as compared with the simple establishment by the nervous system of a difference between stimuli, was seen by Pavlov to start with as lying only in a special inhibitory process (differentiatory inhibition). Later, in connection with study of the differentiation not only of positive agents from inhibitory agents, but of different positive agents linked with different conditioned reflexes, Pavlov began to attribute very great significance in differentiation to the concentration of the stimulatory and inhibitory processes (22; vol. III, book 2, 202) and (23, vol. III, 402–404). The consideration of this question, a most important one for the theory of differentiation, is outside the scope of this paper. It suffices for us to note here that for I. P. Pavlov *differentiation is something more than simple distinction*.

In the present paper we compare the technique of definition of thresholds of distinction with that of elaboration of differentiations, for the purpose of study of the activity of the analysers in man. We will confine ourselves to the consideration of distinction between and recognition (differentiation) of the pitch of sounds.

EXPERIMENTAL MATERIAL
PRECISION OF SOUND PITCH DISCRIMINATION IN DOGS

G. P. Zelyony in 1906 demonstrated that one particular dog could differentiate between sounds at an interval of 50 hundredths (a quartertone), the pitch of the sound being 1740 c/s (12). M. E. Elyason in 1908 advanced the following general thesis: "Sounds differing from one another by half a tone act upon the auditory analyser of the dog as different stimuli" (34). He was thus concerned with differentiation of sounds at an interval of 100 hundredths. V. V. Belyakov (1911) elaborated in one particular dog differentiation of sounds at an interval of 25 hundredths (one-eighth of a tone), the pitch being 800 c/s (6). B. P. Babkin obtained in two dogs differentiation of sounds at an interval of 106 hundredths (a little over a semitone), pitch being in the region of 900–1000 c/s (5). G. V. Anrep (1920) elaborated in four dogs differentiation between sounds at 637·5 and 680 c/s; the interval here is 110 hundredths (quoted following F. P. Mayorov, 16, 123). L. A. Andreyev obtained with two dogs differentiation of sounds at a very high frequency (20,000 c/s), at intervals of about 100 hundredths (4).

The above-mentioned authors were dealing with differentiation of reinforced and unreinforced sounds (negative differentiation). B. V. Rikman (unpublished data discussed at Pavlov's "Wednesdays" in 1932) formed in one dog a conditioned food reflex to a sound at 600 c/s and a conditioned defensive reflex to a sound at 596 c/s (23, vol. 1, 191–192 and 204–205). A "positive" differentiation had thus been formed (a differentiation between stimuli producing two different reflexes) for an interval of 11 hundredths or one-eighteenth of a tone. M. M. Khanashvili (of P. S. Kupalov's laboratory) elaborated in 1953 a differentiation between two sounds, one of which was reinforced with dog meal and the other with milk-and-water (again a "positive" differentiation). The "basic" sound was at 800 c/s. In the case of one dog differentiation was successfully elaborated for an interval of 87 hundredths, in that of a second dog the interval was 65 hundredths, and in that of a third dog it was 54 hundredths (32, 33).

If one leaves out of account the unpublished and quite exceptional data of Rikman (where the precision of differentiation is to 11 hundredths), also Belyakov's results, which are unique of their kind (precision of differentiation being here to 25 hundredths), one may conclude that with many dogs, and under widely varying conditions, it is possible to elaborate differentiation between sounds with an interval of 50–100 hundredths, or from one quarter to one–half of a tone.

PITCH DISCRIMINATION AND RECOGNITION IN MAN

The threshold of pitch discrimination has been measured by many workers, using different techniques.

B. M. Teplov in 1940 came to the following conclusion, after making a survey including data available in the literature and the results of his own experiments: "For the majority of people the figures for pitch discrimination thresholds in the middle octaves are approximately in the region of from 6 to 40 hundredths. In particular cases exceptionally high sensitivity is observed, characterised by thresholds of from 1 to 3 hundredths. In cases of exceptionally low sensitivity the thresholds may be as high as 200 hundredths or more" [25, 133]. These exceptionally high thresholds, however, would seem to be always susceptible of improvement by means of special exercises (ibid., 135 and 139–144). There are no grounds for altering this conclusion in any essential way today.

A recently published paper by R. V. Avakyan, giving details of work done in the laboratory of G. V. Gershuni (1), quotes results which fully confirm the conclusion given above. The author obtained for one subject the following figures for pitch discrimination thresholds: pitch 200 c/s—pitch discrimination threshold 26 hundredths; pitch 500 c/s—threshold 14 hundredths; pitch 1000 c/s—threshold 9 hundredths; pitch 2000 c/s—threshold 9 hundredths; pitch 4000 c/s—threshold 54 hundredths. The last figure is outside the limits quoted above, but it relates to a sound which is likewise outside the limits of the middle octaves of the musical diapason. What is worthy of special note is that Avakyan measured the thresholds not only in terms of the verbal account given by the subject (as is usually done), but also using conditioned nictatory reflexes (one sound was reinforced by a jet of air directed upon the cornea, the other was not reinforced). The thresholds obtained by the two methods were identical. It should be stressed that what Avakyan measured, by the nictatory reflex technique as well as the other method, was the threshold of discrimination, not precision of absolute recognition, which is to be described as differentiation. Judging by an oscillogram given in this paper, the interval of time between the presentation of a sound at 1000 c/s, which evoked a nictatory reflex, and the presentation of a sound at 995 c/s, which did not, was 3·5 seconds—an interval typical for measurement of discrimination thresholds (since it favours comparison of sounds).

On the question of precision of absolute recognition of pitch in man (precision of pitch differentiations), there are very few experimental works to be found. One must first of all refer to the literature on absolute pitch.

It is known that absolute hearing, i.e. the ability to recognise and reproduce the pitch of a sound without recourse to comparison, is a gift possessed by few human beings. In order to make sense of this fact (in itself incontrovertible) in the context of the problem at present concerning us, the following two circumstances must be taken into consideration.

1. Absolute pitch—in the meaning in which the term is used in musical practice—presupposes the recognition (without comparison) of the pitch of *all* degrees of the musical scale, not of two, three or four sounds only, the demand usually made in the elaboration of differentiations. Absolute pitch therefore makes much higher demands than does ordinary differentiation[1]. What is more, it seems probable that this is not simply a matter of elaborating a great many differentiations; "systematic perception" of the musical pitch sequence plays an undoubted but as yet uninvestigated part in the elaboration of absolute hearing.

2. Musical practice "demands" of absolute pitch the recognition of sounds at an interval of a semitone (100 hundredths) from one another. Absolute hearing as a "musical ability" is cultivated in the form of the ability to recognise in the pitch sequence "zones" of a given width, not separate "points" in the sequence. This circumstance is of great importance and provides the basis for the theory advanced by N. A. Garbuzov on the "zonal nature" of musical hearing.

In the majority of works devoted to absolute hearing the "precision" of the latter is measured in terms of the percentage of correct replies given when the subject is required to recognise the sounds in a musical sequence (or in plain words, the notes of a piano); these sounds, let me repeat, being at an interval of 100 hundredths from one another[2]. This index shows 100 per cent correct replies only in rare cases.

There are some data obtained by Abragam and Garbuzov which show the precision of absolute hearing in some people with an outstanding degree of this ability. Abragam assessed the precision of his own absolute pitch at 16 hundredths (whereas his pitch discrimination threshold was 2 hundredths), and that of the pianist Raif at 32 hundredths. N. A. Garbuzov once made a communication on precision of absolute hearing in

---

[1] Differences in pitch of sounds will be expressed in hundredths of a semitone. A semitone will thus equal 100 hundredths, a tone—200, a minor third—300, and an octave—1200.

(*Translator's note*: the unit of measurement used in Russian is called a "cent"; There appears to be no equivalent English term for this, so the term. Hundredth has been retained although a hundredth of a half is rather confusing).

[2] For this reason one cannot agree with the following assertion by Ya. P. Frolov: "It transpired that the vast majority of dogs possess what is known as absolute pitch, i.e. are capable of reacting adequately to any sound which we made active or inactive, and of so reacting, and this without previous comparison with other sounds, contrary to what is found with most human beings" [31, 123]. It is unlikely that anyone has ever seen a dog with genuine absolute pitch, i.e. capable of reacting differently to all the degrees of the musical scale.

certain musicians, which gave figures of from 32 to 80 hundredths [cf. 25, 124–125]. At a later period Garbuzov described experiments performed with three musicians specially chosen for the excellence of their absolute hearing; in experiments involving the reproduction of a given pitch of sound they exhibited "zones of non-discrimination" (or zones of generalisation) equal to 42, 48 and 132 hundredths [10]. It is clear that the precision of absolute hearing, even in the case of persons possessing this ability, is of another order than the precision of pitch discrimination.

One should not, however, lose sight of another aspect of this matter, which is that every human being can recognise the pitch of a sound with some minimal degree of precision. It would be difficult to find a man who could not recognise the pitch of a bass voice and confused it with that of a coloratura soprano.

In some early works in Ivanov-Smolenskii's laboratory pitch differentiation of a minor third (300 hundredths) was used. These experiments were made with normal children, not selected in any way for their "good ear". Judging by the results of these, such a differentiation was within the capabilities of the majority of children (though not of all) [14, 20, 21, 30].

Recently a number of works have been published which were carried out in the Institute of Higher Nervous Activity (USSR Academy of Sciences), and devoted to the elaboration of fine differentiations in human beings. These include a number of works by V. G. Samsonova, and one by L. I. Mkrtycheva published in the first volume of the Works of the above-named Institute. These works, however, deal with visual differentiations. A work by N. Y. Alekseyenko [2] published somewhat earlier, and coming from the same Institute, is concerned with pitch differentiations. Formally speaking, the author was elaborating differentiations, not measuring discrimination thresholds. But the time intervals between the stimuli were very short—10 seconds. This is rather more than the intervals most suitable for comparison of sounds and usually employed in threshold measurement, but it is too short to entitle one to speak of absolute recognition of pitch, recognition without comparison. The results of Alekseyenko's experiments show that all his subjects (there were 5 of them) succeeded in attaining stable differentiation of sounds at 500 and 520 c/s (an interval of 70 hundredths), whereas differentiation of sounds at 500 and 510 c/s (an interval of 35 hundredths) proved unstable in every case. For the reason mentioned above it is difficult to place any definite interpretation upon these results. They should most probably be looked on as results of measurement of pitch discrimination thresholds under conditions making comparison difficult.

In our experiments the aim was to compare the elaboration of pitch differentiations and the measurement of pitch discrimination thresholds in the same subjects.

The experiments were made with 7 adult subjects, members of the staff of the Institute of Psychology. Sounds were presented through a dynamic loudspeaker from a ZG-10 sound generator, and differed only in frequency, loudness and timbre remaining the same for all the experiments. Pitch differentiations were elaborated first, then pitch discrimination thresholds measured.

A peculiarity of our technique was that we elaborated simultaneously differentiation of three, not two, stimuli. We are quite conscious of the fact that this makes the task somewhat more complex than it is when the usual technique is followed. We chose to introduce this complication for the following reason. When there are only two stimuli to be differentiated the subject's judgment may depend too markedly on chance. At the same time, the elaboration of a differentiation makes it impossible to present stimuli to the subject sufficiently frequently (or else there will be comparison, not "absolute recognition"). It is therefore desirable to find a method enabling one to consider even a small number of judgments of one and the same stimulus as yielding statistically trustworthy results. It was with this in mind that we increased the number of stimuli to be differentiated at the same time to three. It should be added that we were also thinking in terms of making a closer approach to the conditions of any practical activity; such activity hardly ever requires of a man the ability to differentiate ("recognise") two degrees only of any quality. It would even be difficult to name any case of elaboration of differentiations in ordinary life when the course of such elaboration starts with discrimination between two degrees only.

In the first experiment three sounds were presented to the subject, and the experimenter described each of them verbally as either "upper", "middle" or "lower". In all the succeeding experiments three sounds were first presented, with a two-minute pause between them (these pauses were normally occupied by conversation between subject and experimenter). The subject was required to describe each sound as either "upper", "middle" or "lower". The three sounds were not always all different; sometimes the experimenter would present the same sound twice, so that one of the three would be missing from that particular experiment. Without this precaution the third "recognition" would be without meaning; if the subject knew that all three sounds would always be given in each experiment, after assessing the first two as, say, "upper" and "lower", he would be able to answer "middle" automatically to the third. Our practice meant that the subject had to make all three "recognitions" while completely unaware of what the sound coming next would be. The sounds were presented each for 5 seconds, in varying order. After the three "recognitions" the experimenter would tell the subject the result, e.g. "You recognised all three sounds correctly", or "you were right in assessing the first sound as the "lower", but the second sound was the upper one, and you said it was "middle", while you called the third one "lower" and it was in fact the middle one", etc. Then the subject was allowed to hear all three sounds again each preceded by the experimenter's verbal description. This concluded the experiment. Such experiments were made with each subject three times a day, as a rule. The intervals between experiments were not less than two hours.

All possible steps were thus taken to ensure that the subjects were always presented with the task of recognising pitch without comparison, as is done in strict tests for absolute hearing, and in experiments with animals for elaboration of differentiation. One might wonder whether perhaps it is only the first recognition in each experiment that fully meets these requirements, since the two succeeding recognitions are only separated from it or one another by two-minute pauses. We made a special check of the comparative accuracy of the first, second and third answers in each experiment, and this showed that there was no difference between them; the first answer was no more difficult than the other two. Evidently a two-minute pause, which was in most cases occupied by remarks exchanged by subject and experimenter, was quite sufficient to exclude the possibility of direct comparison.

With all the subjects the experiments began with the elaboration of differentiation between three sounds—at 390, 435 and 490 c/s respectively. The interval between the neighbouring sounds is here equal to 200 hundredths, or 1 tone. Our criterion for the satisfactory elaboration of the differentiation was faultless recognition of all three sounds in 6 experiments running (i.e. 18 successive answers without mistakes). This is, of course, a very strict criterion. We considered, however, that only such a strict criterion entitles one to speak of a properly elaborated differentiation having practical value.

With five out of the seven subjects it proved possible (after a varying number of experiments) to elaborate this differentiation for an interval of 200 hundredths. With these we then went on to the elaboration of a finer differentiation. The middle sound (435 c/s) remained the same, but the other two were gradually made closer to this. With the other two subjects we had to "retreat", i.e. to change to more obvious differentiations, and only after these were satisfactorily elaborated go back to finer ones. Such "retreats" had sometimes to be made in the case of the first five subjects too, in passing subsequently to finer differentiations. We judged when a "retreat" was called for not so much by the number of experiments which passed without our criterion being attained (I repeat

TABLE 3. *Results of experiments in measurement of pitch discrimination thresholds*

| Subject | Thresholds of differential discrimination | | | Thresholds of simple discrimination | Threshold of differentiated discrimination after "training" |
	Threshold for rising interval	Threshold for falling interval	Average fig. for threshold		
1	8	11	9·5	—	—
2	14	24	19	—	—
3	12	8	10	2	—
4	9	27	18	7	—
5	14	22	18	16	6
6	18	31	24·5	10	16
7	94	36	65	6	35

TABLE 2. *Results of experiments in information of pitch differentiations*

Subject	Fineness of differentiation achieved (in hundredths)	Total No. of experiments
1	60	138
2	80	159
3	80	154
4	150	148
5	200	115
6	200	112
7	500	134

that it was a very severe one) as by absence of any noticeable progress (i.e. absence of any approach to a less strict standard). The course of the experiments with all seven subjects is shown in Table 1, and the final results in Table 2.

After the completion of the experiments just described we measured pitch discrimination thresholds for the same subjects.

Here also the sounds were transmitted from a sound generator; in timbre and intensity they did not differ in any way from those used in the differentiation experiments. The subject was presented with two sounds, the pause between lasting 1·5–2 seconds. He then had to say whether the second sound had been higher or lower than the first, or the same. The first sound was always at 430 c/s. The pitch intervals given were mixed up without any sort of order—large, small, rising or falling, quite unsystematically. The figure for the pitch discrimination threshold we took as that interval for which the subject *always* gave the correct answer. The figure commonly taken is that which gives 75 per cent (sometimes even 50 per cent correct answers. We took a different criterion in order to make our results comparable with those on elaboration of differentiations, where we considered the differentiation fully elaborated only when the answers were constantly correct. Two experiments in threshold measurement were made with each subject; during each experiment 30–50 pairs of sounds were presented (the number varying according to the results obtained). The threshold figure given in Table 3 is an average of the results of the two experiments. Separate measurements were made of "rising interval threshold" (second sound higher than first) and "falling interval threshold" (second sound lower than first).

With five out of these seven subjects some further experiments were made a month or two after the completion of those described above, the new experiments differing from the old only in the instructions given to the subjects. They now had to say only whether the two sounds were different or the same, without going into the matter of "higher" or "lower". It has long been noted in the literature that when the task is set in these terms the discrimination threshold is less (see, for instance, Whipple [29, 199] and Titchener [28, 215]. Titchener calls the object of measurement in such experiments "an impression of difference without knowledge of the direction of the difference". We will refer to the threshold measured in these terms as the "threshold of simple discrimination", as opposed to the "threshold of differentiated discrimination" obtained when the subject is saying whether the second sound is higher or lower than the first. Table 3 shows figures for thresholds of both kinds (in hundredths) for our subjects.

One very real technical difficulty in experiments of this pattern should be mentioned. Some subjects have a tendency never to admit that the sounds are the same, answering "different" even when the same sound is repeated; our subject No. 3 exhibited this tendency at the beginning of the experiments. Only after suitable explanations did her answers become normal in this

TABLE 1. Course of formation of pitch differentiations

Subjects	1st stage			2nd stage			3rd stage			4th stage			5th stage			6th stage			7th stage		
	Diff. between sounds in hundredths	No. of experiments	Result	Diff. between sounds in hundredths	No. of experiments	Result	Diff. between sounds in hundredths	No. of experiments	Result	Diff. between sounds in hundredths	No. of experiments	Result	Diff. between sounds in hundredths	No. of experiments	Result	Diff. between sounds in hundredths	No. of experiments	Result	Diff. between sounds in hundredths	No. of experiments	Result
1	200	11	+	100	52	−	150	6	+	100	18	+	80	35	+	60	16		18	17	+
2	200	30	+	100	38	+	80	26	−	100	15	+	80	17	+	60	33				
3	200	27	+	100	24	−	150	25	+	100	6	+	80	43	−	100	12				
4	200	26	+	100	38	−	150	24	−	200	8	+	150	15	+	100					
5	200	46	+	150	40	−	200	8	+	150	21	−									
6	200	43	−	400	6	+	300	16	+	200	28	+	150	19	−						
7	200	43	−	400	28	−	500	14	−	600	12	+	500	26	+	400	1?				

With a positive result (+) the tests also include the last 6 tests, in which were obtained completely correct replies.

respect. This undesirable tendency may well arise from a subject's natural desire to exhibit the greatest possible sensitivity in discrimination (for it is clear to any and every subject that what is being tested is his ability to distinguish sounds from one another), and in these particular experiments there is no "check" in the form of the need to say in what direction the difference lies. In order to combat this tendency, which can ruin all the results obtained, one must explain carefully at the very beginning to each subject that identical pairs of sounds will be given as well as differing ones, and that under test is his ability to distinguish differing pairs from identical pairs. After which care must be taken to see that identical pairs of sounds are in fact presented quite frequently.

For four out of the five subjects (Nos. 3, 4, 6, and 7) the "threshold of simple discrimination" is much less than the "threshold of differentiated discrimination". Subject No. 5 is an exception, the two thresholds being almost identical. The reason for this is the fact that this subject was in fact acting upon the instructions for the previous series of experiments, i.e. was saying whether the second sound was higher or lower than the first. The experimenter's exhortations to the effect that this was not necessary made no difference: the subject explained that in order to determine whether or not the two sounds were the same, he had to take into account in his own mind the direction or nature of the possible difference. The most he could do was refrain (and that only for short periods) from actually saying aloud "higher" or "lower"; in fact he always made the comparison in those terms.*

Especially striking is the low figure for the threshold of simple discrimination in the case of subject 7. Her threshold of simple discrimination —6 hundredths—is lower than the threshold of differentiated discriminations of any of the subjects, including subject 1, who in general shows the best results in threshold measurements and differentiations—this subject had received and was still receiving at the time of the experiments specialised musical training, in singing. Yet at the same time subject 7 showed exceptionally poor results for "threshold of differentiated discrimination" (65 hundredths, i.e. a figure outside the limits of the "usual" for pitch

---

* It should be noted that this subject had in the past devoted a lot of time to music and had much experience in working by ear, although he had had no special musical training. It is very possible that the simple judgment "the sounds are different", with no assessment of the nature of the difference, appeared to him unnatural and meaningless in the light of his musical experience. The deliberate formation of judgements more simplified than those to which a man has become firmly accustomed in the course of some practical activity, is clearly no easy thing.

discrimination) and for differentiations. In her case we could not achieve any differentiation finer than $2\frac{1}{2}$ tones (500 hundredths, a fourth). It is interesting that the threshold of differentiated discrimination in the case of subject 7 is greater than the interval for differentiation (60 hundredths) of subject 1; but the threshold of simple discrimination for subject 7 is in the region usual for musicians playing stringed instruments (violin or 'cello), people having the highest possible sensitivity to pitch (of course in their case one is speaking of a threshold of differentiated discrimination).

The results of our measurements of thresholds of simple discrimination raised the question of whether the latter may not reflect some function essentially different from that reflected in the threshold of differentiated discrimination. The next step was an attempt to reduce, by means of special "training", the threshold of differentiated discrimination of certain subjects. For a number of reasons we were not able to carry out this work with all our previous subjects, but only with subjects 5,6 and 7.

The "training" experiments were made as follows. Two sounds were presented, as usual, and the subject required to say whether the second was higher or lower than the first. If the answer was correct the experimenter would at once tell the subject so. If it was incorrect, the experimenter would tell the subject what the correct answer should have been, and would let him hear the two sounds again straight away, now knowing what their real relation was to one another. Sometimes the subject would persist in his first opinion (this did not happen very often). If so, the experimenter would give a demonstration of what "higher" or "lower" meant, using pairs of sounds with a slightly more obvious difference. In these experiments the subject was also allowed, if in doubt, to hear a pair of sounds again.

For subject 5 the threshold of differentiated discrimination had been on the average 18 hundredths. The first training experiment began with the presentation of sounds at 430 and 435 c/s (a difference of 16 hundredths). The subject replied that the sounds were "the same". The experimenter explained the real state of things, and let him hear this pair of sounds repeated several times. Then sounds at 430 and 426·5 c/s were given (a difference of 14 hundredths). The answer was "the same", and the same kind of work was repeated. Strictly speaking, this was the end of the "training"; the following 30 pairs of sounds produced correct answers in all cases without exception in which the rising interval was not less than 4 hundredths (1 c/s) and the falling interval not less than 10 hundredths (2·5 c/s). The experimenter confined himself to "reinforcing" the answers given by saying "Correct". Only where even finer distinctions were involved was any "training" work needed. Thus the very first training experiment reduced the threshold of differentiated discrimination for this subject from 18 to 7 (taking the average between 4 and 10) hundredths. The next experiment, carried out 4 days later, gave a threshold (for rising and falling intervals) of 6 hundredths. At this point the training of subject 5 was brought to a close. The exceptionally rapid results obtained in this case are probably to be explained by his great experience of music, which was "brought to bear" on the task of threshold measurement as soon as the experimenter gave the first "push" in that direction.

Only one training experiment was carried through with subject 6, but this yielded definite results. This subject had never practised music at all. The training process—similar to that described above, but more thorough—was for the most part concentrated around the subject's first 5 answers. If we take the rest of the experiment, it gives a perfectly clear picture: the threshold (for rising and falling intervals) was 16 hundredths (4 c/s). Prior to the training session the threshold had been on the average 24·5 hundredths, the threshold for rising intervals being especially great—31 hundredths. After the training the subject's judgements for both rising and falling intervals became equally accurate.

With subject 7, who was of particular interest to us, 6 training experiments were made (over a period of just over three months). These experiments brought out with remarkable clarity this subject's peculiarity: she could distinguish perfectly whether sounds were the same or not (her threshold of simple discrimination, let us recall, was 6 hundredths), but did not "know" (where comparatively small differences were concerned) which difference should be called "higher" and which "lower". This subject is a scientific worker with a learned degree, loves music, and likes going to serious concerts, though she has never been an active musician herself. There can of course be no question of her not knowing, literally, what is meant by a high-pitched or low-pitched sound, in the way in which small children do not know what this means. She can say quite promptly and correctly which sound is higher or lower, when wide intervals (over a tone) are involved. But when the intervals are small (less than a semitone, roughly) judgment of pitch becomes extremely difficult to her, and her answers are often mere guesses.

The first three training experiments not only failed to reduce this subject's threshold, they may even have made it greater. In the course the third experiment she made mistakes at times in distinguishing sounds at an interval of 100 hundredths (a semi-tone). It seemed as though in the search for some precise criterion, beyond her reach, for upward and downward changes in pitch, she was losing even those approximate criteria she had previously gone by. No verbal descriptions of the sounds concerned were of any use, naturally enough. A peculiar conflict was set up between her accustomed (and as we know, very inaccurate) means of distinguishing between "higher" and "lower", and the new, more exact means required of her. For example, she would be presented with sounds at 435 and 390 c/s. The second sound is a whole tone lower than the first. But the subject says "It's what you call "higher", though I think the second sound is lower".

Some positive results of the training appeared in a sudden leap forward in her progress during the fourth training experiment, when the subject did not give a single wrong answer in comparing sounds at an interval of 20 hundredths or more (in either direction). For this experiment the subject's threshold of differentiated discrimination was 20 hundredths. After this, work with her had to relinquished for two and a half months. In the first experiment after this interruption the subject's first two answers again showed complete inability to judge of the direction of pitch difference even between pairs of sounds where the difference was strongly marked; but analysis of the two pairs of sounds given yielded good results. In the further course of this experiment the threshold for rising intervals did not go higher than 60 hundredths, and that for falling intervals no higher than 40 hundredths, giving an average threshold of 50 hundredths. The next experiment showed further marked progress: both thresholds (for rising and falling intervals) were at 35 hundredths.

The training experiments with all the three subjects who underwent these thus demonstrated the possibility of marked and speedy reduction of the threshold of differentiated discrimination, which is in confirmation of the data of Seashore (1935) [35], Teplov (1940) [25] and Wyatt (1945) [36]. Our materials, however, do not indicate the possibility of improving elaboration of pitch differentiations within comparatively short periods of time.

CONCLUSIONS

On the basis of analysis of the facts given above, one can advance (though only hypothetically as yet) some general theses:

1. The most simple form of experiment in the field of the phenomena connected with discrimination and differentiation in man, is the measurement of thresholds, the subject being given the task of determining whether or not there is any difference between stimuli (the "threshold

of simple discrimination"). The pitch discrimination thresholds obtained in such experiments lie for the majority of subjects within the limits of 10 hundredths (subject No. 5 showed a threshold of 16 hundredths because he was in fact answering a different question). There is ground for supposing that in experiments of this kind we are dealing with an orienting reaction. The subject's reactions are the response to a simple change of stimulus. Such a form of experiment is the simplest way to put into practice in research on human beings Pavlov's idea that it is the orienting reaction which can serve as the most direct index of the subtlety of the nervous system's analyser activity, in relation to a given property of stimuli. The advantage of this form of experiment lies in its avoidance of the extinction of the orienting reaction, an obstacle commonly met with sooner or later when the vegetative components of the orienting reaction are under study.

There scarcely seem to be any grounds for supposing that thresholds of this kind can be noticeably lowered by "training". Learning always means the formation of connections of one sort or another. But here it would not appear that any conditioned connections have any essential significance. The result depends, literally and precisely, upon the sensitivity of the analyser to change in the given property of the stimulus. Investigation of the threshold of simple discrimination is for this reason of great importance, but serious work is still needed to perfect techniques for measuring this threshold.

2. Measurement of the "threshold of differentiated discrimination", when the subject has to decide which of two possible directions an observed difference takes—higher or lower, faster or slower, softer or louder, lighter or darker, etc.; this probably implies the presence of a differentiation of these two directions of change in the given quality. The training which was given in the last of the experiments described earlier amounted to the elaboration of fine differentiations of this sort, *sensory* differentiations, pertaining to the first signalling system, whose "content" cannot be reflected in speech, although the differentiations may be linked up with certain words.

One can say that the judgement "the second sound is higher than the first" requires recognition, recognition without comparison, but this is recognition *not* of the pitch of a particular sound, but *of the nature of the relationship between two sounds*. It is "recognition without comparison" in the sense that the subject says "the second sound is higher than the first" without having the chance to compare that pair of sounds with another pair in which the second sound is lower than the first.

It should be strongly stressed that here we are speaking of recognition not of the actual relationship itself (as in the case of tests of "sense of intervals" or "relative musical ear") but of the nature only of that relationship; not of recognition of the degree of change, but recognition of the direction of change.

3. The third case which interests us—the elaboration of differentiations—requires absolute recognition of the given quality (pitch of sound, speed of successive blows, loudness, brightness etc.), without any possibility of relying upon a relationship between stimuli.

It is precisely this feature—*the impossibility of relying upon perception of relationships*—which makes so special a case of elaboration of differentiation, or elaboration of the capacity for absolute recognition. Reactions to relationships probably do ·play some part even here, but they are reactions *to remembered relationships*, to relationships which are imagined, not perceived.

The amounts of thresholds of differentiated pitch discrimination are, as we have seen, much less than the amounts of differences in pitch typical for subtlety of differentiation. True, if one takes extreme cases it is possible to find examples of subtlety of differentiation in *one* person (e. g. our subject 1) giving a smaller pitch difference than the threshold of differentiated discrimination in *another* person (such as our subject 7). But such a relationship of indices can never be observed in one and the same person; furthermore the threshold of differentiated discrimination can, even in persons like our subject 7, be lowered very quickly by training. Therefore the thesis with which we opened this paragraph is undoubtedly of general import. It is much more difficult to recognise the absolute pitch of a separate sound than to determine the direction of the pitch difference between two sounds.

In relation to other sensory qualities this difference may be less sharply expressed. In the field of discrimination between and recognition of differing tempos, for a start, this difference is not so great—as unpublished experiments by us have shown—though it is still considerable. There are grounds for supposing that it is still less in relation to discrimination between and recognition of colour (wavelength). Evidence of this is provided by experiments of our own not yet completed, and by the work of L. I. Mkrtycheva (18).

5. One may advance the hypothesis that the threshold of simple differentiation is wholly determined by sensory function (the function of sensitivity), whereas subtlety of differentiation is determined mainly by the mnemonic function, seeing that in man subtlety of differentiation

always lags behind the discriminatory capabilities of the given analyser. Differentiation (absolute recognition) is primarily a characteristic of the *sensory memory* of man, in relation of course to given sensory qualities.

In connection with what has been said above under point 2, it would seem to be more difficult to answer this question in relation to the threshold of differentiated discrimination. It does seem as though it is still sensory rather than mnemonic function which is of decisive significance here, and what has just been said under point 4 also weighs in favour of this. But the most important thing is to stress that what comes out in the results of tests measuring thresholds of differentiated discrimination is *memory for relationships,* and for relationships *in their most generalised form,* wheareas in the results of elaboration of differentiations what comes out is *memory for absolute sensory qualities.*

6. In studying sensitivity by the method of measuring thresholds of differentiated discrimination, it is essential to bear in mind the possibility of lowering these thresholds *very rapidly* by training. The question therefore arises: would it not be more correct to take as the "index" the threshold of differentiated discrimination *after* training, not that obtained without any training whatsoever, as is the usual practice?

7. One cannot agree with the view, having some currency, that sensitivity in sound discrimination is higher in dogs than in man. Even a serious and qualified investigator like E. G. Vatsuro writes thus—"... it has been shown that a dog distinguishes sounds differing from one another by one—eighth of a tone, which is beyond the capabilities even of a musically gifted man" [9, 54]. It has been demonstrated above that the majority of people without special musical gifts can distinguish sounds differing from one another by one-eighth of a tone (25 hundredths). On the other hand we have seen that the possibility of elaborating a differentiation with a precision of one-eighth of a tone in a dog has been proved only in a few rare cases.

The hypothesis that it is easier to elaborate fine pitch differentiations in a dog than a man still remains unrefuted. But this hypothesis (and it is only a hypothesis, not a proven fact!) can only indicate that in dogs *sensory memory* for the absolute pitch of a sound is better than it is in man, although sensitivity for pitch discrimination is much higher in man than in the dog. Even if this hypothesis is correct, we consider it to be no indication of the limited capabilities in this respect of the sound analyser in man. In a work by I. P. Nechaeva it has been shown that by the method of conditioned reflexes with reinforcement by food one can elaborate in a seven-month-old child a differentiation to a precision of about half a tone (80–130 hundredths) [19] *. Surely a brilliant proof of the very great capabilities in man of sensory memory in the field of the sound analyser! The point would appear to be that in the majority of people these capabilities are never realised, since there are very few forms of activity which require precise memory of absolute pitch of sounds (even music does not require this). Many forms of activity, on the other hand, require from men subtle discrimination of pitch—and it is in this direction that the capabilities of man's sound analyser are developed.

Translated by RUTH KISCH

REFERENCES

1. AVAKYAN, R. V., (1955). Ob izmerenii porogovykh intensivnostei zvukov i differentsial'nykh porogov po chastote s pomoshch'yu uslovnykh migatel'nykh refleksov. (On measurement of threshold intensities of sounds and differential frequency thresholds with the help of conditioned nictatory reflexes). "Problemy fiziologicheskoi akustiki", Vol, III.

2. ALEKSEYENKO, N. Y., (1953). Nekotorye osobennosti tonkikh zvukovykh differentsirovok u cheloveka v svyazi s voprosom o vzaimodeistvii pervoi i vtoroi signal'nykh sistem (Some peculiarities of fine differentiations of sound in man in connection with the question of interaction of the first and second signalling systems). *Zhur. vyssh. nerv. deyat. im. I. P. Pavlova*, III, 6.

3. ANAN'EV, B. G., (1955). Prostranstvennoye razlicheniye (Spatial discrimination). University of Leningrad.

4. ANDREYEV, L. A., (1934). Sposobnost' razlichennii tonov vysokoi chastoty u sobak (The ability to distinguish between high frequency tones in dogs). *Fiz. zhur. SSSR*, 17, 6.

5. BABKIN, B. P., (1911). Dal'neishiye issledovaniya normal'nogo i povrezhdyënnogo zvukovogo analizatora sobaki (Further studies of the normal and damaged sound analyser of the dog). *Trudy Obshchestva russkikh vrachei v Sankt-Peterburge*, No. 78 (Jan.-May).

6. BELYAKOV, V. V., (1911). Materialy k fiziologii differentsirovaniya vneshnikh razdrazhenii (Thesis. Materials on the physiology of differentiation between external stimuli). St. Petersburg.

7. BOGOSLOVSKII, A. I., (1940). Vopros o sootnoshenii razlicheniya, uznavaniya i differentsirovochnogo tormozheniya (The question of therelationship between discrimination, recognition and differentiatory inhibition). *Fiz. zhur. SSSR*, 28, 4.

* I. P. Nechayeva, expressing in c/s the differences in pitch of the sounds, with which she was working, for some reason calls a difference of 40 c/s, the basic pitch being 810 c/s, "a difference of two-thirds of a musical tone", and a difference of 60 c/s "a difference of one musical tone", though in actual fact the first difference is one of 82 hundredths (less than half a tone), and the second is one of 130 hundredths (about two-thirds of a tone). By so doing she has incorrectly reduced the full impact of the results she obtained.

8. BREITBURG, A., (1953–4). Znacheniye fiziologicheskogo ucheniya I. P. Pavlova dlya muzykal'noi pedagogiki i muzykal'nogo ispolnitel'stva (The significance of Pavlovian physiology for the teaching and practice of music). *Voprosy muzykovedeniya* (annual pub.), 1, Moscow.

9. VATSURO, E. G., (1955). Ucheniye I. P. Pavlova o vysshei nervnoi deyatel'nosti (Pavlov's teaching on higher nervous activity), Uchpedgiz, Moscow.

10. GARBUZOV, N. A., (1948). Zonnaya priroda zvukovysotnogo slukha (The zonal nature of the hearing of pitch in sound). U.S.S.R. Acad. of Sci., Moscow.

11. ZAPOROZHETS, A. V., (1953). Psikhologiya (Psychology. A textbook for colleges training nursery school teachers). Uchpedgiz, Moscow.

12. ZELYONY, G. P., (1907). Materialy k voprosu o reaktsii sobak na zvukovye razdrazheniya (Materials on the question of the reaction of dogs to sound stimuli) Thesis. St. Petersburg.

13. KOLESNIKOV, M. S. and TROSHIKHIN, V. A., (1951). Malyi standart ispytanii dlya opredeleniya tipa vysshei nervnoi deyatel'nosti sobaki (A review of tests for determining the type of higher nervous activity of a dog). *Zh. vyssh. nervn. deyat. im. I. P. Pavlova*, I, 5.

14. KOROTKIN, I. I., (1930). Sravnitel'naya kharakteristika vysshei nervnoi deyatel'nosti rebionka pri pishchevom i oboronitel'nom podkreplenii (A comparative characterization of the higher nervous activity of the child under food or defensive reinforcement). *Osnovnyye mekhanizmy uslovnoreflektornoi deyatel'nosti rebenka.* (Essays. "Basic mechanisms of the conditioned-reflex activity of the child".)

15. MAYOROV, F. P. and TROSHIKHIN, V. A., (1952). Chap. VI, Metodika izucheniya uslovnykh refleksov, (Techniques for studying conditioned reflexes) N. A. Podkopayev, Third ed.

16. MAYOROV, F. P., (1954). Istoriya ucheniya ob uslovnykh refleksakh (History of the theory of conditioned reflexes), 2nd ed., U.S.S.R. Acad. of Sci., Moscow.

17. MAKAROV, P. O., (1952). Neirodinamika zritel'noi sistemy cheloveka (Neurodynamics of the optic system in man), University of Leningrad.

18. MKRTYCHEVA, L. I., (1955). Analiz pazlichnykh svoistv uslovnogo svetovogo razdrazhitelya pri vyrabotke u cheloveka tonkikh differentsirovok na monokhromaticheskiye izlucheniya (Analysis of different properties of a conditioned light stimulus in the course of elaborating in man fine differentiations of monochromatic radiations). *Trudy Inst. Vyssh. Nervn. Deyat. AN SSSR*, 1.

19. NECHAYEVA, I. P., (1954). K funktsional'noi kharakteristike slukhovogo analizatora rebenka rannego vozrasta (Towards a functional characterisation of the sound analyser in the young child), *Zhur. vyssh. nerv. deyat. im. I. P. Pavlova*, IV, 5.

20. NOVIKOVA, A. A., (1930). Issledovaniye propriotseptivnykh statokineticheskykh uslovnykh refleksov u detei (An investigation of proprioceptive statokinaesthetic conditioned reflexes in children), *Osnovnye mekhanizmy uslovnoreflektornoi deyatel'nosti rebenka.* (Essays. "Basic mechanisms of conditioned reflex activity of the child").

21. NOVIKOVA, A. A., (1930). O podrazhatel'nykh uslovnykh refleksakh u detei (On imitative conditioned reflexes in children), *Opyt sistematicheskovo issledovaniya vysshei nervnoi deyatel'nosti rebenka.* (Essays. "An experiment in systematic investigation of the higher nervous activity of the child").

22. PAVLOV, I. P., (1951–2). *Pol. sob. soch.* (Collected Works), 2nd ed.

23. "Pavlovskiye sredy" (1949). ("Pavlov's Wednesdays"), Moscow–Leningrad.

11*

24. RUBINSTEIN, S. L., (1946). Osnovy obshchei psikhologii (Foundations of general psychology), 2nd ed., Moscow.

25. TEPLOV, B. M., (1940). Oshchushcheniye muzykal'nogo zvuka (The sensation of musical sound), Uchënyye zapiski Gos. nauchno-issled. inst. Psikhologii. (Learned proceedings of State Institute for Research in Psychology), 1.

26. TEPLOV, B. M., (1947). Psikhologiya muzykal'nykh sposobnostei (The psychology of musical ability), Moscow.

27. TEPLOV, B. M., (1953). Psikhologiya (Psychology. A textbook for the secondary school), 7th ed.

28. TITCHENER, E. B., (1914). Textbook of psychology; a university course. Translated by A. P. Boltunov, vols. I–II, Moscow.

29. WHIPPLE, G. M., (1913). A guide to research into physical and mental activity of school-age children (Title re-translated from Russian). Translated from English by M. V. Raikh, Moscow.

30. FADDEYEVA, V. K., (1930). Vyrabotka uslovnykh refleksov i differentsirovok na tsepnyye razdrazhiteli vozrastayushchei slozhnosti (Elaboration of conditioned reflexes to chain stimuli of increasing complexity), Opyt sistematicheskogo issledovaniya vysshei nervnoi deyatel'nosti rebenka. (Essays. "An experiment in systematic investigation of the higher nervous activity of the child").

31. FROLOV, Y. P., (1936). I. P. Pavlov i yego ucheniye ob uslovnykh refleksakh (I. P. Pavlov and his teaching on conditioned reflexes), Moscow–Leningrad.

32. KHANASHVILI, M. M., (1953). Differentsirovaniye blizkikh uslovnykh razdraz-hitelei, podkreplyayemykh odnorodnymi bezuslovnymi refleksami (Differentiation between closely related conditioned stimuli reinforced by homogeneous unconditional reflexes), "16-oye soveshchaniye po problemam vysshei nervnoi deyatel'nosti; tezisy i doklady" (Papers read at 16th conference on problems of higher nervous activity).

33. KHANASHVILI, M. M., (1955). Differentsirovaniye polozhitel'nykh uslovnykh razdrazhitelei, podkreplyayemykh odnorodnymi bezuslovnymi refleksami (Different-iation between positive conditioned stimuli reinforced by homogeneous unconditional reflexes), Zhur. vyssh. nerv. deyat. im. I. P. Pavlova, V, 4.

34. ELYASON, M. E., (1908). Issledovaniye slukhovoi sposobnosti sobaki v normal'nykh usloviyakh i pri chastichnom dvustoronnem udalenii korkovogo tsentra slukha (An investigation of the auditory capacity of the dog under normal conditions and after partial bilateral removal of the cortical hearing centre) Thesis. St. Petersburg.

35. SEASHORE, R. H., (1935). Improvability in Pitch Discrimination, Psychol. Bull., 32.

36. WYATT, R. F., (1945). Improvability of Pitch Discrimination, Psychol. Monographs, 58, 2.

THE GENESIS OF VOLUNTARY MOVEMENTS *

A. R. LURIA

Department of Psychology, Moscow University

1

IN ORDER to study those forms of a voluntary human activity which will reveal its mechanism most clearly, we must first isolate the basic unit in which the characteristic features will be most clearly revealed, and construct an experimental model which will enable us to follow how a voluntary act is made up of a number of successive stages.

A unit of this kind can be observed when *a simple voluntary act is performed in response to verbal instruction,* while the most convenient form in which to study such a unit is that which occurs in a *"psychic response".*

In Soviet psychology it has been established that voluntary activity does not originate from any primordial properties of an internal life, but from the relations between a child and an adult. The adult at first describes certain tasks to the child, who is later able to carry them out in response to his own verbal instructions. L. S. Vigotskii indicated the basis of a child's development when he pointed out that "a function which is first divided between two people later becomes a method of organisation of the activity of a single individual".

It may be supposed therefore that early experiments involving a "psychic response" in which there was the simplest possible relationship between the verbal instruction and the task carried out may acquire a new interest if we apply their result to the problem as stated above.

Indeed, experiments with either a simple or a psychic response may be of particular value in our investigation. Here we study reflex processes of a special kind: they originate in the experimenter's verbal instructions, and form a certain conditioned association in the child's brain: according to the conditions of the experiment, this association may become

* *Voprosy psikhologii*, No. 6, pp. 3–19, 1957.

dominant and resistant to other extraneous stimuli which do not belong to the relevant system. Finally, in its most complex form, this association is extended and strengthened by words uttered by the child itself, who may formulate the appropriate method of response, so regulating its own reactions. It would appear likely that a careful analysis of how the child's response to such a task originates in experiments involving a simple psychic reaction may lead to a new approach to such experiments, and may reveal other aspects of behaviour.

We will now go right back to the beginning of the problem and consider how a child obeys adult instructions, what form this obedience takes and how as it is gradually learnt the child is able to regulate its actions accordingly.

A great deal has been published concerning the early stages of the effect of adult verbal orders on child behaviour.

From the numerous work on the psychology of the young child by M. M. Shchelovanov, G. L. Rozengart-Pupko, M. M. Kol'tsova and others it has been established that these instructions are by no means immediately distinguished from the affective forms of contact between the child and its environment. Only if the command (for instance, "hold out your hand") is pronounced in a certain way and forms part of a certain situation can it evoke the appropriate response. At this early stage, the whole affective situation acts as stimulus, and a considerable time is required before the adult speech can be recognized as a part of this situation or is able to elicit the required response.

It would appear as if the power to respond to speech as a stimulus does not develop until the beginning of the second year: if we say to a child of one and a half years "hold out your hand" or "clap your hands" it is easy to obtain the appropriate response. However, careful observation will show that at this stage the effect of speech is still very limited, and if there is any conflict with some act the child may have started already, the order may be quite ineffectual. Following Shchelovanov we may tell a child who is putting on a stocking to take it off, or one who is taking rings off a stick to put them back, and it will be seen that the intended effect on the original act is not produced, but that on the contrary the action proceeds more vigorously. At this stage of development, a child's actions are dominant and adult speech has merely a release function; it is not able to suppress an act already begun and still less to deflect a child from one task or another.

There is nothing easier than to illustrate this result by preforming an experiment developed by S. V. Yakovleva.

A child of 1·5–2 years is given a rubber bulb and told to squeeze it. He does so, but having started, cannot stop. Gradually the kinaesthetic stimulation of the palms from pressure on the bulb will induce him to exert a continuous pressure; having started this action verbally we cannot stop it by further verbal instructions. If we say "stop pressing", the child is unable to arrest the widespread excitatory process, and quite often he may even press harder, because the excitation has irradiated widely and become dominant (Fig. 1).

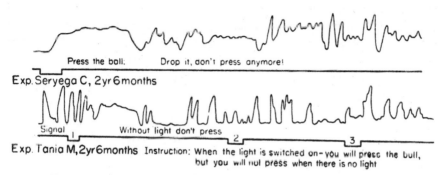

Press the ball.   Drop it, don't press anymore!

Exp. Seryega C, 2yr 6months

Signal   Without light don't press

Exp. Tania M, 2yr 6months   Instruction: When the light is switched on-you will press the bull, but you will not press when there is no light

FIG. 1. Motor responses to verbal instruction in young children.

Thus the release function of speech is well developed at this age, but inhibitory power is not yet established.

A far more complex effect of speech is exerted when it acts as a pre-release mechanism and establishes conditioned associations, and so acts in a regulatory capacity. As an example we may quote the usual experiment with a simple psychic response. If we say to a child "when the lamp lights, press on the bulb" it appears as though we do not set in motion any complex form of activity. But in fact it is quite otherwise. In this instance the verbal instruction does not act as a simple release mechanism in the same way as does a direct command. As A. G. Ivanov-Smolenskii pointed out long ago, before it has any overt effect it adds significance to a *future* stimulus and associates it with a *future* response which is not to be carried out until the actual word of command is given. In this case the verbal instruction represents an *inhibition* both of direct release signals as well as of direct movement; it presupposes a previous *synthesis* of two verbal functions, so that its distinctive feature is that it represents a *pre-release system regulating subsequent action.*

We must enquire whether a one and a half year old child in whom the direct release speech function is already developed is able to have its pre-release system operated by verbal instructions.

V. V. Yakovleva's experiments have shown that often this task is impossibly difficult, particularly under laboratory conditions. In the present study, the verbal instruction does not operate only in the pre-release *synthetic* system, but continues to act fragmentarily: the words "when the lamp lights" cause the child to look round to see where the lamp is; when he is reminded "to press" he makes responses which, on account of conditions of which he is reminded, are diffuse, and he continues to execute a set of movements which are not controlled by the instruction received. It is because of this direct release action of the separate components of the instruction that the appropriate reaction of pressing on the balloon may not occur, but instead there may be an orienting response so that when the lamp is presented it does not convey the appropriate message. Instead, it begins to act as an external inhibitor, and so paradoxically causes the reaction to stop (Fig. 2).

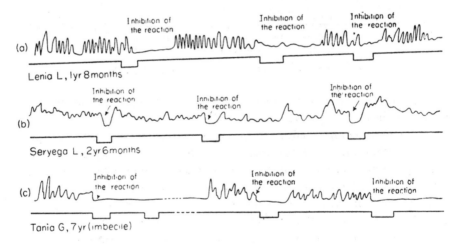

FIG. 2. Inhibition of motor orienting response to a signal:
(*a*) and (*b*) — normal young children; (*c*) — imbecile.

Under these conditions, any generalised form of verbal instruction, not to press when the lamp is off will have the effect as will any repeated inhibitory order (not to press) and will not have any restraining influence. on the contrary, they will act only in a non-specific way to induce a still stronger pressure, or else, at best, cause a completely irradiated inhibition and failure of all motor responses.

Only by working with the child for a long time and developing each separate portion of the verbal instruction and demonstrating the act as it should be performed is it possible to form the association required for the instruction to be carried out, and only in this way can the child become conditioned to respond to the signal.

However, even in this case we do not obtain a stable, clear-cut reaction: for a long time the response consists of a series of movements not implied by the signal and which indicate the diffuse nature of the induced excitation. For a considerable period the child is not conscious of these movements, which remain undirected.

2

We have described the phase when a child's behaviour is controlled only by the simple release function of speech, and when attempts to inhibit an action already begin to fail.*

Does this mean that in general at this early stage it is impossible to inhibit by word of command the fulfilment of an action already started? By this stage adult speech has not yet acquired an inhibitory function, and instructions to a child to stop performing involuntary actions may act *non-specifically* and so increase them: this does not mean that no further search must be made for some earlier form of organization of voluntary action.

Many proposals made long ago by I. M. Sechenov and supported more recently by P. K. Anokhin are of help in attacking this problem. These authors repeatedly pointed out that the inhibition of any action usually results from the encounter of two excitations, so that one inhibits the other. It would, therefore, appear possible to make use of the already established excitatory and release function of adult speech to induce in the child just such an encounter of two excitations, and in this way to inhibit an action already under way.

A very simple experiment proposed by A. I. Meshcheryakov and carried out by S. V. Yakovleva showed that this could in fact be done. When it had been found impossible by word of command to prevent a child pressing on the rubber bulb, we then told him to carry out two simple acts successively; after the lamp had lit he was to press the bulb, and then

---

* The results show that the artificial conditions obtaining in a laboratory experiment, and which we have mentioned previously, have a very considerable effect on tendencies which in more complex and sometimes in concealed forms occur as part of the child's natural behaviour. The child's natural behaviour is somewhat in advance of that which is observed in their laboratory experiment, but the fundamental features are the same in both cases.

immediately afterwards to move his hand away, e.g. to put it on his knee.
When this two-fold release instruction had been fulfilled (and it caused
no great difficulty) we began gradually to *reduce* the action required,
telling the child to press on the bulb and then to put his hand not on his
knee but on the table near the bulb; this process was then taken further,
and after a short period of exercise we were able to dispense with the
instruction to take the hand away. By learning to carry out the second
action, the child was able to inhibit the first, and so could now do what was
previously impossible, and co-ordinate his movements in accordance
with the signal without giving any superfluous pressure responses on the
bulb between signals. The inhibitory verbal command now produces the

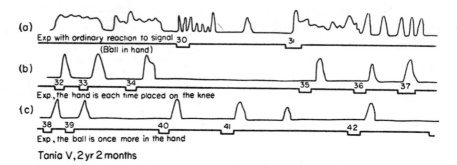

FIG. 3. The part played by the inhibitory component of the motor response during
the encounter of two successive actions which are later performed in more rapid
succession (from V. V. Yakovleva):
a.—Experiments with a simple response to a signal (bulb in hand all the time); *b.*—
Experiment in which the hand is moved to one side: *c.*—Effect of developing inhibition (bulb again in hand all the time).

intended effect: on account of the inhibitory influence derived from the
previous encounter of successive excitations, a child is now able to hold
the bulb in the hand and to press it when instructed without continuing
to apply successive uncontrolled pressures (Fig. 3). V. V. Yakovleva obtained this result in the great majority of 1·5–2 year old children and in
all those of the 2·5–3 year old group.

Having obtained a simplified picture of an organization of an action,
and having prevented the diffusion of motor impulses, we can now see
how right I. M. Sechenov was in considering voluntary human movements
as being "learnt", and are encouraged to undertake further investigations.

The organized action which we obtained arose from the encounter of
two excitations each of which was induced from without by the experi-

menter. As a further step, we must now attempt to obtain a completely voluntary movement in which the inhibition of the superfluous motor impulses is produced by the child itself.

To induce experimentally a simple voluntary act involving a typical inhibitory component, we must change the principle of the experiment.

In the experiment as performed, the verbal instruction was purely excitatory, and the inhibitory signal which restrained superfluous movements was not part of the experiment. This inhibition should be performed by kinaesthetic stimulation originating from contraction of the finger muscles and indicating that the movement has been completed; they should serve to inhibit subsequent movements. However, we could not be sure that the incompletely developed motor system of a child does have available the necessary kinaesthetic signals for arresting an action when it has been completed; because the inhibitory function of speech is not yet established, the command from the experimenter was also inadequate for this purpose. On this account the experiment failed. Not having received any definite signal that its task was completed, the child did not arrest its movements but applied superfluous pressures when it should have stopped. We were therefore faced with the problem not only of starting but also of stopping the child's response. An analysis of the reflex structure of the motor act indicated a solution.

Neuro-physiologists have frequently pointed out that control of an action requires afferent ("feedback") impulses which signal the end of an action, and that without such a system of signals resulting from the act itself, movements would be uncontrollable; this modern cybernetic view has been advanced by several English and American psychologists, and considerable support to it has been given by the Soviet Physiologists, L. A. Orbeli, N. A. Bernshtein and P. K. Anokhin.

With this in mind, we must now consider whether it will be possible to arrange an experiment so that the child's *movement itself* initiated by the adult's command shall itself *produce a sufficiently definite and as far as possible exteroceptive signal which will indicate the end of the action, and by acting on the feedback principle will extinguish the irradiated motor impulses.*

We now re-designed our experiments in order to obtain self-regulation of this kind. All the conditions remained as before except that the child was told that when the lamp lit he was to press on the bulb and in this way to extinguish it. Again, in a more complex form of the experiment, when the lamp lit he was to press on the bulb and so cause a bell to ring. A simple mechanical arrangement enabled the lamp to be turned off by pressure on the bulb, and, in a second arrangement the same device caused a bell to ring. The signal given to the child elicited a movement from him, while the movement itself induced a clear exteroceptive signal which gave rise to afferent impulses indicating that the task had been fulfilled and so acting as a secondary inhibitory stimulus.

Experiments of this kind carried out by V. V. Yakovleva gave interesting results. In half the 2-year-olds and in three quarters of the 2–3 year old group, this arrangement eliminated chance pressures occurring between signals and elicited clear-cut co-ordinated reactions to the signal; however,

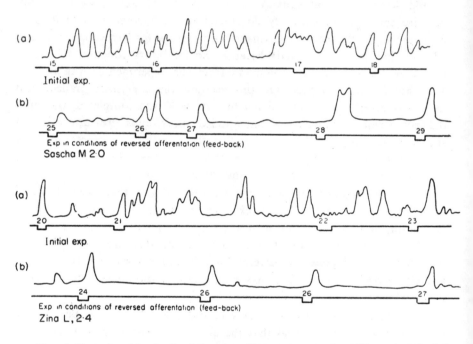

FIG. 4. Part played by feedback in controlling movements in children aged 2—2·5 years. (From V. V. Yakovleva).

if the feedback was eliminated then the great majority of the children returned to the original diffuse motor reaction, and only in one third of the older group (2–3 years) was any noticeable effect retained, and the movements co-ordinated (Fig. 4).

These experiments need to be refined and the results confirmed, but it is difficult to interpret them otherwise than as illustrating *a first and very simple plan of a definitely voluntary action in a young child*. The movement is set in motion by the verbal instruction, and is arrested by an exteroceptive signal which results from the child's movement itself. While remaining reflex in nature, the action acquires all the features of a voluntary act under the control of the subject. By means of a signal derived from the child's movement it was possible to obtain a result which it was impossible to elicit by means of an inhibitory word of command.* It seems that we have here a simple illustration of a self-regulated act to the analysis of which so much attention has been given recently, and that it might be expected that the same effect would be obtained from an experiment of this type even in cases where it would not be thought possible that a true voluntary act could occur.

3

Having revealed the simple plan of a voluntary act in a 2–2·5 year old child, it now remains to consider further possible developments.

The first and simplest voluntary act was controlled by an external signal which, it is true, was derived from the movement itself. It might, however, be possible to organize the experiment in such a way that the self-regulatory movement will be derived from the child and will no longer require an external regulatory signal to be applied.

It then occurred to us to present the command given by the adult, which initially controlled the child's behaviour and then, following it, the child's own speech. By this means it might be possible to solve the problem and to develop a method of inducing a true voluntary action.

The features by which the child develops the power to obey a verbal instruction and to become capable of regulating his actions by his own speech should now be recalled.

At 3–4 years the child's speech advances greatly. It has been shown that at 3–3·5 years it is possible to set up by a simple spoken order the necessary pre-release system of associations, and to tell a child not to carry out a certain set of movements immediately but to react only when an agreed signal is given; in the same way it is possible to form a more elaborate set of associations, for instance by telling him to respond by pressing only when the signal is red, and not to press at green. However, according to work which N. P. Paramonova has done in our group, the excitatory component of the verbal instruction is still considerably stronger

* At the present time more precise experiments are in progress which will determine the limitations of responses of this kind.

than the inhibitory, and the motor response is still very diffuse. Therefore, as a rule, a child of 3–3·5 years reacts readily to the positive signal,
and sometimes continues to give uncontrolled responses between signals;
it can be restrained from movement only for very short periods after the
inhibitory order has been given. The direct stimulating effect of the signal
is so great and the inhibitory so weak that the child can withhold the
response only for a short time. Therefore, in these cases we have to resort
to another method, and to reinforce each stimulus by a special verbal
instruction in order to strengthen the inhibitory significance of the signal
and so gradually to elaborate the necessary differentiation of the response.

The fourth year, which is the first year of the pre-school period is not
only the time at which the child becomes capable of carrying out comparatively complicated instruction, but it is also the stage when its own
speech becomes much more rich and varied.

This last fact would suggest that new pathways become available for
behavioural control.

We have seen that at the first stage of development we were able to
regulate movement if the motor response itself was made to produce
a signal which indicated the result of the action; it was also shown that
at the next stage this regulating influence may be exerted by verbal reinforcement of its reaction by the adult.

We now have to consider whether such a regulatory effect can be taken
over by *the speech of the child itself.*

For this purpose we once more changed the arrangement of the experiment and told the child that at each movement made in response
to the signal he should say, "Now!".

There is reason to suppose that the child's speech, which by this time
is well formed and quite varied and not under the continuous influence
of any external stimulus such as that corresponding to the kinaesthetic
stimulation of the hand receptors by the bulb, will be better able to follow the agreed signal. It is a product of more highly developed nervous
processes, and will now constitute a means by which the motor response
may be controlled.

An attempt to study the regulatory function of the child's own speech
in the 2–2·5 year old group met with no success. At this stage speech
is very imperfect, and attempts to obtain even the simplest verbal responses
to the signals given did not help but actually hindered the organization
of the child's movements. In these experiments, it is true, the child began
to reply to the signal by saying, "now!" (or by the even simpler expression "Oh!"), but at this age these response were every unstable, and it often

appeared to be unable to say "now!" while at the same time pressing on the bulb; the verbal response was either very easily extinguished, or else came to be repeated mechanically, irrespective of the signals, or again through a process of negative induction, it began to inhibit the motor response.

Quite a different condition was found in 3–3·5 year old children, and particularly in those whose speech had been well-developed by kindergarten training.

Unlike the 2 year olds, these children never found any noticeable difficulty in replying to the signal with the word "now!". They were highly interested in the task, their replies were always well-timed to follow the signals and the latent period was much more stable than was that of the motor response. By contrast with simple motor responses unaccompanied by speech, we practically never found any cases of a perseverative verbal response occurring independently of the signal or continuing after the signal had been withdrawn. Thus, all the results indicate that the *neutral processes associated with simple verbal replies are at this age considerably in advance of those which control motor responses, and that they are well defined and adaptable.*

We must now consider the possibility of using this sufficiently perfect and therefore controllable nervous system in the place of the signals previously derived from the act itself, thereby effecting the necessary control.

It will be recalled that a clearly marked control over young children's reactions was produced by additional signals, whose effect was still better shown in the 3–3·5 year old group.

In the normal experiments in which actions were carried out in accordance with instructions previously given, we were not able to arrest diffuse motor responses, but the introduction of the additional signal eliminated them completely. Whereas in the usual experiments the response is directly related to the stimulus, so that a stimulus of long duration would induce a pressure lasting for some time, or would cause a child to press several times during the whole of the period that the stimulus was applied, according to O. K. Tikhomirov, the introduction of feedback eliminates such a relationship and the movement becomes more subordinate to the verbal instruction.

It is extremely important at this stage, however, that the *same results can be obtained by using the child's own speech in place of the additional signals.* If the child is told to respond to each illumination by saying "now" or "oh", and at the same time to press on the bulb, we *replace the control of the external signal by the child's own command,* which, because of the more highly perfected nervous organization underlying it can be more accurately directed, and serves as an effective control mechanism.

We will now consider the results obtained in such experiments performed in our group by M. R. Peskovskaya and O. K. Tikhomirov. According to them, use of the child's own verbal command completely eliminates the diffuseness of the response and causes the movement to be accurately related to the signals, so that it is clear-cut and appropriately directed. If however the verbal accompaniment is not given the child once more responds in the diffuse and unorganized way. Thus, the

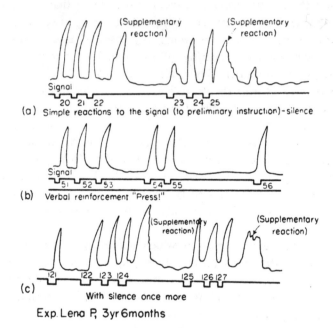

FIG. 5. Regulation of motor responses using supplementary verbal instructions by the child (from O. K. Tikhomirov).

introduction of the child's own command eliminates the direct relation between his response and the nature of the stimulus, and his reaction becomes subordinated to his own verbal instruction. A child who was not able to react appropriately to either a short or a long-lasting stimulus may now begin to do so easily, regulating his action by bursting out with the word "now!" by which means he controls his own movements.

It is possible to elaborate the experiment further and to demonstrate the regulatory function of the child's own speech even more clearly. If a 3–3·5 year old child is given the problem "when the lamp lights, press twice", he will be unable to do so; even when he understands perfectly well the significance of the number "two" he will perform the task correctly only one or twice, and then only if the signal presented to him is not maintained for too long. The motor excitation induced in the child radiates readily, the reactions induced perseverate, and instead of pressing twice he presses a third, fourth, and finally many times. We have, however, only to go over to an experiment where, besides pressing the bulb, the child also exclaims "one, two!" for the irradiation of the excitation to be arrested, and the child will again press twice, as required. When he no longer gives the verbal response he once more returns to the diffuse motor reaction. (Fig. 5).

The facts expounded above are of considerable significance. Whereas in experiments which revealed the effect of the extra signals, we demonstrated, even though artificially, a model of a simple externally controlled voluntary act in the later experiments which included verbal control by the child himself we were able to follow the *initial stages of the formation of a self-regulatory system,* in which the self regulation is natural and in which the more highly *perfected nervous linkage (association) plays the part of a control mechanism* which reinforces the verbal instruction and allows a true voluntary act to take place.

4

We will now try to examine more closely the mechanism by which the child's speech exerts its controlling influence. We require to know whether the regulatory effect is brought about by the motor response becoming included in a system of selective mental associations belonging to the word, or whether the influence of the child's speech which we have observed in our experiments is much simpler, and the possible effects of this influence much more limited.

In considering the various possible forms the effect of speech may take we have already mentioned that it may have an excitatory, release, or inhibitory function, and that it may act specifically by completing some nervous circuit, or finally that it may exert a regulatory influence. We must now consider whether it is possible to use these different criteria in determining what part of the child's verbal reaction is responsible for the regulatory function.

There is no doubt that the exclamation "now!", acting as negative feedback, operates as a complex stimulus. The child's subsequent behaviour may be influenced on the one hand by the production of the verbal response, which will include the innervation of the different organs of speech and the establishment of an appropriate excitatory level in the cortical speech areas. On the other hand the verbal reaction will include the system of selective thought associations which elaborate from the word a complex signal which brings about a reaction closely associated with the child's previous experience of the word. It has to be decided which of these two aspects of the word, the non-specific impulsive or the specifically thoughtful, acts at this early level of behavioural organization to regulate the response.

O. K. Tikhomirov's recent experiments give no answer to the problem: both functions, the impulsive and the thoughtful, coincide during the child's verbal response, and *they must be separated* in order to solve the problem.

We may make use of a simple device. Let the conditions of the experiment be changed so that a 3–4 year old child, who has successfully pressed twice in reply to the signal, instead of accompanying his action by saying, "one, two" shall each time give the generalized instructions "I will press twice!".

It might seem that we have changed our experiment very little. In fact we have altered it fundamentally. In the first arrangement, the regulatory effect of speech might be derived from the two isolated impulses "one, two", "oh, oh", but now these *two isolated impulses* have been completely eliminated, and the regulatory effect proceeds only from their *significance;* in other words the control will proceed only from that selective system of associations with those particular words which have been firmly established in the previous experiment. Furthermore, in this new arrangement, the nature of the impulses associated with the commands the child gives to himself may even conflict with their meaning: the child means that he ought to press twice, while the impulses derived from the phrase "I will press twice" will consist only of a single extended nervous signal.

In this case, to what is the motor response of the child subordinated?

O. K. Tikhomirov's experiments on 3–4 year old children leave no doubt as to the answer. Whereas the child's cry of "one, two!" successfully controlled the motor response, in all cases without exception the exclamation "I will press twice!" failed to lead to the desired effect, and as a rule the child made one long lasting movement. This showed clearly that the regulating effect is not derived from selecting the relevant thought association, but is determined by the impulsive aspect of the speech (Fig. 6).

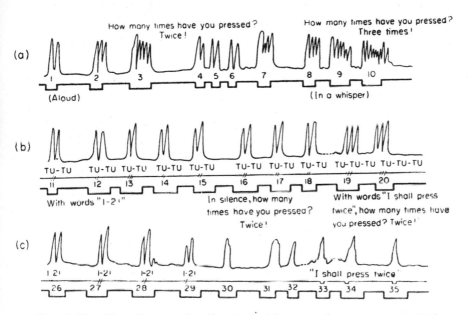

FIG. 6. The effect of nervous impulses derived from speech as compared with that of the thought contact in regulating motor responses in 3 year old children (from O. K. Tikhomirov):

a.—Development of motor response from the instruction "when the lamp lights, press twice;" *b.*—Same instructions, and child accompanies response by saying "oh, oh!" (correct response now obtained); *c.*—ditto, and while reacting the child says "I will press twice" or merely says "twice!"

There is, however, a further even more convincing experiment which shows that the effect is derived from the impulses and not from the selective thoughtful aspect of the speech.

Until now we have investigated the regulatory effect of speech only in experiments in which there is a simple response to a signal, and when the speech impulse necessarily has only an excitatory or release function.

However, we can successfully change over to experiments in which a system of differentiated associations is formed, and in which one signal is positive and the other negative. We have already seen how difficult it is for a child of this age to inhibit the impulse to react directly to a signal which his instructions tell him to be inhibitory.

It might, however, be possible to inhibit this impulsive reaction by using the child's own speech to coincide with each appearance of the stimulus and so to reinforce the signal conveyed by it. For this purpose we used E. D. Khomskaya's method, and told the child to say at each positive signal: "I must press" or simply "I must", and at each negative signal to say "I must not press" or simply "I must not".

It was found that there was no great difficulty in developing such a differentiated verbal response to signals in children of 3 to 4 years old. However, in the light of what has just been said, it can be understood that considerable difficulties are encountered when the attempt is made to regulate action by means of such verbal responses.

Indeed, if when the child says "I must" at the positive signal, a positive signal is derived both from the significance of the remark and from the signal represented by the associated nervous impulses; it is quite otherwise with the response "I must not" which accompanies the inhibitory signals. From its significance it ought to be restraining and inhibitory, but from the nature of the nervous impulses conveyed by it it still constitutes an additional innervation, in just the same way as did the positive signal "I must". It remains to find what component of this complex verbal response, the impulsive or the thoughtful, will be dominant and will determine the influence on the motor reaction.

The experiments on 3–4 year old children gave a completely unambiguous answer. When the child said "I must" at the positive signal, there was an increased excitation and clear-cut appropriate responses to the signal were made. When the child said "I must not" when given the inhibitory signal, this reply did not cause an inhibition but a *disinhibition* of the motor reaction which was futher stimulated by the verbal response to the signal (Fig. 7). From O. K. Tikhomirov's experiments in the "silent" experiment in which differential responses were elicited in the 3–4 year old children, there were 42 per cent impulsive motor responses to the inhibitory signal, while when the child said "I must not" on being presented with the signal, the number of disinhibited reactions was as high as 70 per cent.

It is only when we told the child to say "I must" at each positive signal and at the same time to press on the bulb, and in response to each inhibitory signal not to press on the bulb and not to say anything, that the conflict was eliminated. The child who was previously unable to develop a stable differentiated response was now able to make appropriate responses with the help of his own speech as controlling factor.

The effects described show that in the 3–4 year old child it is possible to effect a definite control over movement by means of the child's own

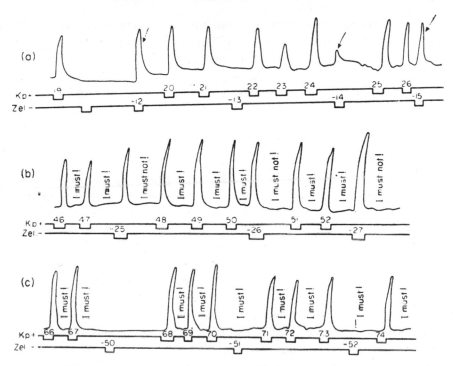

FIG. 7. Effects due to the nervous impulses derived from speech on the motor responses in a child of 3 years 2 months (Test on Vasya, D). (From O. K. Tikhomirov): (a)—Carrying out the differentiated response in silence. (b)—ditto, replying verbally to both signals; (c)—ditto, during silent inhibition of the motor response to the negative signal.

speech which serves to reinforce the previous verbal instruction and acts on the principle of feedback. However, at this early stage, and at any rate under the conditions of our laboratory experiments, the regulatory effect of the speech *of the child itself* does not originate from the selective or thoughtful side so much as from the non-specific, action of the nerve impulses; whereas the non-specific aspect of outside speech is completely without effect at this time, the child's own words may nevertheless exert a considerable influence.

5

We have been considering the earliest and the least known stages of the formation of a voluntary act in a child, and have described the characteristics and the simplest ways in which the child's own speech may serve to regulate its behaviour.

It remains to say something about the subsequent stages in the development of this regulatory function. The essential feature of these stages will be no surprise to us: it is that *regulation shifts over more and more from the mediation by the nervous impulses associated with speech to that system of separate selective thought associations which are stimulated by the word;* what is most interesting, is that at the same time control becomes transferred *from the child's spoken word to its own internal speech.*

For this purpose we need not necessarily apply special tests, but an experimenter always requires to follow any process as far as possible to its origin, and to do so by means of the original set of experiments.

The facts indicate that the essential change which we have just mentioned occurs in children between 4·5 and 5·5 years old. It is at this time that it becomes possible to develop in the child a sufficiently stable system of motor responses solely in terms of previous instruction. The child may grasp quite complicated instructions, to press in response to one signal but not to another, and by regulating his own behaviour by a rule which he has learnt he gives no impulsive reaction to an inhibitory signal. It is only when the conditions of the experiment are complicated, for instance by giving the signals more rapidly or by making them more difficult to distinguish, that the inhibitory stimuli may elicit impulsive responses. It is in these cases that it can quite often be seen how the child begins to resort to speaking aloud. But now the response "I must not press" does not act in the capacity of a set of nervous impulses, but by virtue of the significance of the statement, so that it does not disinhibit but rather inhibits the sponteneous response. It is for this reason that in children of 5–6, as O. K. Tikhomirov has shown, the learning of the significance of the inhibitory signal can by itself cause a considerable reduction in the number of spontaneous motor responses in these relatively complex experiments. At this age the child's own spoken words have the same effect, when because of the complexity of the experimental conditions some of the verbal instructions begin to lose their regulatory function. This can be clearly seen, for instance, in cases when the child is set a difficult task requiring more complex forms of delayed inhibition. He may be told to press in response to short signals and not to long ones, or again to press when two equal signals are given and not to press in response to a third. These experiments show that the correct carrying out of the instruction is often beyond the powers of a 5 year old child if he attempts to work in silence, but that he can succeed if he speaks while responding, so that his verbal replies can serve to reinforce the delayed inhibition and to determine the order of the positive and the inhibitory responses.

However, under these conditions it is by no means always necessary for the normal child to produce a spoken accompaniment of the motor response, but it becomes necessary only in certain special cases which we shall consider in another connection. It is, therefore, often sufficient to extend the verbal analysis of the signals presented to the child, and the internal speech associations so formed are then adequate to regulate his motor response.

The use of speech as a regulator, the gradual transition of the regulatory function from the nervous impulses derived from the child's own speech to the system of selective thought processes, and finally the transition from the regulation by the child's spoken word to the formation of verbal associations represents a highly complex process during which the characteristic "following device" of internal speech is developed.

Internal speech is a method of selection and of generalization and a means whereby a human being may orientate himself with respect to his environment and so comes to be a mechanism which allows new temporary connections to be developed, and which endows them with certain specific features peculiar to man.

A comparative analysis of the results obtained in the very simple experiments confined to studying relatively simple motor responses, with which we have been concerned in this article helps to demonstrate this conclusion.

We will now leave for the time being the method of formation of motor responses based on previous verbal instructions and following A. G. Ivanov-Smolenskii will attempt to establish for man the normal framework of the conditioned reflex, as proposed by I. P. Pavlov. Let us show to a child one signal, for instance a red light, and at the same time say "press this"! (or, what is the same in principle reinforce it with an interesting picture), and then give another signal, which may be a green light, and each time give the inhibitory order "don't press" (or show no picture as reinforcement).

We now have to find whether the differentiated conditioned response to press at the red signal and not at the green will be developed as well in a 3 year old, in whom the regulatory function of speech is still poorly developed, as in a child of 4·5–5 years in whom internal speech plays an active part in determining his behaviour.

Facts given by N. P. Paramonova in her lifetime showed that it was possible to demonstrate how different is the nature of the conditioned reactions in these two cases.

There is every reason to suppose that in the first case in which a conditioned reaction is developed under artificial laboratory conditions, many of the features which were studied by I. P. Pavlov in animals appear. New associations are formed which require repeated reinforcement, there is a period when the associations are generalized and for some time are not sufficiently stable so that each external agent or inhibition, or a short pause, or even a simple failure to supply reinforcement may easily destroy the association which is being formed. The selective nature of the reaction develops only gradually, and in the first trials each inhibitory reinforcement ("do not press") causes the whole reaction to stop, and each positive reinforcement ("press") likewise forces the whole reaction to continue. The development of the inhibitory reaction occurs only gradually, passing through stages of smaller and smaller responses to the inhibitory signals; it becomes extremely difficult to alter the system which has developed, and an extended period of re-learning is required. Do we expect to find all the properties of this primitive development of a new artificial association in the young child?

The nature of the formation of the new system of selected responses in a 4·5–5 year old child is quite different. We can be sure that a signal accompanied by verbal reinforcement will already constitute the certain system of information, which becomes generalized with the help of speech. The first presentation of the conditioning signal with its verbal reinforcement ("press") induces in the child an active generalized verbal reaction to the effect: "does that mean I must press at red?" Even by the first presentation of the inhibitory signal accompanied by the instruction "don't press", he has formulated the rule: "ah—ha, that means I must press at red but not at green", and the rule formulated by the child himself is now firmly included between the signal and the response so as to regulate all further activity. Thus it assumes an indirect quality through being mediated verbally, and remains of this indirect kind when the child begins to perform his movements silently.

Accordingly, the way in which the new association is formed is fundamentally different; it develops at once, and does not pass through a phase of generalization, but immediately forms a clearly defined complete system. The new association formed by bringing the reaction into the system formulated by the child's speech does not require continual reinforcement and is not destroyed either by an external inhibitory agent, or by a pause or by withholding the external reinforcement. It may be rapidly reinforced, and equally rapidly reversed. If a child is shown a signal which was previously inhibitory, but is given the new instruction "press";

the rule is easily and immediately formulated; "ah ha, that means now it's the other way round".

There is no single rule in the development of a new temporary connection which does not undergo profound change as soon as the child's reactions begin to be based on information which is systematised in a verbal form. It is this critically important fact which allows us better to understand the new factor introduced by speech into the organization of behaviour. The second signalling system is, of course, a part of the work of the same nervous system, but, as I. P. Pavlov has pointed out, it introduces a *new principle of nervous activity*. This new principle involves a close association of speech and behaviour and transforms man into the "most advanced self-regulatory system".

Translated by H. ASHER, B.A.

REFLEX RECEPTOR MECHANISMS *

YE. N. SOKOLOV

Department of Psychology, Moscow State University and Institute of Defectology, Academy of Pedagogical Sciences of the R.S.F.S.R.

THE ACTION of a stimulus on any sensory system brings about a number of changes in its different parts, including the receptor itself, as a result of which the sensitivity of the system to external stimulation changes. On this account, during the action of a stimulus its action on the system is altered, and this in turn produces further changes in sensitivity. In this way, the reception of a stimulus takes place as a series of reflex acts occurring within the sensory systems concerned in the perception of any particular stimulus.

A very important part in perception is played by the orienting and adaptive reflexes.

G. V. Gershuni [1] first raised the question of the part played by the orienting reaction in the reflex control of the sensory sensitivity of other systems, after which a number of experimental studies followed. The importance of adaptive reflexes in influencing perception has recently been stressed by P. O. Makarov.

Work carried out by us in the Laboratory of the Physiology of Analysers, Moscow State University, and in the Institute of Defectology of the Academy of Pedagogical Sciences [2, 3, 4], has shown that in considering the perception of external stimuli, special attention must be paid to the relationship between the orienting and adaptive reflexes.

The two adaptive reflexes which we have studied are those of thermoregulation and light adaptation. They were compared with the orienting reactions developed in response to sound, light and temperature stimuli.

* Conference on Psychology, 1–6 July, 1955 (*Materialy Soveshchaniya po psikhologii,* 1–6 iyulya 1955 g.), pp. 250–256. Acad. Paed. Sci. of R.S.F.S.R., Moscow, 1957.

COMPARISON OF THE ORIENTING
AND THERMOREGULATORY REFLEXES

An attack was made on this problem, working with O. S. Vinogradova and using a plethysmographic method. Simultaneous records were made of the increase in blood volume of the fingers and of the skin of the forehead in the region of the temporal artery. Also, N. I. Danilova, M. V. Mikhalevskaya and the author used the method of recording skin resistance with the aid of a self-setting potentiometer EPP–09.

As heat stimuli we used infra-red radiation obtained from a ceramic heater element with reflector. The light stimulus was supplied by an incandescent lamp whose intensity could be varied from 0·1 to 50 lux. The sound stimulus was supplied by a pure-tone ZG–10 generator. The cold stimulus was supplied by a glass filled with ice.

The experiments showed that the first applications of the heat, cold, or sound stimulus produced the same reaction: there was a constriction of the vessels of the hand and a dilatation of those of the skin of the forehead. However, after several applications, there was a marked change: heat now produced a dilatation of the vessels of the hand and head, cold caused both sets of vessels to contract, while sound ceased to produce any reaction at all. However, if the same stimuli were used immediately after some other stimulus such as the ringing of a loud bell or a knock, then the previous reaction returned for one or two trials, so that heat, cold and sound again caused constriction of the vessels of the hand and dilatation of the head vessels. After this, the reaction reverted to its previous stage.

Recording of the C.G.R., which consisted in measuring the change in the skin resistance of the palm in response to the action of heat, cold, or sound, showed that all these stimuli give the same reaction in which there is a temporary reduction in the resistance of the skin to direct current. The resistance of the skin fell at the moment of application of the stimulus, was restored while it continued to act, and again fell on its withdrawal—Repeated application of any of the stimuli led to an extinction of the C.G.R. Unlike the vascular reaction, we found no specific feature associated with thermal stimuli. After applying the extraneous stimulus, subsequent application of heat, cold, or sound once more induced the previous reduction in the resistance of the skin of the hand, which occurred either when applying or at the moment of cessation of the stimulus; subsequently the C.G.R. to all stimuli once more disappeared.

We must now consider how these facts may be explained. Constriction of the vessels of the fingers and dilatation of those of the hand may be involved in several different processes, including the orienting reaction and the process of thermal regulation. The first application of any of the stimuli always brings about an orienting reaction, which consists of a constriction of the vessels of the hand and a dilatation of those of the head; this reaction disappears with continued application of the stimuli. The thermo-regulatory reflex is increased when the orienting reaction to heat or cold is inhibited. Therefore, when after many applications sound has ceased to induce any reaction, heat produces only its specific effect in dilating the blood vessels in the hand and the head, while cold produces only a constriction of both sets of vessels. When an extraneous stimulus is applied and the orienting reflex becomes disinhibited, there is temporary inhibition of the adaptive reflex. The original orienting reaction is then temporarily restored for sound, heat, and cold equally.

Unlike the vascular reaction, the C.G.R. is associated chiefly with the orienting reflex. For this reason the first applications of heat, cold or sound produce an identical reduction in skin resistance of the palm of the hand, which becomes extinguished as the stimuli are repeated (Fig. 1). Extraneous stimuli disinhibit the orienting reflex, and in particular

Stimulus	Place of registration	Vessel responses			Skin–galvanic responses		
		To extinction	After extinction	After release	To extinction	After extinction	After release
Heat	Head						
	Hand						
Cold	Head						
	Hand						
Sound	Head						
	Hand						

FIG. 1. Diagram showing the relation between the orienting and thermo-regulatory reflexes. It can be seen that dilatation of the vessels in response to warming and contraction caused by cooling occurs only when the orienting reaction is extinguished. The C.G.R. is entirely in the nature of an orienting reaction. Extraneous stimuli disinhibit the orienting reflex and inhibit the adaptive reflex.

a. Stimulus b. Heat c. Cold d. Sound e. Recording made from:
f. head   i. Before extinction j. Dilatation k. Constriction
   hand   l. Vascular reactions
g. head   m. After extinction
   hand   n. After disinhibition
h. head   o. C.G.R.
   hand   p. Before extinction q. After extinction r. After disinhibition.

its manifestation in the form of a change in skin resistance, so that their effect is to restore temporarily the original orienting reflex, which again subsides after further applications.

The results indicate the differences between the orienting and adaptive reflexes. The former, which develop in response to any change of stimulus, become extinguished by repetition, while the latter, which are elicited only by adequate stimuli, become strengthened by repeated application.

A COMPARATIVE STUDY OF THE ORIENTING AND ADAPTIVE REFLEXES OF THE VISUAL SYSTEM

The relationship of the orienting and adaptive reflexes is of great importance in the functioning of the human visual system.

To investigate the relationship, we worked on the pupil reaction, where the reflex change is particularly clearly shown. The pupillary reaction to light and sound was recorded with a ciné camera working at 32 or 250 frames per second. Light stimulation was applied by switching on the 500 Watt lamp used for photography. The sound stimulus was the noise of the motor switched on at the moment of making the film. The films were taken by E. A. Pokrovskaya, an operator in the Department of Scientific Cinematography, Moscow State University.

The second visual reaction used was the change in electrical activity of the occipital region which was recorded in several experiments by use of a thermo-electric integrator, which allowed a direct determination of the level of electrical activity in the brain to be made and to be recorded by a selfsetting electronically controlled potentiometer.

For comparison, we measured the cutaneous galvanic reaction to light.

In the transition from darkness to light, as many investigators have shown (V. A. Smirnov [5], S. V. Kravkov [6] and others), there is a maintained constriction of the pupil whose extent depends on the strength of the light. As our experiments showed, this reaction shows some variation in latent period and in the amplitude of the contraction, and is maintained with some fluctuations during the whole period of action of the light stimulus. However, even when applied together with a powerful light stimulus, the effect of a loud sound is always to produce a dilatation of the pupil, which, however, disappears if the sound is maintained, and becomes inhibited if it is applied repeatedly; this was previously shown by A. E. Liberman and N. I. Strel'tsova [7]. Extraneous stimuli disinhibit the reaction.

The C.G.R. occurred when switching the light either on or off, and the resistance change occurring in response to the light signals was in no way different from that induced by sound stimulation. The skin resistance recovered during exposure to a sound, and the reaction became extinguished by repetition of the stimuli and was restored by the application of extraneous stimuli.

Changes in the electroencephalogram of the occipital region induced by light have much in common with the pupil reaction as affected by sound, and with the C.G.R. induced by light and sound stimuli. The recording of the brain potentials using an integrator shows very clearly that when the light is first applied the alpha-rhythm becomes depressed, but that it is restored, the curve returns to its initial value. Repeated applications of the light stimulus cause less and less depression of the alpha-rhythm, until finally no depression at all may occur. However, in most cases, a long period elapses before the first switching on of the light fails to produce any effect.

A particular feature of the electrical response of the visual cortex to light is that its sign may depend upon the initial level of electrical activity. Thus, if light is applied during a period when the alpha-rhythm is well developed, it is depressed. But when the level of activity is low, the same light stimuli may enhance the alpha-rhythm. Switching off the light, i.e. the transition from light to darkness, also causes depression of the alpha-rhythm. However, usually the depression is less when changing from light to darkness than when the change is in the reverse direction. Both sound stimuli and light depress the alpha-rhythm, but in the case of sound the alpha-rhythm recovers much more quickly, and becomes much more rapidly extinguished when the stimulation is repeated. Just like visual stimuli, sound stimuli may also enhance the alpha-rhythm if it is initially weak. Switching off the sound, just like switching off a light, may cause alpha-rhythm depression. A feature common to the electrical responses to sound and light, to the pupillary reaction to sound, and to the C.G.R., is that extraneous stimuli restore the reactions after they have become extinguished.

It remains to consider the relationships between the pupillary reaction, the electrical cerebral response, and the C.G.R. to light or sound.

The pupillary reaction, just like the vascular constriction in hand or forehead, may form part of several different processes involved in various reflex acts. In our experiments, it formed part of the orienting reflex, when the dilatation of the pupil in response to sound was a component of the orienting reaction which results from the application of any change in the external environment; it was also a component of the adaptive reflex, when the dilatation caused by the change from light to darkness, and its constriction on illumination, was a component of the adaptive visual reflex. Dilatation of the pupil as a component of the orienting reaction enhances the effect of the stimulus by temporarily increasing the sensitivity of the eye, and it shows all the features of an orienting reflex: it disappears if the stimulus is maintained, and becomes extinguished by repetition and disinhibited by extraneous stimuli. The pupillary component of the adaptive reflex remains constant at a level determined by the intensity of the stimulus and does not disappear on repetition of the light stimulus.

The C.G.R. is a component of the orienting reaction closely similar to the pupillary component: it has the same sign irrespective of whether the stimulus strength is increased or decreased, it disappears when the stimulus is maintained, becomes extinguished through the action of sound or light stimulation, and disinhibited by the application of sudden or strong stimulation.

The electrical response of the brain at first sight appears to differ from the pupillary and cutaneous galvanic components of the orienting reaction in that the sign of the response depends upon the initial activity level. However, on looking further, it can be seen that precisely the same reactions, consisting of an increased cortical excitation, are responsible for both depression and enhancement of the alpha-rhythm. In both cases the direction of the frequency change of the potentials is the same: when an alpha-rhythm is present initially, depression corresponds to a shift towards the higher frequencies, and when the alpha-rhythm is absent, or when medium frequency oscillations take place, enhancement also corresponds to a shift towards the higher frequencies. Both kinds of reaction represent an increased lability of the cortical cells, indicating a heightened reactivity of the visual system.

Whereas the C.G.R. is not selective with respect to the stimuli applied, being the same for both light and sound, the cortical responses to light and sound are different. The reaction to sound resembles the cutaneous galvanic response and the pupillary component of the orienting reflex. The response to light shows certain special features indicating that it is a type of orienting reaction: it disappears when the light is maintained, becomes extinguished by repetition, and is disinhibited by extraneous stimuli. However, the fact that the reaction to light becomes extinguished much more slowly than that to sound, and sometimes never extinguished at all, suggests that it is a special component of the orienting reflex and intimately associated with the visual system. The fact that this consistently maintained reaction is elicited selectively by light shows that it is in the same category as the adaptive reflex (Fig. 2).

Comparison of the results of the first and second parts of the experiment shows the resemblance between reflex temperature regulation and

Stimulus	Pupillary response	Electric response			Skin–galvanic response		
		To extinction	After extinction	After release	To extinction	After extinction	After release
Light	Dilatation	Exaltation — or	or — or	or	Rise in resistance	—	
Darkness		— or	or — or	or		—	
Sound	Contraction	Depression — or	—	or	Fall in resistance	—	

FIG. 2. Diagram of relationship between the orienting and adaptive visual reflexes. The pupillary reaction may be either adaptive or orienting. When a strong light is applied, the orienting reaction does not appear immediately, and the first response is a pupillary constriction. Sometimes, however, there may be a delay in the response which is evidently caused by the inhibitory effect of the orienting reflex. The appearance of the orienting reflex during the action of light is indicated in other ways (chiefly by the cutaneous galvanic reflex). It is therefore only the component of the orienting reflex which has the same manifestation as the adaptive reflex (i.e. the pupillary response) which is inhibited. Depression of the alpha-rhythm by sound takes place together with the C.G.R. However, the depression to light is better conserved, and is extinguished only with difficulty by a great many applications of the light stimulus.

    a. Stimulus *b.* Light *c.* Darkness *d.* Sound
    e. Pupillary response *f.* Dilatation *g.* Constriction
    h. Electrical response
    i. Before extinction *j.* or *k.* Enhancement *l.* Depression
    m. After extinction *n.* After disinhibition
    o. C. G. R.
    p. Before extinction *q.* After extinction *r.* After disinhibition.

control over the sensitivity of the eye. In both cases there is a complex interaction between the orienting and adaptive reflexes, which despite the similarity of their outward form may take place not only to a certain extent independently, but also show a reciprocal relationship. According to the conditions, this orienting reaction may temporarily inhibit one or other adaptive reflex, as occurred when recording vascular reactions, or under the influence of the adaptive reflex, one or other of its manifestations may be disinhibited, as in the pupillary reaction during strong light stimulation. When stimuli are applied frequently, the orienting reaction becomes extinguished, and then its inhibitory effect on the adaptive reflex becomes weaker. Therefore, in many cases the orienting reaction may become replaced by an adaptive reflex. Extraneous stimuli, by increasing the orienting reaction, may temporarily inhibit an adaptive reflex.

By comparing the vascular, cutaneous galvanic, and cortical electrical responses it is possible to establish certain properties of the orienting and adaptive reflexes.

Orienting reactions:

(a) develop only in response to a change of stimulus;

(b) in all cases the sign of reaction is the same, and is such as to increase sensory sensitivity;

(c) they disappear during the maintained action of the stimulus, to appear once more when it ceases;

(d) they develop in response to a wide range of stimuli;

(e) they include many components affecting many different organs;

(f) they may be divided into general and special orienting reactions;

(g) they become extinguished by repetitions;

(h) they are restored by the application of extraneous stimuli or by a change in the conditions of the experiment.

Adaptive reactions:

(a) the response is proportional to the strength and to the quality of the adequate stimulus;

(b) the sign of the reaction differs according to whether the stimulus is applied or withdrawn;

(c) they are maintained during the whole of the period of application of the stimulus;

(d) they represent special reactions which occur only in response to adequate stimuli;

(e) they are not extinguished by repetition;

(f) they may be inhibited by extraneous stimuli, being temporarily replaced by orienting reactions.

In spite of the differences between them, the orienting and adaptive reflexes are intimately associated. Their interaction at a cortical level represents the reflex basis of perception.

Translated by H. ASHER, B.A.

REFERENCES

1. GERSHUNI, G. V., (1950). Fiziologicheskoye obosnovaniye ob'ektivnoi audiometrii (The Physiological Basis of Objective Audiometry). *Problemy fiziologicheskoi akustiki* ("Problems of Physiological Acoustics"), Vol. II.
2. SOKOLOV, YE. N., (1954). Orientirovochnyi refleks i problemy retsepsii. Doklady na soveshchanii po voprosam psikhologii 3–8 iyulya 1953 g. (The Orienting Reflex and Problems of Reception. Reports to the Conference on Problems of Psychology, 3–8 July, 1953), p. 12.
3. SOKOLOV, YE. N., (1955). Vysshaya nervnaya deyatel'nost' i problema vospriyatiya (Higher Nervous Activity and the Problem of Perception), *Vop. psikholog.*, No. 1, p. 58.
4. SOKOLOV, YE. N., (1955). Reflektonyye osnovy oshchushcheniya. Tezisy dokladov iz yubileinoi sessii MGU (The Reflex Basis of Sensation. Abstracts of the Reports to the Jubilee Session of the Moscow State University).
5. SMIRNOV, V. A., (1953). The Pupil in Health and Disease (Zrachki v norme i patologii). Moscow.
6. KRAVKOV, S. V., (1950). The Eye and its Work (Glaz i yego rabota), 4th ed., Moscow.
7. LIBERMAN, A. E. and STREL'TSOVA, N. I., (1952). Some Features of the Pupillary Component of the Orienting Reaction in Man (Nekotoryye osobennosti zrachkovogo komponenta orientirovochnoi reaktsii u cheloveka). *Zh. vyssh. nervn. deyat.*, II, 6

APPLICATION OF ELECTROMYOGRAPHY
TO THE STUDY OF SPEECH *

F. V. BASSIN and E. S. BEIN

Institute of Neurology, Academy of Medical Sciences, of the U.S.S.R., Moscow

BEFORE electromyography can be usefully applied to speech mechanisms, it is important that the following questions be answered :

What results can be derived from studying the electrical changes in muscle associated with speech? What is the nature of the relationship between muscle potential changes and the second signalling system?

If electrical recording is used as a means of analysing this most complex psychic mechanism without a clear answer to these questions, there is danger that a wrong approach may be made and in particular that the treatment may smack of psychophysical parallelism. To begin with, therefore, we will define our standpoint clearly.

By the term "electromyography of speech", we mean the recording of the variable bioelectric potentials originating principally but not exclusively in the muscles concerned with articulation. Since these potentials reflect to some extent the regulatory processes controlling the muscles, their study will give information on certain aspects of the physiology of speech mechanisms.

The recordings can be made in two distinct ways: by making the measurements either during audible speech or during the process of "speaking to oneself", i.e. while the subject mentally performs various experimental speech tasks.

The first method gives information concerning the muscular contractions on which articulation depends. The second shows the changes in muscular tone which accompany subliminal speech and which represent to some extent the internal changes associated with it. This association between small variations in muscular tone and thought processes was,

* Conference on Psychology, 1–6 July, 1955 (*Materialy soveshchaniya po psikhologii*, 1–6 iyulya 1955 g.), pp. 315–327. Acad. Paed. Sci. of R.S.F.S.R., Moscow, 1957.

as is well known, stressed by I. P. Pavlov, who pointed out that one had only to think about hand movements for such movements to be initiated and that it was possible to record them by means of appropriate apparatus.

The fact that the minute changes of muscle tone which accompany speech are associated with electrical potentials enables the electromyograph to be used to investigate these movements, as well as to study many of the features of the silent processes which are made as a preliminary to audible speech.

A detailed analysis of the nervous changes preceding and preparing the words actually spoken constitutes an important part of the psychology of this problem. Of that there can be no doubt.

The present trend in Soviet psychology is to consider internal speech as a process of great complexity. This is true of both the changes concerned in the translation of the thought into the spoken word and of the stages and separate phases in the waxing and waning of the verbal expression of thought. For this reason any attempt at an accurate analysis of the changes preceding and preparing the act of speech represent a correct approach. If the use of the electromyograph gives any information whatsoever as to the nature of these silent reactions, its use will have been abundantly justified.

The foregoing are the general considerations concerning the possibilities of the application of electromyography to the study of speech.

It can thus be seen that the principal task was to use the muscular potentials generated in speech to reflect the changes in tone associated with internal speech.

What published information is there concerning these mechanisms?

Muscular potential changes arising as a result of various forms of mental activity have been frequently investigated. We refer to the works of Jacobson, Allers, Sheminskii, Davis, Bychkov, and many others. However, in most of these studies the effect of mental activity was investigated only as affecting the limbs. Studies of the muscles of articulation are rarely found in either Russian or foreign publications.

The first Soviet author to work in this field was Iu. S. Iucevich of the A.M.N. S.S.S.R. Institute of Neurology. The present study is a follow-up of her work, and makes extensive use of the methods she used several years ago. She also helped in obtaining the present results.

A two-channel oscillograph giving high distortionless amplification over a wide frequency range was used for recording the electrical changes. Both the normal type of electrode applied to the skin and others of special construction were used. Recordings were made from various muscles of the articular apparatus, chiefly from the muscles of the lower lip, as well as from those of the distal part of the arm.

In selecting subjects we were guided by the following considerations. In a modern speech defect clinic various forms of organic and functional disturbance corresponding to the various facets of speech activity are represented. Because of this, a study of speech disturbances frequently allows information about functions and features of verbal activity to be inferred which could not be found by studying normal subjects.

On this account we investigated both healthy subjects and patients with organic and functional speech disorders, including aphasia and hysterical mutism. Altogether more than 50 subjects were tested.

In all cases the EMG record was made by assigning various experimental speech tasks which the subject had to carry out silently, and these were based on a preliminary psychological study of the subject. In patients, the nature of the task was based on a clinical and psychological study of the speech defect.

Studies of the normal subjects will be reported first.

The following are the three principal features which are shown:

If a normal subject finds a given verbal task simple, then when performing it silently, only the very slightest increase of the amplitude of the potentials above normal in the lip muscles can be recorded. Usually no definite changes can be recorded from the hand muscles (Fig. 1).

If the task presents some difficulty, then the increase in the potentials in the lip muscles becomes much more marked (Fig. 2). One particular set of experiments showed that the factor chiefly responsible for evoking these electrical changes was the difficulty of the thought rather than the articulation.

In cases where the subject adopted a negative attitude to the experiment, for example when he was tired or when compulsion was applied, etc. the increase in the amplitude of the potentials in the muscles might not occur during the execution of the verbal task, although the problem would be correctly solved. However, quite frequently in such cases a considerable increase could be observed in the electrical activity of the flexors and extensors of the wrists (Fig. 3).

The results obtained in tests on patients with organic speech disorders show certain differences in comparison with the normal. The following points are to be noted. If a speech task which involves some specific difficulty associated with his defect is given to a patient, as a rule this causes a considerable increase in the amplitude of the lip muscle potentials (Fig. 4). If the task is clearly beyond his powers, then instead of the normal

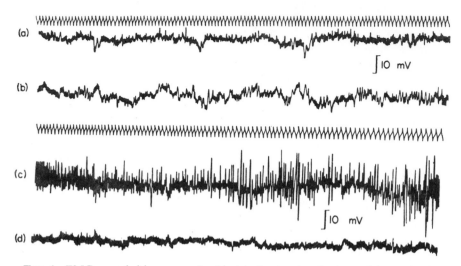

FIG. 1. EMG recorded in a normal subject both at rest and when solving a simple
mental task (repeated subtraction of 3 from 100) (a) and (b)—EMG of lower lip and
extensors of fingers of right hand at rest; (c) and (d)—ditto during solution of problem
Time marking on each trace, and in subsequent traces, 50 cycles/second.

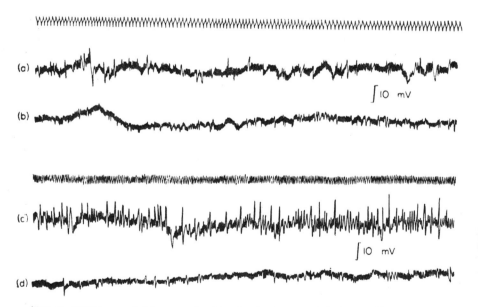

FIG. 2. EMG recorded in normal subject both at rest and during a difficult mental
task (reading a text consisting of jumbled words and letters) (a) and (b)—EMG of lower
lip and extensors of fingers at rest; (c) and (d) ditto during solution of problem.

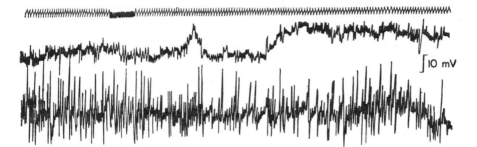

FIG. 3. EMGs recorded in a normal subject having a negative attitude to the experiment. (The subject was invited to read "to himself" a text having missing words and letters—a task which he carried out unwillingly). Upper oscillogram: EMG of lower lip; lower: EMG of finger extensors of right hand. The beginning of the task is indicated by a mark on the time line at the upper left part of the figure.

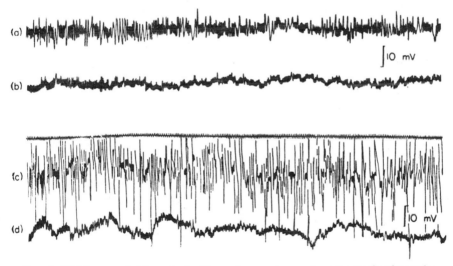

FIG. 4. EMGs recorded in patient with syndrome of amnesia and aphasia of vascular origin; recordings made at rest and during execution of difficult task (naming in thought an object represented on the card shown)
(a) and (b)—EMG of lower lip and finger extensors (on the functionally "uninvolved" side) during rest; (c) and (d)—ditto during solution of problem.

amplification of the potentials during the attempted solution there may be an actual reduction (in comparison with the initial resting conditions), whereas in the hands there may be a marked increase in the amplitude of the potentials. After some practice in the task, the normal type of potential change is once more recorded (Fig. 5).

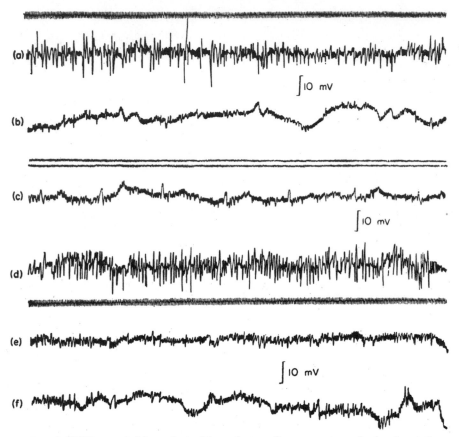

FIG. 5. EMG recorded in patient with syndrome of severe motor aphasia of vascular origin at rest during unwilling execution of a task which he found difficult—the mental repetition of a word pronounced by the experimenter, and during the satisfactory execution of the same task after preliminary instruction

(a) and (b)—EMG of lower lip and finger extensors (on the functionally "uninvolved" side during rest); (c) and (d)—the same during attempts to carry out the task without preliminary instruction; (e) and (f)—ditto during fulfilment of task after instruction.

In patients with aphasic disturbances, the usual response is that of a "disinhibition" of the EMG as recorded from the lips at rest, i.e. the potentials increase in comparison to the normal mean amplitude; the shape of the electromyogram also changes. It is particulary interesting to note the tendency to increased electrical activity which occurs in the hand and arm muscles in patients who are using writing as a method of compensation for a speech defect.

What results were found in a case of hysterical mutism where the disturbance was purely functional? If such a patient was asked to pronounce mentally any of the words which were affected by his condition of inhibition, i.e. any of the words which he could not pronounce aloud, then in many cases it was possible to observe a reduction in the amplitude of the lip potentials as compared with the resting condition. When the request was repeated insistently by the experimenter, the depression of the potentials became even more marked (Fig. 6).

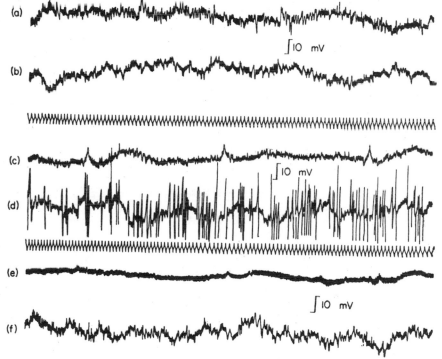

FIG. 6. EMGs recorded in patient with syndrome of hysterical mutism during rest and during the task of mental pronunciation of one of the words which he was unable to pronounce aloud.
(a) and (b)—EMG of lower lip and finger extensors of right hand during rest; (c) and (a)—ditto during taks of mental pronunciation of one of the words affected by the inhibition; (e) and (f)—ditto during repetition of insistent request to carry out the task.

A second characteristic feature was also found in functional cases.

In organic speech disturbances and in normal subjects, the extent of the increase in the amplitude of the potentials was associated in a definite

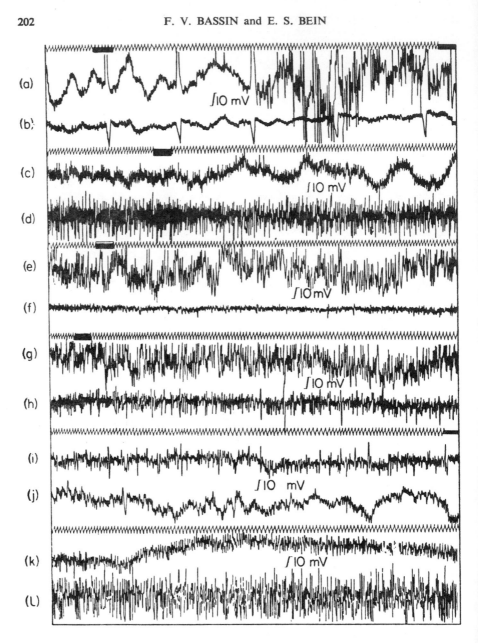

FIG. 7. EMGs recorded during fulfilment of the same speech problems by patients
with different types of speech defect

(a) and (b)—EMGs in patient with syndrome of motor aphasia recorded from finger
extensors and lower lip during execution of simple task (finding picture named by
experimenter on card); (c) and (d)—ditto during execution of difficult task (mental
repetition of a word pronounced by the experimenter); (e) and (f)—EMGs in patient

way with the degree of difficulty of the task assigned. This relationship was clearly brought out by the EMG recording when the series of tasks was made to increase gradually in complexity. In functional disturbances no such correlation could be found.

Thus the results obtained in investigating organic and functional speech disorders show that, as with normal subjects, the effect on the EMG must be considered in relation to the difficulty of the task and to the attitude of the subject, but that the effect of these factors on patients is not the same as on normal subjects.

The dependence of the potentials in the articular muscles on the difficulty of the verbal task was the basis of the method used in our investigations for revealing small individual features of the speech mechanism. Since different features of the tasks will affect the various structural defects unequally, the electromyogram may be used to find just which features of the speech of a particular subject are a consequence of the absence or of the reduced availability of certain of the normal components. The same information also allows us to obtain information about the fine structure of speech and about changes in this structure occurring under the influence of various factors.

We have realized this in electromyographic studies by selecting problems appropriate to patients with clinically distinct types of aphasia. With appropriate choice of problem, the electromyographic indices characteristic of each particular type of speech disturbance may be observed, since the solution of particularly difficult problems in one form of aphasia causes EMG changes which are quite distinct from those associated with similar problems in other types of structural speech defect (Fig. 7).

It must be noticed that in this figure only, the electrical activity of the lips is shown in each of the six photographs of the lower but not of the upper oscillogram. In all cases the transition to a task which presented a difficulty for the particular speech defect involved is accompanied by a sharp rise in the amplitude of the oscillatory potentials.

In these cases the differences between the different lines of the electromyograph indicate only coarse features which were already apparent

←————————

with syndrome of sensory aphasia recorded from finger extensors and lower lip during execution of simple task (mental repetition of a word pronounced by the experimenter); (g) and (h)—ditto during execution of difficult task (finding picture on card of object named by experimenter); (i) and (j)—EMGs in patient with syndrome of amnesia and aphasia recorded from flexors of fingers and from lower lip during execution of simple task (finding picture corresponding to object named by experimenter); (k) and (l)—ditto during execution of difficult task (mentally naming an object drawn on a card).

before using it. In many other cases the differences revealed by the EMG may be used to reveal finer details which were either not manifest before or about which there was some doubt. We will give two typical examples.

Two patients who might be thought to show different degrees of involvement of the internal or silent speech mechanism were told to name "to themselves" the object represented on a card. Subsequent questioning showed that both patients solved the problem incorrectly, but the electrical activity shown during the solution was different in the two patients: in one there was a sharp and in the other a very weak increase in the amplitude of the potentials (Fig. 8).

Subsequent investigation showed that the patient in whom the sharp increase occurred usually made poor use of the inner speech mechanism when solving problems, while the patient who did not give this response found problems of this type much more manageable.

This observation shows that a study of the EMG during the solution of a problem may allow a more correct interpretation of the nature of any speech defect than if the diagnosis was to be based only on the results of a purely verbal examination. In this case, the EMG helps towards understanding the nature of the defect, thereby supplementing and amplifying its psychological analysis.

Another example in which fine details of a speech defect were revealed through the use of the electromyograph is the case of a patient who solved the same problem at different stages during the restoration of his speech. In this kind of case the changes in the general clinical and psychological condition of the patient usually run closely parallel to those shown by the electromyograph, so that both improve together (Fig. 9). A feature of particular interest is that if in such a case, during the late stages of restoration of speech the patient fails to carry out a particular task set, nevertheless the kind of potentials occurring during the attempted solution may be more nearly normal than when the same task is attempted at an earlier stage of recovery (Fig. 10).

Examples of this kind show that the data obtained from the electromyograph may be of use in revealing very slight speech disturbances. The results obtained are evidently to some extent specific because they may reveal changes which could not always be detected by means of purely verbal examination.

The indication which we have used has been the increase in the amplitude of the EMG potentials which reflect the physiological changes in the innervation and functional condition of the effector organs—the so-called motor units. This may be interpreted in two distinct ways.

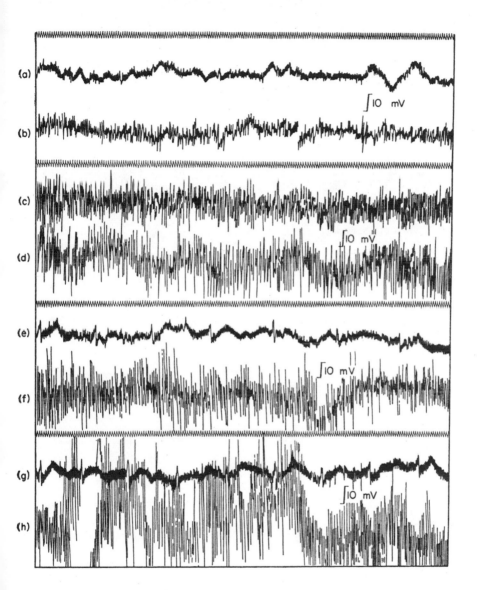

FIG. 8. EMGs of patients with profound and mild disturbances of "internal" speech. (a) and (b) — EMGs of lower lip and of finger flexors in patient with profound disturbance of "internal" speech (amnesic aphasia) recorded at rest; (c) and (d) — ditto during execution of task involving "internal" speech; (e) and (f) — EMGs of lower lip and of finger extensors recorded in patient with slight disturbance of "internal" speech at rest; (g) and (h) — ditto during execution of task involving "internal" speech.

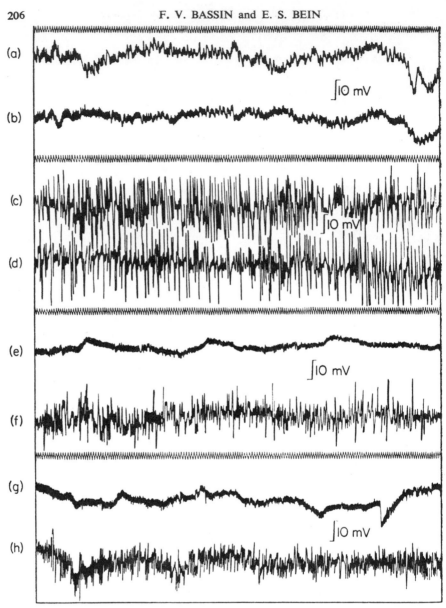

FIG. 9. EMGs recorded in a patient with motor aphasia during solution of the same problem at various stages during recovery

(a) and (b)—EMGs of lower lip and of finger extensors recorded at rest when the treatment was started; (c) and (d)—while carrying out a verbal task; (e) and (f)—record taken from the same points at a later stage during recovery and under resting conditions; (g) and (h)—ditto while carrying out verbal task; comparison of (e) and (g) show no increase in amplitude of the potentials during successful fulfilment of verbal task during the later stages of speech recovery.

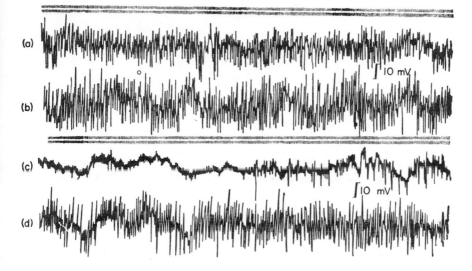

FIG. 10. EMGs recorded in one patient with motor aphasia during solution of the same problem at an early and late stage of speech recovery; the latter was a phase of "chance" error

(a) and (b)—EMGs of lower lip and of finger extensors during execution of difficult verbal task (mental repetition of a word pronounced by the experimenter) at the beginning of treatment; (c) and (d)—ditto at a later stage of speech recovery.
Comparison of (a) and (c) shows that during the late recovery stage, no increase in amplitude occurs, even though because of a slip, the task set was not correctly carried out.

It may be that the increase in amplitude is a reaction which is connected in some way with the activity of the second signalling system, but nevertheless does not form an essential part of it; in other words the changes in the EMG are related to speech in the same way as, for example, is an increase in sweat secretion, bodily conductivity, or a vasomotor reaction which occur in a perfectly regular manner when speech difficulties are encountered.

There is, however, a second possibility. These tonal changes may be thought of as being associated with speech, not only by occurring at the same time but as being a part of the speech mechanism and reflecting the innervational processes involved in articulation. According to this view, changes in the amplitude of the potentials associated with speech difficulties are not mere indicators of the degree of difficulty, but occur simultaneously as an actual expression of the nervous activity involved in the very act itself.

One observation allows us to distinguish between these two possibilities. We tried to find to what extent the potential changes occurring during difficult tasks are characteristic of the different muscles of the articular apparatus. To do this, we compared the EMGs recorded under such conditions as those described above, from both lips, cheeks, base of mouth, and various closely related muscular structures. From these traces it could be seen that the changes which interest us occur most markedly in the lip muscles, i.e. in the groups whose articulatory function is most fully differentiated (Fig. 11).

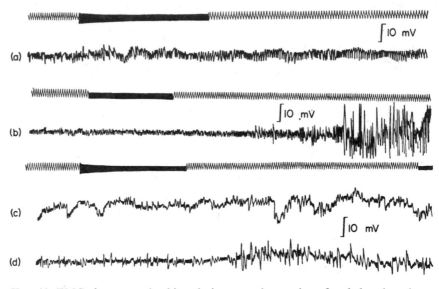

FIG. 11. EMGs in a normal subject during mental execution of verbal tasks taken from neck muscles (a) and upper lip (b); (c) and (d)—records taken under identical conditions and from the same points simultaneously.

In this respect, therefore, the muscles of articulation resemble those of the limbs, since in the latter the changes in muscle tone caused by activity of the second signalling system are more clearly marked in EMG records taken from the more distal parts of the upper extremity, i.e. from the muscle groups involved in fine specialized movements.

This selective localization of alterations in tone accompanying verbal thought appears to us to constitute an argument in favour of the second of the two views described above, i.e. it shows that these fine changes in tone should not be considered merely as indications of the speech difficulty but should be interpreted as processes closely linked with thes physiological mechanism of the very act of speech, and as essential functional components of this act.

In the present communication we have presented results which illustrate only some of the possible applications of electromyography to the investigation of speech mechanisms. There is no doubt that the range of possibilities extends much further than the ground covered here. The use of the EMG to evaluate the difficulty of a verbal task may be useful in explaining all kinds of speech activity mechanisms. By applying this method to psychological experiments we can not only obtain more precise information on just what speech components are preserved or involved. We can also obtain a clear idea of the affective attitude of the subject during the tests, and the role and the degree of activity of the different elements of the articulatory apparatus involved in speech can be compared, and this is of considerable importance in speech therapy; we can assess the value of various methods, such as articulation, as methods for compensating speech defect. Finally, the use of electromyographic investigations in the speech clinic may enable us to solve a number of important clinical and psychological problems.

All these considerations indicate that serious attention must be given to extending the applications of electromyography in speech studies.

Translated by H. ASHER B.A.

ELECTROPHYSIOLOGICAL INVESTIGATION OF SPEECH *

L. A. NOVIKOVA

Institute of Defectology, Academy of Paedagogical Sciences of the R.S.F.S.R., Moscow

THE first statement about the reflex nature of the thought process was made by I. M. Sechenov in his well-known work "Brain Reflexes". Sechenov's great achievement consisted in producing the idea of the direct relation between thought and the speech reflexes. He wrote: "At least I know that in my own case while my mouth is closed and motionless my thoughts are often accompanied by internal speech, i.e. by movements of the tongue and oral cavity. In every case when I wish to give priority to one thought over others I invariably express it in a whisper" [3; 151].

The study of speech reflexes was subsequently developed further by I. P. Pavlov. He pointed out the part played by the kinaesthetic impulses in bringing about reactions associated with the second signalling system. These impulses pass from the speech apparatus into the cerebral cortex, and as Pavlov explained, represent the "basic component of thought".

There have been various experimental approaches to the problem of demonstrating the leading part played by the kinaesthetic impulses in mediating the second signalling reaction. One has consisted in making a study of the higher cortical processes under conditions in which motor control has been partially eliminated. Thus Sokolov [4] found that there was considerable difficulty in understanding and remembering a text when the speech organs of the subject were occupied in pronouncing words. From these observations he concluded that thought cannot take place in the absence of the so-called "internal speech" and that the thought processes of an adult are built up on the basis of a shortened "condensed" internal speech.

The experiments of L. K. Nazarova on young schoolchildren showed that when speech movements were partially excluded by pressing the tongue with the lips, there was some interference with complex forms

* Conference on Psychology, 1–6 July, 1955 (*Materialy soveshchaniya po psikhologii,* 1–6 iyulya 1955 g.), pp. 337–351. Acad. Paed. Sci. of R.S.F.S.R., Moscow, 1957.

of cortical activity [2]. Still more serious disturbances of the higher proces-ses on compressing the tongue were found by A. R. Luria in patients with damage to the kinaesthetic areas of the cerebral cortex. Tests applied to these patients showed just which thought processes were most disturb-ed by elimination of tongue movements.

While this type of investigation is no doubt valuable, the possibility of objective recording is of considerable interest.

The first work of this kind was that of Cartis, 1899, followed by that of Courten, 1902, who recorded tongue movements using a pneumatic drum. Wycoikowski, 1919 *, placed the tongue in a small glass balloon connected with a kymograph. Thorson, 1925, used a complex system of levers for recording tongue movements. The results obtained by these authors led to no clear conclusion as to the part played by these move-ments in the thought process, and this is partly due to the fact that they used cumbersome apparatus of high inertia which made the investiga-tions very difficult.

In 1930 Jacobson [6], using a string galvanometer, first recorded the action potentials of the tongue muscles and observed an increase in electri-cal activity when counting "to oneself" and during the solution of arith-metical problems. In 1935 A. M. Fonarev, a student at Moscow Uni-versity, working in A. N. Sokolov's laboratory, used a special method for recording tongue movements which allowed small changes of muscle tone to be observed, but which required complicated apparatus. With this method the author has succeeded in recording tongue movements during various thought processes.

From what has been said above it follows that the best method of objective study of speech movement is that of recording the electrical potentials of the tongue muscles. By using high gain amplifiers, it is pos-sible to detect tensions in the tongue muscles which are associated with the corresponding speech mechanisms. By using several oscillographic channels it is possible also to record the electromyograms of any muscle as required. With these considerations in mind we chose the electrophys-iological method of investigation.

Our object was to study speech movements in subjects with normal hearing and in deaf and dumb patients. The studies made on deaf and dumb subjects using sign language to communicate with each other are of particular importance in connection with the part played by these move-ments in the thought process. Here, in addition to oral movements, the

---

* The work of Cartis, Courten and Wycoikowski is given as reported by Sokolov [4].

more accessible finger movements may be used, because in deaf and dumb subjects using sign language this takes the part of the equivalent speech process.

METHOD

Special electrodes were constructed for recording the electrical potentials of the tongue muscles. These electrodes consisted of small suckers inside which were fixed a hook-shaped loop of silver wire 5 mm in diameter. The bent surface of the hook came into contact with the tongue and allowed potentials to be led off from it; a 0·2 mm enamelled wire soldered to the hook was taken to the input stage of the amplifier. The sucker itself consisted of the end of the rubber teat of a glass pipette stretched over a flat metal ring having external and internal dimeters of 1·2 cm and 0·6 cm (Fig. 1). For bipolar recordings, two of the electrodes were

FIG. 1

placed on the dorsum of the tongue at a distance apart of 2·5–3 cm. Owing to the suction force, the silver electrode remained firmly pressed against the surface of the tongue and was not disturbed by movements. In all the experiments, the subjects were placed on a couch and told to arrange themselves comfortably so that the body and tongue muscles were relaxed. After a few minutes of training, most subjects managed to achieve a fairly relaxed condition of the tongue so that the resting potential could be recorded. In some cases continual movements of the tongue occurred, and in these cases the experiment had to be abandoned. In many experiments, besides measuring the electrical potentials of the tongue muscle, recordings were also made of the potentials of the flexors or extensors of the fingers of the right hand. For this purpose two round lead plate electrodes 8–10 mm in diameter were placed on the dorsal surface of the forearm. Recordings of the tongue and hand muscle potentials were made using a four-channel ink-writer from the Experimental Works of the U.S.S.R. Academy of Medical Science.

TESTS OF SPEECH MOVEMENTS IN ADULTS
WITH NORMAL HEARING

The first set of experiments was carried out on adult subjects with normal hearing. The object was to study speech movements during various kinds of mental activity.

In all, 11 subjects were investigated. Usually the experiments started by recording tongue muscle potentials generated by counting aloud, and this allowed the correct placement and fixation of the electrodes to be checked; after this, various tasks were assigned. A marker was used to indicate the beginning and end of its execution (Fig. 2).

The first operation to be performed was to count mentally up to 10. The results obtained are shown in Fig. 2, a. The first part of the curve represents resting potential and shows that the initial tone of the tongue muscle is quite low. During the counting, the amplitude of the potentials increases considerably. At the end of the count the curve returns to its initial level.

Thus in this first arrangement of the experiment it was possible to discover how mental operations (mental counting) lead to an increase in the potentials of the tongue muscle, and to obtain information about the increase in speech movements.

Similar results were obtained when mentally reciting the months, or days of the week, or poems. Interesting results were obtained in experiments on remembering groups of numbers and words. The subject was told to look for a few seconds at a board carrying figures or words. After this the board was removed and the subject pronounced aloud what he had been able to remember. Fig. 2, b shows the strong impulses from the tongue muscle recorded during the period of memorizing. Usually in such cases there is a greater activity during the memorizing of words than there is in the case of figures.

In studying a number of curves we were struck by the following feature: in several of the subjects there was an increase in the amplitude of the potentials recorded from the tongue even while listening to the instructions. Thus, for instance, one subject was told to multiply 125 by 7. It can be seen from Fig. 2, c that there was a considerable increase in the potentials from the tongue while the problem was being presented to him.

Most of the experiments involved solving arithmetical problems. One of the curves obtained in this way is shown in Fig. 2, d. It can be seen from the electromyogram how sharply the action potentials of the current increased during the solution of one of these problems, which consisted of multiplying together a pair of two-figure numbers. The burst

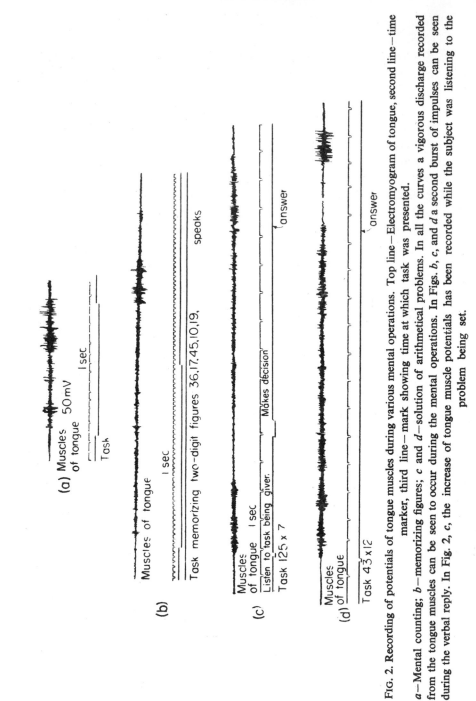

FIG. 2. Recording of potentials of tongue muscles during various mental operations. Top line—Electromyogram of tongue, second line—time marker, third line—mark showing time at which task was presented.

a—Mental counting; *b*—memorizing figures; *c* and *d*—solution of arithmetical problems. In all the curves a vigorous discharge recorded from the tongue muscles can be seen to occur during the mental operations. In Figs. *b*, *c*, and *d* a second burst of impulses can be seen during the verbal reply. In Fig. 2, *c*, the increase of tongue muscle potentials has been recorded while the subject was listening to the problem being set.

of impulses at the end of the record occurs when the subject announces the answer aloud.

Fig. 3 shows the electromyograms of the tongue in a single subject who has been set arithmetical problems of various degrees of difficulty. It can be seen that the potentials increase in proportion to the difficulty of the task. In this experiment, besides leading off potentials from the tongue, the electrical activity of the cerebral cortex was also recorded. During the solution of a difficult arithmetical problem, a depression of the activity of the brain could be seen to coincide with the period of activity in the tongue.

An increase of impulses from the tongue muscles was also found on increasing the complexity of the task in experiments involving memorizing one or two digit figures. The same differences can be found in the electromyogram of the tongue in the case of mentally repeating the days of the week or months directly or in reverse order.

In connection with Sokolov's experiments [4] mentioned above, tongue electromyograms recorded while a dominant centre was established are of particular interest. To make these recordings, the subject was instructed to carry out some mental process and at the same time to tap out the rhythm of a tune by hand. Fig. 4, *a* is a curve showing the increase in potentials from the tongue during the solution of the arithmetical problem. After this, he was told to solve a simpler problem but at the same time to beat time to a tune with his hand (Fig. 4, *b*). In spite of the fact that the second problem was the easier of the two, the time taken to solve it was longer and the potentials of the tongue muscles were greater, which indicated an increase in the number of motor impulses.

Fig. 3, *d* shows simultaneous recordings of the electroencephalogram (first line) and electromyogram of the tongue (second line). It can be seen that the increase in the electrical activity from the tongue coincides with the depression of the electroencephalograph.

From the first set of experiments described above we concluded that the method used was suitable for the study of speech movements. Owing to the firm fixing of the electrodes it was usually possible to make uninterrupted observations of changes in the tongue muscles during rest, during various mental tasks, and also during the spoken replies.

The results are collected in Table 1 and clearly show the speech kinaesthetic effects in response to various kinds of mental activity. From the table it can be seen that during the execution of simple tasks, such as mentally counting up to 10, reciting poems, or solving simple arithmetical tasks, some subjects showed no increase in the tongue potentials

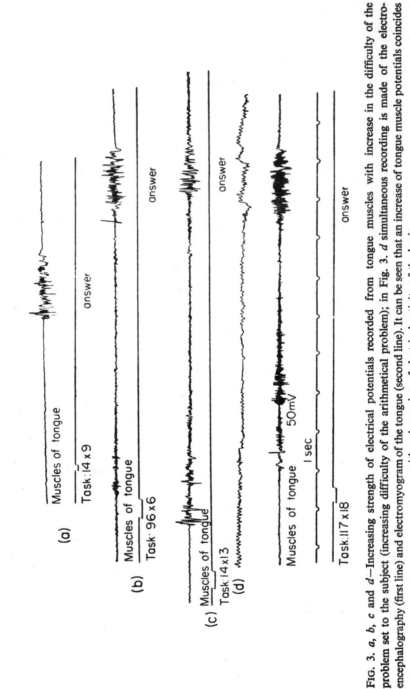

FIG. 3. *a*, *b*, *c* and *d*—Increasing strength of electrical potentials recorded from tongue muscles with increase in the difficulty of the problem set to the subject (increasing difficulty of the arithmetical problem); in Fig. 3. *d* simultaneous recording is made of the electroencephalography (first line) and electromyogram of the tongue (second line). It can be seen that an increase of tongue muscle potentials coincides with a depression of electrical activity of the brain.

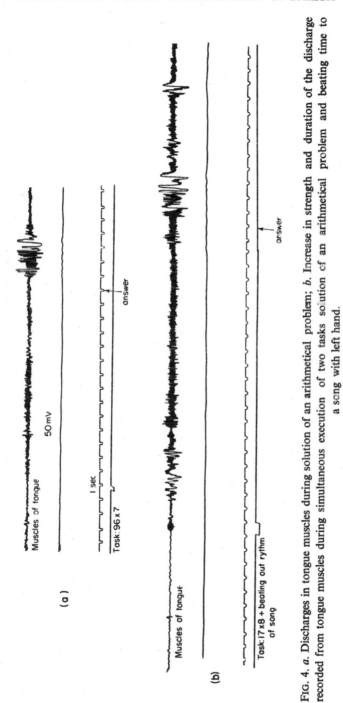

FIG. 4. *a.* Discharges in tongue muscles during solution of an arithmetical problem; *b.* Increase in strength and duration of the discharge recorded from tongue muscles during simultaneous execution of two tasks solution of an arithmetical problem and beating time to a song with left hand.

TABLE 1. *Expression of verbal movements during various, mental operations and during manual speech*

Task set	Cases investigated	Tongue movements well shown	Tongue movements not well shown	Total No. of cases showing verbal movements	No tongue movements shown
Mental counting	9	4	2	6	3
Mental pronunciation of poem	11	5	3	8	3
Mentally naming months in sequence	7	1	2	3	4
The same in reverse	17	4	1	5	2
Problem of 1st degree of difficulty	13	5	4	9	4
Problem of 2nd degree of difficulty	19	12	3	15	4
Problem of 3rd degree of difficulty	26	20	5	25	1
Manual speech	14	8	1	9	5

and so gave no objective sign of active speech movements. Clearly—as A. N. Sokolov said, in the performance of simple mental tasks by literate adults, verbal movements may be abortive or smothered: in these cases it may be impossible to record activity from the tongue muscles even using a sensitive oscillographic method. Evidently it is *also* possible that verbal movements may be absent during simple mental operations, owing to the formation of a stereotype. On the other hand, when the task is made more complicated it is almost always possible to observe well marked oral movements (as found in 25 out of 26 cases of solving complex arithmetical problems). Here we must once more recall what I. M. Sechenov said about the necessity the individual has for some sort of speech movements when engaged in complex mental tasks (3; 151).

One striking feature of the results was as follows. Out of 11 subjects tested, 8 were adult literate people having had school or higher education, and 3 were illiterate. In these 3, the increase of potentials from the tongue was particularly well shown and occurred in all the tasks set.

Clearly manifest verbal movements occur more frequently in illiterate than in educated people. This observation suggests that it would be possible to use the method of recording electrical potentials from the tongue muscles to study the evolution of the habit of oral movements during the development of the child. It is likely that this would give information as to how the mechanism was gradually elaborated during the process of mastering the language and during the acquisition of other knowledge. It would seem to be useful to employ the method of recording muscle potentials to study afferent pathways associated with speech, and to use it also for the purpose of developing temporary linkages in children with impaired development.

STUDY OF VERBAL MOVEMENTS IN DEAF-MUTE CHILDREN *

As has been described above, tests of speech movements made by recording electrical potentials from the tongue muscles sometimes fail because of the very high mobility of the tongue and because of its tonus. It therefore seemed well worth while to investigate deaf-mute children who had been taught sign language as well as true speech and writing. These children could not only speak and write but could also use the deaf and dumb hand alphabet. It was clear that besides kinaesthetic impulses from the speech organs and from hand movements in writing, deaf and dumb children who had learned the sign language might be expected to show impulses from the fingers when using it. Thus verbal movements could be studied in both tongue and finger muscles in deaf-mute children who had been taught speech and sign language.

In all these experiments simultaneous recordings were always made of the electrical activity of both tongue and hand muscles. The tasks were presented in writing, using boards hung in front of the subjects. The movements were investigated among pupils of Classes I–VIII of a school for deaf-mutes. The tests revealed that when they were learning the language not only in the written and spoken from but also in the form of the hand alphabet, there was an increase in potentials from muscles of both tongue and hand. The traces which illustrate this are shown in Fig. 5. The subjects were given a problem in mental arithmetic (Fig. 5, *a* and *b*), or were told to remember a group of figures (Fig. 5, *c*). In both cases there was a marked increase of muscle potentials from the tongue and the hand both at the time of performing the task and during the verbal reply.

Thus tests on deaf-mutes and on normal subjects reveal an increase in tongue muscle potentials which is evidently to be interpreted as an indication of the development of oral movements.

* This section of the work was carried out together with S. A. Zykov and F. F. Rau.

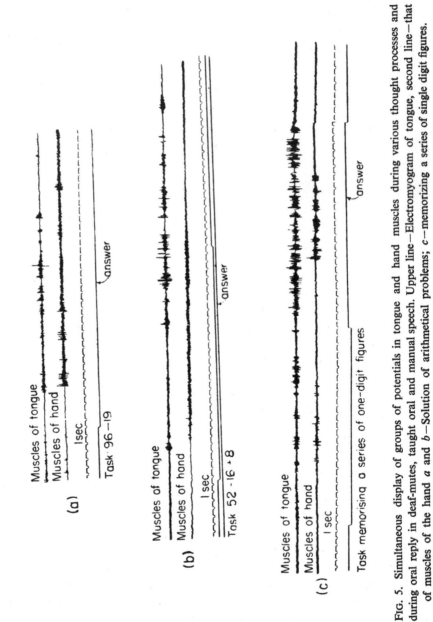

Fig. 5. Simultaneous display of groups of potentials in tongue and hand muscles during various thought processes and during oral reply in deaf-mutes, taught oral and manual speech. Upper line—Electromyogram of tongue, second line—that of muscles of the hand *a* and *b*—Solution of arithmetical problems; *c*—memorizing a series of single digit figures.

However, in dumb children who had been taught both verbal speech and the hand alphabet, besides an increase in potentials from the tongue, there was also an increase recorded from the hand muscles. This shows still more clearly the presence of speech movements during different kinds of mental work.

From the curves shown it can be seen also that in children with oral and manual speech there is a "co-operative" spread of the excitation to include both tongue and hand muscles, and this indicates the activity of a single functional system within the motor speech analyser. The formation in deaf-mute children of a single system embracing finger and tongue movements may be understood in terms of Ukhtomskii's conception of constellations [5] and Anokhin's idea of functional systems [1]. The functional system of tongue and finger movements develops in deaf-mute children during instruction, and appears to be a direct consequence of it. Simultaneous instruction in both sign language and speech has the result that deaf-mutes pronounce a word and make the sign for it at the same time, and conversely when making the sign they also pronounce it verbally. The following curves will serve to illustrate the fact that the functional system of tongue and finger movements develops simultaneously during the instruction of deaf-mutes in verbal and manual speech.

Figure 6 shows electromyograms from the tongue and hand of a deaf-mute taught both oral and manual speech, and of another who was taught oral speech and writing but not sign language. The upper curve (Fig. 6, a) is that of the teacher of the first year class in a deaf and dumb school who could use both oral speech and sign language; here it can be seen how the traces correspond by showing an increase in tongue and hand muscle potentials during the execution of the task (memorizing cards); by contrast, in another teacher of the first class who had been taught only verbal and not manual speech, as would be expected, there was an increase only from the tongue muscles while the task was being performed (Fig. 6, b).

The close relation between the tongue and finger movements, and the formation in deaf-mutes of a single functional system is also demonstrated by the following experiment. A teacher of the eighth class of the school for deaf-mutes was set the task of expressing manually the phrase "Today the weather is fine". Fig. 6, c shows how while expressing this idea with her hands, potentials were developed from the tongue muscles. Thus in the deaf children who can use both oral speech and the manual alphabet, although when communicating with each other they chiefly use gestures and manual speech, the movements of the tongue are so closely associated with those of the fingers, and the two are so closely linked to form a single

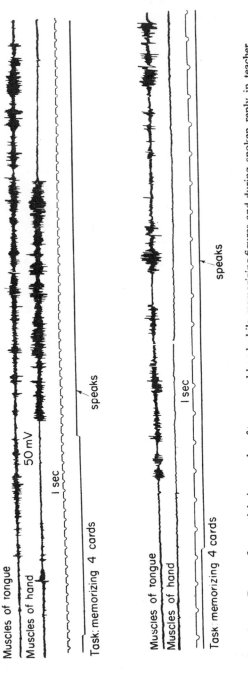

FIG. 6. *a* — Bursts of potentials in muscles of tongue and hand while memorizing figures and during spoken reply in teacher of Class I in a school for deaf-mutes; the teacher had learned oral and manual speech; *b*—appearance in same problem of bursts of electrical potentials in muscles of the tongue only in another teacher of Class I in a deaf-mute school who had been taught oral speech only and not manual speech. Upper line—Electromyogram of tongue; second line—electromyogram from hand.

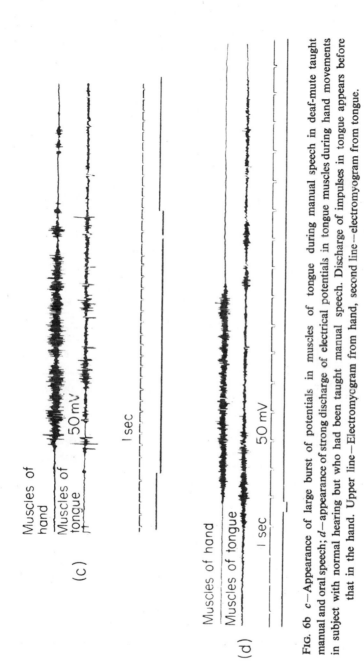

FIG. 6b c—Appearance of large burst of potentials in muscles of tongue during manual speech in deaf-mute taught manual and oral speech; d—appearance of strong discharge of electrical potentials in tongue muscles during hand movements in subject with normal hearing but who had been taught manual speech. Discharge of impulses in tongue appears before that in the hand. Upper line—Electromyogram from hand, second line—electromyogram from tongue.

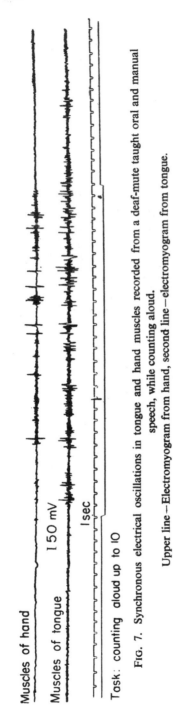

Muscles of hand

150 mV

1 sec

Muscles of tongue

Task: counting aloud up to 10

Fig. 7. Synchronous electrical oscillations in tongue and hand muscles recorded from a deaf-mute taught oral and manual speech, while counting aloud. Upper line—Electromyogram from hand, second line—electromyogram from tongue.

functional system, that when contractions take place in the fingers, they also occur at the same time in the tongue.

We decided to follow up this experiment by investigating the relationships between tongue and finger contractions in normal subjects who could use manual speech.

Figure 6, *d* shows the curves obtained in this experiment. The trace shows how, when told to express some idea with the hands, unlike deaf subjects, people with normal hearing start by producing contractions in the tongue, and then later begin to move the hands. Also it can be seen on both curves that the potentials from the tongue are best shown at the onset of the hand movements and become reduced subsequently; however, it is interesting to note that they once more show an increase when the manual expression has been completed.

Thus in subjects with normal hearing who use manual speech frequently, for instance in teachers in schools for deaf-mutes, functional systems may also be developed in which tongue and fingers are united into a single functional system. However, examination of the curves shows that here the chief part (P. K. Anokhin's "initiating afferentation") is that of the tongue. In manual speech, in subjects with normal hearing, movements start first in the tongue and then in the fingers.

Examination of the curves obtained in the experiments allows one important conclusion to be reached concerning the problem of the interaction of the mechanisms controlling tongue and finger movements in deaf-mute children who have been taught both manual and oral speech. In many cases it can be seen that the "combined operation" of the excitation of tongue and hand muscles in deaf-mutes with oral and manual speech is particularly well shown when speaking aloud (Fig. 5, *c*, Fig. 6, *a* and *b*). The almost complete coincidence of the bursts of impulses recorded from tongue and hand muscles can be seen in Fig. 7, which is a record taken from a Class V teacher of a deaf-mute school who was asked to count aloud up to 10. Evidently, in deaf-mute children taught both languages, during different kinds of activity (mental operations and oral speech) various relations between tongue and finger movement control in the speech movement analyser are possible.

The problem of the relation between lingual or digital movements in deaf children and their age, state of education, and individual peculiarities is particularly important in relation to the theory of education of the deaf, and must be studied further.

CONCLUSIONS

1. An electrophysiological method has been described which allows minute movements of the tongue to be recorded during various kinds of mental activity and for the associated control mechanism to be determined.

2. During various mental operations, as for instance counting "to oneself", solving arithmetical problems, memorizing words and figures, a noticeable increase in tongue muscle potentials is recorded, and this is a definite indication of an increase of verbal movements.

3. On complicating the task set, the muscle potentials increase according to the difficulty of the problem.

4. Establishing a dominant centre during the execution of the task leads to a noticeable increase of tongue muscle potentials.

5. In some subjects an increase in these potentials is observed while they are listening to the problem.

6. Tongue muscle potentials in illiterate adults observed during the memorizing of words and solving of arithmetical problems are shown much more strongly than in literate subjects.

7. In deaf-mute children who have been taught both oral and manual speech, an increase in both tongue and finger potentials is found during various mental processes. The increase of potentials from both tongue and hand muscles affords an even clearer demonstration of the verbal movements occurring during the thought process.

8. Simultaneous recording of electricals potential from tongue and hand muscles in deaf-mute children demonstrated that there was a "combined operation" in which both sets of muscles were involved, and this applied to the performance of most mental operations, particularly when speaking aloud.

9. The simultaneous excitation of tongue and hand muscles during various kinds of mental activity in deaf-mutes having both oral and manual speech shows that a single functional system has developed within the motor speech analyser and that this includes the control of both the tongue and the fingers. The various ways in which interaction can occur depends on the kind of education the subject has had, and will vary according to the kind of task performed.

Translated by H. ASHER B.A.

REFERENCES

1. ANOKHIN, P. K., (1949). The Reflex and the Functional System as Factors in Physiological Integration, *Fiziologicheskii zhurnal SSSR*, 35, No. 5.
2. NAZAROVA, L. K., (1952). The Role of Verbal Kinaesthesias, Communication to "Soviet Pedagogy", No. 6.
3. SECHENOV, I. M., (1952). Selected Works, Vol. I, Moscow.
4. SOKOLOV, A. N., (1941). Internal Speech and Understanding, *Science Notes of the State Scientific Research Institute of Psychology*, Vol. II, Moscow.
5. UKHTOMSKII, A. A., (1950). Collected Works, Vol. I, Leningrad.
6. JACOBSON, Ed. *Am. I. Physiol*, 1930, p. 94.

LEARNING AS A PROBLEM
IN PSYCHOLOGY *

A. N. LEONT'EV

Department of Psychology, Moscow University

LEARNING is one of the fundamental problems in the science of education. It is at the same time one of the basic problems in general psychology. The experimental treatment of this problem as one of general psychology started with the very first investigations on memory.

An enormous amount of highly significant material on the problem of learning has been accumulated by physiologists in the course of the past sixty years. The physiology of higher nervous activity, created by Pavlov, is—in one of its aspects, of course—the true physiological doctrine on learning. It has very naturally had an enormous positive effect on the development of this problem in psychology.

Despite the very extensive and fruitful research of physiologists and psychologists in the field of learning, there are still, however, quite a number of important problems in urgent need of theoretical analysis and review.

It is my intention to touch on some of these problems in this paper.

1

The conception of learning is used in a very broad sense. We speak of learing to write and count at school; yet we may also say that the young child learns to walk or—still earlier—learns to follow objects with its eyes. We can, of course, speak of learning with reference to animals: animals learn to open a problem box, to go by the shortest route through a labyrinth and so on.

We set aside the question of whether such a wide conception of learning is valid as an educational conception. In general psychology, as in physiology, this wide interpretation of the concept of learning is scientifically justified. It is sufficient to consider how important the classical

* *Voprosy psikhologii*, No. 1, pp. 3–17, 1957.

investigations of Pavlov, on animals, were for an understanding of the mechanisms involved in the process of learning.

In speaking of learning in this broad general meaning of the word, we are thinking of the process whereby the living being acquires its individual behavioural experience. Learning in this wide sense is a universal phenomenon in living organisms. It occurs wherever there is adaptation of the individual in the form of change of behaviour in response to new conditions. It constitutes an obligatory and constant condition in the lives of both animals and man.

A more complete definition of learning in this wide sense is, of course, possible. One could, for example, introduce into this definition references to the absence of learning in the process of behavioural change through fatigue or in the process of organ adaptation and so on. Yet this broad conception is not essentially changed thereby, and it is not this which constitutes the subject of scientific controversy [16].

The matter is quite different when we come to deal with the investigation of learning in its concrete forms. Here, one can no longer be satisfied with the notion of learning in its wide sense. The task now is to discover *specific* features in the process of learning, its mechanisms and the laws governing it. At the same time these features must be understood as arising *of necessity* in the course of development. In other words, the investigation of the learning process must start from the conception that this process develops, from the conception that it undergoes qualitative changes at genetically different stages and when conditions change. But this will not, of course, dispose of the problem of the most general mechanisms and laws of learning. The problem merely emerges as one of the initial, genetically primary forms of learning and its mechanisms.

What then are the most general and genetically the earliest mechanisms of learning?

Before learning has become differentiated and specialized in its functions and forms its mechanism coincides with the general mechanism for adaptation of the individual's behaviour. This is, in fact, the mechanism of conditioned connections.

The concept of the conditioned connection, advanced by Pavlov, is well known. I shall therefore dwell only on certain of its aspects.

First of all, I would draw attention to the intrinsic connection that exists between this concept and another in Pavlov's theory, namely the concept of signal stimuli.

The fundamental fact is that initially the direct, unmediated connections of organisms with the external medium at a certain stage in evolution, formed the basis for the development of connections which were indirect and mediated. Animals acquired the capacity to react in the same way to agents which *of themselves* had no biological significance for them. Agents obtained this significance only by virtue of their connection with other agencies on which the existence of the individual or species already depended *directly*. This type of agent fulfilled a signal role for the direct, biologically important agent; it became a signal stimulus. Thus, rustling sounds acting on an animal are of themselves neutral, but they may become for the animal a signal of food or of danger. In this case they become signals *orienting* the animal in relation to properties of the medium which are at that moment hidden from it and are not acting directly on it.

The formation of a time connection is also the commonest mechanism for change in the organism's reaction in accordance with the signal significances of the stimuli which are experienced in the course of behaviour directed to satisfaction of its needs by the organism. This mechanism is also the most general mechanism concerned in the development of the organism's orientation in the surrounding medium, that is, the mechanism for development of reflection and recognition by the organism of the properties of the medium and their objective connections and relationships.

As we know, the problem of temporal connections was developed by Pavlov and his pupils in respect of the stage in the evolution of the animal world at which temporary connections are nerve connections in the cerebral cortex. They are in fact cortical conditioned reflexes.

Pavlov's classical experiments with conditioned reflexes were directed to elucidation of the laws governing movement of the nervous processes effecting the conditioned reflex activity of the brain—activity which is the physiological basis of all behaviour, including also its most complex, specifically human forms.

Another objective was to extend the physiological explanation, based on these laws, to the widest possible range of phenomena in normal and pathological behaviour and so to create possible superposition "of the psychological pattern on the physiological canvas", of which Pavlov spoke.

These are interconnected but not simply identical tasks.

Here it may be noted that the classical arrangement of Pavlov's experiments with salivary reflexes corresponds directly with only the first of these problems. While it affords the best method of tracing such cerebral processes as are examined, this arrangement does not reproduce the complete structure of the behaviour of the higher animals under natural conditions.

For experimental demonstration of the laws governing the dynamics of nervous processes in the cortex, it was essential that all conditions of behaviour should be strictly constant and controllable. This required that these conditions should be reduced to the minimum necessary. Consequently the structure of the actual behaviour of the animal examined was also simplified.

This simplification of the structure of behaviour affected all its links. The simple and relatively constant need for food, which could be measured easily by the degree of the animal's excitability, was selected. Indifferent stimuli were then given an artificial character which excluded the effect of past experience on the process under examination, and the orientated reflexes evoked by these stimuli were rendered uniform in direction and result. This was achieved by the maintenance of absolute constancy in the setting of the experiments, by careful isolation of the animal from chance effects and by the definite, orderly sequence of the stimuli. On the other hand, in the conditions of experiments in which the animals were placed in a stand, the actual response reaction (salivary reflex) was, as it were, detached from their motor behaviour. As, however, the salivary reaction manifests itself in a perfectly simple form, its arousal neither created any problems nor introduced any changes into the system of operating stimuli, such as occur in the case of motor behaviour. Finally, a characteristic feature of classical experiments with salivary conditioned reflexes is that direct reinforcement is used in them.

This simplification of the entire system of behaviour in the classical Pavlov experiment sets us a further problem, namely, that of the analysis of behaviour under natural conditions, which is always of more complex, more extensive structure.

It must be emphasized at this point that, far from excluding the analysis of complex behaviour under natural conditions, Pavlov's theory of higher nervous activity actually suggests transition thereto.

This theory does not reject anything in the structure of complex behaviour and does not in any way degrade the complex in behaviour to the elementary. It analyses complex behaviour.

2

It is impossible, within the scope of a paper, to examine all the problems arising in connection with transition to the analysis of complex behaviour and which are already present in undeveloped form in the arrangement of the classical experiments with salivary conditioned reflexes. I shall therefore dwell only on some of these problems.

First of all there is the problem of the sensory, cognitive link in behaviour.

Whereas this link is more or less completely undeveloped in the classical experiments with salivary reflexes, it inevitably figures in its most developed form in the natural conditions of behaviour.

Under these conditions the neutral stimuli, which in experiment stand out against a specially "extinguished" background, give place to a whole stream of effects coming from the multiform properties of the innumerable objects surrounding the animal.

These agencies can acquire significance for the animal only as a result of the manifestation of relationships connecting them, and this requires a special process, answering to the task of orienting the animals in the complex medium surrounding them [18]. It follows, therefore, that the presence of developed orienting activity, whether immediate or created in past experience, constitutes under natural conditions of behaviour the same obligatory behavioural link as the existence of the unconditioned orienting reflex to the indifferent stimulus, artificially distinguished from the general background in the conditions of the classical Pavlov experiment.

The role of this orientational, cognitive link in behaviour is that it mediates the final, executive behavioural links. This cognitive link may be very largely undeveloped, being restricted by the inborn adaptational reaction of the organ-analyser, developed in the course of biological evolution, or it may acquire the form of well-developed processes of listening or watching and so on, but this link must always be present.

This, incidentally, is the reason why the Pavlov theory cannot be classed with the theories of direct connection between stimulus and reaction, and so be set in opposition in this respect to the so-called "cognitive" theories of learning, as is done by many foreign authors [15]. This antithesis is the more unjustified in that, as Pavlov repeatedly pointed out, the development of this very orienting activity in the course of evolution constitutes one of the most important conditions for the progressive development of behaviour.

It must at the same time be emphasized that the doctrine of higher nervous activity bases its understanding of the nature and mechanism of this cognitive link in behaviour on grounds which are essentially different from those in the theory of contemporary behaviourists. The latter, faced with the impossibility of explaining the true complexity of behaviour completely by means of the simplified $S \rightarrow R$ schema, introduce into their explanation references to this link, which is in the path between stimulus and reaction, as if to the manifestation of a special principle intervening in the process of behaviour.

The Pavlov doctrine provides the investigator with quite a different outlook: it reveals this highly complex link as the product of the reflex analytical-synthetic work of the brain, controlled by the objective laws of nervous process movement, and thus applies to it a strictly deterministic interpretation.

In this connection I would first recall the results of experiments with the formation of conditioned reflexes to compound stimuli and relationships. Special investigations on the conditioned reflex mechanisms of sensory processes, which have now led to the accumulation of a large mass of experimental material, bring us still closer to analysis of this link in behaviour. Among these reference may be made to the investigations of Sokolov and his co-workers, carried out over the last few years in the Department of Psychology of Moscow University [14]. It can now be regarded as established that even elementary sensations are the product of a whole chain of reflexes, including both intra-analyser (intramodal) and inter-analyser (intermodal) conditioned reflexes.

Even more complex are the processes of pure perception which represent what may be termed special "sensory behaviour". The feature of this behaviour is that in its complex forms it appears to have no effector links, that is, it takes place entirely within the system of sensory connections. Analysis reveals, however, that these sensory connections and relationships are the product of the combination into dynamic systems of completely constituted reflexes, the external motor effects of which are, however, reduced. Analysis of these more or less stereotyped systems also created the picture of, as it were, a purely sensory conception of the world, a picture in which there was manifestation of a capacity for direct insight into the relationships of the "field of perception" [10].

At this point we naturally come up against the Gestalt conception. Without at the moment discussing this conception as a whole, I limit myself to the one observation, that what the Gestalt psychology turns into a *postulate* we regard as a *problem* for investigation. From the standpoint of the theory of learning this means that where structuralism sees a *factor* of learning, we see its *product*.

3

The second great problem that arises on transition from the general schema of the conditioned reflex to the analysis of behaviour in natural conditions is in regard to its motor, executive link. The conditions of the classical experiments with salivary reflexes ruled out this problem as a special one. This did not, however, remove it from the programme of investigations. It will suffice to point, for example, to the experiments of Konorskii and Miller [9], which were analysed by Pavlov.

As some foreign authors are inclined to see in the theory of conditioned reflexes merely a conception based on the simple "substitution" of external stimuli, I must mention that, on the contrary, Pavlov ascribed a particularly important role, I might almost say a creative role, to the motor link, with the central processes produced by it, in the development of recognition and behaviour.

If the adaptation function is to operate effectively, the motor act cannot be completely determined solely by the direct effects of the external situation on exteroceptors. The effects of these agencies alone can never exhaust all the properties, connections and relationships of the actuality completely. The motor acts elicited by these effects cannot, therefore, lead automatically to the required adaptational result. This is not merely a question of the strengthening or suppression of movements by virtue of their direct reinforcement or nonreinforcement by the terminal effect: it is a question of the readjustment and the perfecting of the very system of movements, in accordance with the objective conditions, for the successful accomplishment of the motor act.

This is one of the problems of extreme importance for the theory of learning that was developed by the Pavlov school. Here I am thinking mainly of the investigations carried out by Anokhin and his co-workers [2]. These investigations enabled us to distinguish the conception of return afferentation as long ago as 1935 [3].

Return afferentation plays a very important part in the structure of behaviour. Investigations have shown that the accomplishment of a motor reaction not only requires transfer of the system of excitations evoked by the action of the external situation to the effector paths but also presupposes the simultaneous actualization of a special sensory system carrying, as it were, the "image of the action" undergoing execution. This "action image" is the product of return afferentation. By receiving and fixing motor behaviour experience within itself, it also plays the role of "acceptor" in relation to the action being executed (Anokhin).

The return signals reaching the brain during the performance of a motor act are also addressed specifically to this sensory formation. If they are adequate, there is acceptance of the movement and the act of behaviour continues to evolve. If, on the other hand the return afferentation signals arriving are not adequate for the system of excitations in the acceptor, the developent of the act is interrupted, and an orientation reaction develops in the animal. There is mobilization of the cognitive processes— a fresh analysis, a fresh examination of the situation, leading to change and development of the specifically cognitive link in behaviour, that is, its sensory link turned directly to the external world.

The discovery of return afferentation and acceptance of action made it possible to explain one of the most important phenomena in learning, namely, the development of compound motor acts by experience gained in their performance, which is the process of developing the *act itself*. And in this, of course, lies the central problem of motor learning.

Knowledge of the mechanisms concerned in the development of action has also even more general significance for psychology. The analysis of behaviour brings us face to face with a dual "cyclic" relationship: the action reveals its dependence on cognition, and cognition reveals its dependence on the action. How then is this "sensorimotor cycle" interrupted? Its interruption occurs in the motor, executive part—in the action. It is the action that makes active *practical* contact with the external world; coming up against the resistance of real objects, it not only is subordinated to them but, figuratively speaking, it "learns" from them.

If then, we take learning in its initial form, or in its most general features, it emerges as a process consisting of the formation of conditioned connections.

As we have already seen, however, learning has already in the higher animals acquired a very complex character, and is effected by special functional mechanisms. The general laws governing the conditioned reflex activity of the brain retain their validity completely, of course, but the development of the aggregate effect of these laws is now subordinated to new, more complex laws. These latter laws arise from development of those components in activity which, by their interconnections form a reflection of the objective world in the brain.

These are psychological laws.

At the highest level of behaviour, namely in man, learning acquires completely new features.

4

It is not merely that the process of learning becomes more complex in man. It acquires qualitatively different forms. The important point is that in man learning has acquired a new function by virtue of which its role has undergone infinite growth.

All this is determined by the fundamental change in behaviour and in the form of psychical reflection which took place with the appearance of man and the formation of a human society based on work [1, p. 452].

The pattern of life peculiar to animals, which is characterized by adaptation to the actual external conditions, is replaced by a pattern of life which is based on purposeful, premeditated change in these conditions, on their creation. The main "unit" of behaviour becomes action realizing conscious ends.

The development of these actions engendered yet another new form of reflection of activity—its reflection in the form of consciousness.

Only conscious images, conceptions and ideas can command action and be realized in it and can be translated into objective phenomena. Thus, the technical idea is realized in the physical construction, the image of an object in its depiction, the intention in the actual deed.

In order that images, conceptions or ideas should be able to fulfil this role, it is essential that they should exist for the subject as an activity of which he is fully aware, by which he can be guided and by which he can act. While still mental, subjective, they must at the same time have their objective substrate. This substrate is language, which develops along with work.

Being a product of society, language is objective. For each individual the phenomena of language constitute that special system of stimuli which Pavlov, of course, termed the *second signal system of activity.*

The stimuli which enter into this system are the effects, not of the actual properties of objects in the surrounding world, their connections and relationships, but of these properties, connections and relationships as they are reflected when framed in the sounds and written signs of language.

The stimuli of the second signal system are not therefore merely conditioned stimuli of the second order. They differ from first signal system conditioned stimuli in that they represent in material form, capable of acting on man, the properties and relationships of objects in their generalized grouping and detached from the actual objects. It is for this reason that these stimuli form for man a special system of *reality.* This is the reality of the knowledge and conceptions of the world elaborated by society, expressed in verbal quantities. This is the reality of *social consciousness.*

Man never stands alone before the objective world surrounding him. His connections with the world are mediated by his relationships with men, and this renders intercourse with them by language necessary.

It is by virtue of intercourse through the medium of language that man possesses the knowledge that has been accumulated through many centuries of practical human experience. The reflection of the world in his brain thus becomes, in comparision with his own narrow direct personal experience, immeasurably fuller. This also sets the problem of learning in the case of man on a completely new level.

The main feature of learning in man is the result of the content of experience, differing from that of animals, which he acquires in the process of learning.

The behaviour of animals depends on experience of two kinds. There is, first, the experience consolidated by heredity in the unconditioned reflexes. In its content this is the experience of the species. Secondly, there is individual experience, acquired ontogenetically, as a result of the formation of conditioned reflexes.

It is different in the case of man. There is, of course, in man also the hereditarily consolidated species experience. Another problem is that this experience occupies quite a different place in the behaviour of man and plays quite a different role from that which it plays in the behaviour of animals. Further, the behaviour of man, like that of animals, depends on the experience which is acquired by him in the course of life. This, however, is not merely individual experience, like that of animals. There is still another kind of experience which does not exist in the case of animals; it is species experience (or more accurately, socio-historical experience), which is assimilated, however, in the form of individual experience.

Although the two forms of experience are acquired by way of learning, they cannot be mixed. They differ both in content and in the process and actual mechanism of their formation.

It is true, they are in constant interaction—and this point must be emphasized, but it is specifically for this reason that, in the analysis of learning, it is particularly necessary to differentiate them.

The fact that man acquires species experience, the experience of mankind, not by way of inheritance but in the form of individual assimilation, introduces a decisive change into the whole process of learning and at the same time, as I have said, imparts to it a new function.

This new function of learning is evident in the fact that it changes, develops and perfects behaviour. It *creates* specifically human forms of behaviour. Such, for example, are operations with tools, speech activities and finally, all thought activities.

This, too, is also expressed by the further differentiation of learning. There is development of learning in the strict sense of the word. This is the learning that occurs in the association of man with other men. It plays a decisive role in man.

It is only in the case of man that learning is converted into a special process whereby historically accumulated experience is transmitted from individual to individual. Even in the simplest case of the learning of action as when, for example, the young child is being taught to use a spoon, the process takes place through the active intervention of the teacher in the action which the child is performing. The adult actually places the spoon in the child's hand or corrects the position of the spoon in its hand, helps the child to hold the spoon horizontally, and so on. The action is divided, as it were, between the teacher and the learner. This is the stage in the learning of activity which Vygotskii, giving the term, of course, a certain specific meaning, designated the stage of "collabora-tion".

The extent of and the forms taken by the teacher's participation in the acts of the learner can vary greatly. Such participation is effected verbally in many cases. Yet in learning, in the strict sense of the word, there is always a stage which requires the participation of the teacher. Furthermore, it is the most important stage in the process of learning as it is at this stage that the actual *content* of the process undergoing assimilation is built up.

Vygotskii demonstrated the importance of this stage experimentally. He studied the ability of children to solve various mental problems with the assistance of an adult and, parallel with this, their capacity to solve similar problems independently. Comparing the results of the two sets of experiments with the attainments of the children in the course of their further mental development, he found that the results in the case of the former group were very much more significant. Thus Vygotskii wrote that if the child is capable of doing something with the aid of another today, he will be able to do it himself tomorrow [4, p. 448].

I shall not speak at the moment of the various forms of learning which its further differentiation created. I must first turn to the question of some of the common mechanisms of learning in man.

Learning, *sensu stricto*, always postulates reflection of reality in conscious form. It postulates, in other words, the participation of mechanisms of reflection which are verbal in nature. At the same time, these mechanisms themselves are formed in the process of learning, as a result of the mastery of speech and of language.

Initially, when the young child is just beginning to master language, a word signals to the child the actual object with which adults usually link this word in their intercourse with the child. At this stage the word still does not produce any material change in the processes contributing to the formation of the child's experience. It begins to manifest this specific role only when, in the course of their intercourse with the child, the people around apply the word to other definite objects which the particular word signifies. Now, for the child it brings together within itself these various objects, equates them with each other in some certain respect (and at the same time differentiates them from other objects, including—which is important—objects outwardly similar to them). The decisive step is thereby made: by means of the word, connections are established which might not have been formed in the child as its individual experience is insignificantly small. Indeed the formation of such connections would demand an enormous amount of work on analysis and synthesis of the results of experience. This work is done not only for the individual child but for whole generatious of mankind; the product thereof is also consolidated historically in verbal generalizations and meanings.

It should not, however, be thought that this transfer produced by the child's repeating the word after the adult is a passive process for him. For the child, this, too, is an active form of activity. When an adult names a fresh object with a word known to the child, this is for the child a signal of the presence in the object of properties which have already been linked for him with the particular word; *this signal directs the orienting activity of the child to the finding and distinguishing of these properties in the object.* If this does not happen, there is no abstraction of the properties constituting the object by the child, no fixation of them in the meaning of the word and no conscious recognition of them; which means that the corresponding connections are not formed.

Here, two factors must be mentioned. The first is that the process of mastering words passes through the same very important stage that is characteristic of any form of learning in the strict sense of the word, namely the stage of joint action or "collaboration". In the case of word mastery, however, this stage is masked by the fact that in this case the activity has no deployed outward form.

The second factor concerns interaction between object and word, or in other words, interaction between signals in the first signal system and signals in the second signal system. In the very simple case of the mastery of a word which we have analysed, it becomes particularly clear that the word acquires meaning only through its connection with effect-producing objects. Thus, the source of the content which is reflected in the meaning of the word does not lie in the word itself but in the activity signified thereby.

Another aspect of this interaction, how the word fulfils its cognitive function, should also be considered. As a result of the designation of an object by a word there is equation of this particular object in a certain respect with other objects designated by the same word; there is, in other words, generalization of the word, but generalization which does not, of course, efface the individual features of the object. This result, as I have already said, we owe not directly to the word itself but to the processes of orientation, the processes of analysis and synthesis of the objective phenomena designated by the word, which it, in its capacity as a stimulus, evokes in the subject. The word is not in any way, then, the demiurge behind generalization; it is merely its medium and repository.

At this point we come to the question of the action mechanism of the word. A word, acting on man, actualizes in him the system of reflexes concerned in the orienting, cognitive link in behaviour. Their combined sensory effects, including kinaesthetic and speech, also forms the material for the representation or conception which the content of the meaning of the particular word constitutes. But these are the effects of actualization of complete reflex arcs with their own executive motor terminations; the latter are inhibited, reduced, but not cut off completely.

What happens then in the case of these inhibited motor terminations of the reflexes? When the operating word has a definite and concrete meaning, that is, can be applied directly to concrete objects (and it is only this case that we are examining at the moment), they reproduce the experience of action with these objects. This experience is generalized in quite a different way, however, from the experience which is actualized as a result of the direct effect of the objects themselves. It is generalized a second time as it were—in the process of "repetition" of the word, in the process of operating with it.

5

A new and still higher level of behaviour and learning develops when the child passes on from action with the word to verbal actions, that is, to actions which are effected by speech processes, whether in the form of outwardly expressed speech or in the form of inward thought processes.

The condition for the development of this level is a more advanced stage in the mastery of language, when the child develops the capacity to understand and to use more developed speech, detached from any objective situation. At this stage the common stock of acquired knowledge is transmitted to the child in respect of objects, phenomena and processes which he has never encountered in his own experience. Even in this case, however, it is essential, of course, that the knowledge transmitted to the child in speech form should be linked in him with impressions obtained by him from actual reality. The difference here is merely that now the connection between the content assimilated in verbal form and the impressions from reality is established, not by their direct correlation but through other verbal quantities and conceptions. If, for example, a child who has never seen a polar landscape meets with a verbal description of one, he will be understand it only when he correlates the content of the description with verbal values he already possesses, such as "wilderness", "ice" and so on. If the values which the child has at its disposal are insufficient for this, then it will be necessary to introduce additionally into the verbal description objects which are capable of sensory perception by the child.

This is the classical problem of the relationship between verbal and visual objective learning. Recently it has again been attracting the attention of our psychologists (N. A. Menchinskaya, L. V. Zankov), who have treated it from the standpoint of Pavlov [7], [8], [12].

In the still more complex case of the assimilation of abstract concepts, this correlation process assumes the form of transition from one set of values (concepts) to others, sometimes through a long series of concepts. This transition is effected in mental activities, that is in logical thinking operations.

For this reason the learning of any branch of knowledge, for example, the learning of the elements of sciences at school, *is at the same time a formative process for the students' mental activities.*

The latter also constitutes the main psychological problem connected with human learning.

In its broad aspect, this is one of the main problems in genetic psychology—the problem of the conversion of external actions into inward thought processes, the problem of their "interiorization". Soviet and foreign psychologists have devoted a number of studies to this problem.

This problem has been examined recently in the Department of Psychology of Moscow University by Gal'perin and his co-workers [5], [6]. These investigations were based on the general assumption that the primary source of thought actions was external action. They also assumed that the formation of thought actions—the reflecting mental processes—was not simply a matter of the interiorization of the objective material content of the external actions. If in investigating the process of development of the action from external to inward, one restricts oneself solely to the study of the transformation of its objective material content, as

Piaget does, then the entire process presents itself as the story of the gradual freeing of this content from its material features, as the story of the stages in the transformation of this content into logical operations [17].

The investigations mentioned showed, however, that transformation of the action is characterized by changes in at least three other relatively independent directions (or "parameters of the action") in addition to the interiorization of its material content. Only aggregation and correlation of all these trends or parameters will furnish the characteristics of the action and the stages of its conversion from the psychological point of view that is, as an action of the *subject* as opposed to the abstracted objective content of the action itself which is transformed into logical operations.

The first direction in which the action is changed is in the degree of its generalization, or the extent to which the action, elaborated by the child on one material in one set of conditions, can be transferred by him to other materials and in other conditions.

The second direction taken by change in the action is that of transition to progressive contraction. We know, for example, that a child in counting two groups of objects will count the objects in each group and then again count the objects one by one in the two groups together. Subsequently, however, the child performs this act of summation by adding the total number of objects in the second group directly to the number of objects in the first group.

The third parameter in which the action changes is the extent of assimilation of the action. At any stage in its generalization and contraction the action can manifest a different degree of assimilation. For example, under the guidance of his teacher, the child may effect the summation by adding the number of objects in one group to the number in the other but does not employ this method of his own accord, using the method of counting them one by one, which has been better assimilated by him. Sometimes the degree of assimilation of the action may not be in accord with the indices of the action in its other parameters, and this hinders to some extent the further development of the action.

Finally, the fourth parameter of change is the level of performance. By this is meant the degree of its interiorization.

The process of change in the action in this parameter is, of course, linked with its development in the other parameters, but this connection is relative. For example, even inadequately generalized actions can acquire the form of inward actions.

The results of investigations on the formation in adults and children of many different mental processes during the process of learning makes it possible to distinguish a number of stages in this process.

It begins with the stage of preliminary orientation to the conditions and requirements to which the action must respond. In the next stage the child performs the action with external objects and, for example, learns to count, to add and subtract on rods or other similar instructional material. The most important feature of this stage is that the action performed proceeds under the control of the things themselves; it is at this stage that the content and structure of the future thought action first begins to take shape, and during which its practical basis is formed.

Then comes the stage of action in speech form. For example, the child begins to count aloud, without reliance on the external objects. The significance of this stage is that there is freeing of the action from direct contact with the objects. The action with the objects begins to be converted into action with concepts at this stage, that is, it acquires the characteristics of a theoretical action.

It is only after this that the action is transferred into the inward thought schema. Here it undergoes further changes until, finally, it acquires all the features inherent in inward thought processes.

This, of course, is only the schema of how, from being external and practical, the action becomes inward and cognitive, merely anticipating and orienting the practical activity. As it actually occurs, the formation of thought actions is a process with still more complex and many-sided changes in each of its stages.

It remains for me to turn to the question I have already formulated: can this process be described as a process of formation of logical operations?

Yes, but only in the sense that the logical operations are its product. Logical operations constitute only the capacity to perform a thought action and not the action itself. I have had occasion to show that any operation, including the logical operation, is the product of the specific transformation which the action undergoes when it becomes part of another action which it becomes capable of performing [11]. This, incidentally, makes distinction between the action and operation more difficult. For example, the process of addition or subtraction is, in the case of the pupil in the first class, an action. When later, however, the child learns to solve actual arithmetical problems, these processes acquire in him the character of automatic arithmetical operations.

The formation of mental operations is connected with change in the same parameters as the formation of complete actions, but a specific feature of the former is that it is the most stable content of the actions, the objective material content, and not the psychological content, that is fixed in them. It is for this reason that the performance of mental operations can be transferred to machines, mechanical or electronic.

Study of the development of actions and operations also enables us to approach understanding of the mechanism responsible for the formation of cognitive images and conceptions. These are the result of actions to discover and demonstrate the system of essential features and signs of an object. When these actions become contracted and automatized, they are then effected in the form of a stereotyped reaction in response to action of a specific stimulus. They are therefore experienced by the subject as an action on his part. They are not available for introspection and exist for the subject only in the form of their product—as developing images or conceptions. The successively detected features and properties of the object appear in them as one, just as the picture appears on the screen of a television receiver.

In attempting to outline briefly the process whereby the child acquires the capacity to carry out actions in thought and to reflect reality in cognitive images—ideas and conceptions, I have used the terms, development and formation. These terms do not, however, convey the essential nature of the matter completely. For greater accuracy we should have said development or formation in the process of learning.

It is only in learning in its specifically human forms, that is, when there is transmission from individual to individual of the community's elaborated experience of practical and theoretical actions, that this process, impressive in its complexity and full of dialectical contradictions, is completed. That is why we consider investigation during the process of learning, which is the path particularly followed in the studies I have mentioned, to be absolutely fundamental. It is, of course, possible to detect stage changes in other ways, but it is impossible to understand the movement or transition from one to another as this movement, too, is brought about by learning.

Are we not, however, guilty of overstatement here on the conversion of the subject's mental development into a process, the course of which is imposed from outside by the will of the teacher? The answer is in the negative because the assimilation taking place during the process of learning also effects adaptation to activity which is not only that responding to the specific features of human existence, but activity responding to existence both in the material world and in the world of human relations and also in the world of ideas, concepts and knowledge where the experience of the general social activity is reflected. Learning, then, is one form of manifestation of man's life: it answers his vital requirements and motives; it is motivated purposefully and is itself capable of becoming an end. It is therefore subject to internal laws, the laws governing the development of the life of the individual.

*

It remains for me to sum up our theoretical examination of this problem.

In its primitive, rudimentary forms the process of learning is directly coincident with the process of the formation of conditioned signal connections.

Along with the development and differentiation of processes for the adaptation of the behaviour of animals to the ever increasing complexity of the conditions of life, there is development and differentiation of learning into its various kinds and forms. The mechanisms effecting it increase in complexity and become specialized. The individual reflexes now become linked together into dynamic systems, forming different, comparatively independent behavioural links, between which internal interrelationships are established. The general mechanism underlying the formation of these systems remains, however, the same: this is the mechanism of conditioned reflexes.

Simple recognition of this is still not enough for an understanding of the actual processes of learning. This demands special investigation to determine the regular changes that take place in behaviour, and primarily in its orienting, sensory link in the wide sense of the word sensory. Analysis to elucidate the physiological mechanisms must now take account of the results of this psychological investigation.

This refers particularly to processes of learning in man which not only increase in complexity quantitatively but acquire a qualitatively new form, experience the form transmission and assimilation of socio-historical.

Here the deciding factor is the content of cognitive activity, which itself is formed in the course of learning, in the intercourse of man with other men. The investigation of learning in man cannot, therefore, be effected satisfactorily by methods which merely consider external agencies and the response reactions of the subjects. Pavlov rightly warned against any such attempts. Discussing the results of experiments on man, carried out by the method of motor conditioned reflexes with electrical skin stimulation as reinforcement, Pavlov questioned the experimenter:

"But did he (the subject—*A. L.*) not wonder what all this was about? You see, he had no understanding of what was happening and possibly asked himself this question. . . . . This is all right in dogs, which cannot reason, but in the case of man why not use his brain? I cannot imagine that the man, when placed in the situation of the dog, would also behave like the dog and not reason about anything".

". . . I cannot imagine", Pavlov continued, "that the man went through without questions, without assessing things and the result of such assessments should have been certain. If he decided for himself how he was concerned in the matter, if, when it was painful, he withdrew his hand and, when it was not, let the arm remain in its former position, there you have the equivalent of 100 combinations" [13, p. 103].

It is hardly necessary to say that all this does not in any way mean that the reflex nature of behaviour and of the psychical reflection of the world is in any degree abrogated. On the contrary, it is only an approach from the standpoint of the reflex theory that will enable us progressively and finally to explain man's behaviour and man's consciousness.

The discovery of conditioned connections as a universal phenomenon in the higher forms of life—a phenomenon which is both physiological and at the same time psychological—constitutes a contribution to psychology of enormous importance. Its discovery does not, however, introduce simplified mechanistic conceptions into psychology. It confirms the importance of associations in psychology, but this of course does not mean that it brings us back to the old psychological association theories.

It is in connection with the problem of learning in particular that the inadequacy of these theories is clearly revealed as they ignore an important element, namely, the formation of associations in the process of acquiring knowledge and the formation of associations between new thought actions, thought operations. That is, they ignore the development of the actual mechanisms responsible for the intellectual activity of the child

Translated by DR. R. CRAWFORD

REFERENCES

1. MARX, K. and ENGELS, F., Works, Vol. 14.
2. ANOKHIN, P. K., (1955). Osobennosti afferentnogo apparata uslovnogo refleksa i ikh znacheniye dliya psikhologii (Features of the Afferent Apparatus of the Conditioned Reflex and their Importance for Psychology). *Vopr. psikhologii* No. 6.

3. ANOKHIN, P. K., (1935). Problema tsentra i periferii v sovremennoi fiziologii nervnoi deyatel'nosti, in sb. Problema tsentra i periferii (The Problem of the Centre and the Periphery in Contemporary Physiology of the Nervous System, in symposium on The Problem of the Centre and the Periphery). Gor'kii.

4. VYGOTSKII,, L. S., (1956). Izbrannyye psikhologicheskiye issledovaniya (Selected Psychological Investigations). Acad. Paed. Sci. of R.S.F.S.R., Moscow.

5. GAL'PERIN, P. YA., (1954). Opyt izucheniya formirovaniya umstvennykh deistvii, in sb. Doklady na soveshch. po vopr. psikhologii (Investigation on the Formation of Mental Activities, in Collection of Papers Delivered at Congress on Psychological Problems, 3–8 July 1953). Acad. Paed. Sci. of R.S.F.S.R., Moscow.

6. GAL'PERIN, P. YA., (1957). O formirovanii chuvstvennykh obrazov i ponyatii, in sb. Materialy Soveshch. po psikhologii (The Formation of Sensory Images and Conceptions in the Proceedings of a Congress on Psychology). Acad. Paed. Sci. of the R.S.F.S.R., Moscow.

7. ZANKOV, L. V., (1954). (Editor). Opyt issledovaniya vzaimodeistviya slova i naglyadnosti v obuchenii (Investigation on Interaction between the Verbal and the Visual in Learning). Acad. Paed. Sci. of R.S.F.S.R., Moscow.

8. ZANKOV, L. V., (1956). (Editor), Psikhologicheskiye voprosy sochetaniya slova i naglyadnosti v uchnebnom protsesse vspomogatel'noi shkoly (Psychological Problems Connected with Combination of the Verbal and Visual in the Teaching Process of Special Schools) Acad. Paed. Sci. of R.S.F.S.R., Moscow.

9. KONORSKII, YU. M. and MILLER, S. M., (1936). Uslovnyye refleksy dvigatel'nogo analizatora, Trudy fiziologicheskikh laboratorii akad. I. P. Pavlova (Conditioned Reflexes of the Motor Analyser, in Scientific Papers of the Pavlov Physiological Laboratories), 6: No. 1.

10. LEONT'EV, A. N., (1955). Priroda i formirovaniye psikhicheskikh svoistv i protsessov u cheloveka (Nature and Formation of Mental Properties and Processes in Man). Vopr. psikhologii, No. 1.

11. LEONT'EV,, A. N., (1947). Psikhologicheskiye voprosy soznatel'nosti ucheniya (Psychological Problems Connected with Conscious Learning). 13 v. Akad. Paed. Nauk R.S.F.S.R., No. 7.

12. MENCHINSKAYA, N. A., (1954). Vzaimootnosheniye slova i obraza v protsesse usvoeniya znanii shkol'nikami, in sb. Doklady na soveshch. po psikhologii (Relationship between the Verbal and Visual in the Assimilation of Knowledge by School Children in Papers at Conference on Psychology). Acad. Paed. Sci. of R.S.F.S.R., Moscow.

13. Pavlovskiye klinicheskie sredy (Pavlov's Clinical Wednesdays) Vol. 2. 1956.

14. SOKOLOV, YE. N., (1957). O reflektornykh mekhanizmakh retseptsii, in sb. Materialy Soveshch. po psikhologii (Reflex Mechanisms of Reception, in Papers at Congress on Psychology). Acad. Paed. Sci. of R.S.F.S.R., Moscow.

15. HILGARD, E. R., (1948). Theories of Learning. New York.

16. MUNN, N. L., (1954). Learning, in L. Carmichael (Editor), Manual of Child Psychology. 2nd Edition. New York.

17. PIAGET, J., (1947). La psychologie de l'intelligence. Paris.

18. WALLON, H., (1942). De l'acte à la Pensée. Paris.

FORMATION OF ELEMENTARY GEOMETRICAL CONCEPTS AND THEIR DEPENDENCE ON DIRECTED PARTICIPATION BY THE PUPILS*

P. YA. GAL'PERIN and N. F. TALYZINA

Department of Psychology, Moscow University

1

THE present article deals with certain problems concerning the development of elementary scientific concepts. Our approach to this problem is to consider first the act on which the formation of the concept is based, and which must itself therefore be considered to constitute a mental act. We must start by giving a brief description of the main stages in the development of thought processes.

Mental acts must be considered to be a psychic reflection of external material processes. This statement is of direct practical importance as it requires that a new mental act shall develop from its external material form. If, however, the object itself and the original means for perceiving it directly are no longer available, then the generation of the new mental act must take place on the basis of its materialized form, i.e. on the basis of a process which itself depends on a material representation of essential features and relationships.

A study of thought processes has shown that any single mental act of any subject may take place in several ways. Each concrete form of the act has different fundamental characteristic properties, and we shall refer to these in the way which has now become accepted, as parameters. We have shown (naturally, only to a first approximation) that within the mental act of a subject, it is possible to distinguish four such parameters.

The first parameter—the level of the process. There are three such levels. The first represents the material (or "materialized") level. At this level, the object to which the attention is directed, or the data concerning it

* *Voprosy psikhologii*, No. 1, pp. 28–44, 1957.

which the subject possesses, or finally the process itself of applying a description of its features to the object (material) are associated with the presence of physical objects (or in the material process, with their physical representations). The second level is that of the spoken word. Here the thought process, which is made up of several components corresponding to the criteria defining the concept, takes place in the form of remarks which are made aloud and which are essential to the carrying out of the thought process. Finally there is the third or intellectual level, whose distinguishing feature is that the act is exclusively a mental process.

The great importance of experience involving the objects themselves, and the considerable part played by the spoken word in the acquisition of new knowledge have both been known empirically for a long time, and various explanations of these effects have been offered. In our investigations, both the direct experience of the objects and the spoken word come to acquire a new significance, and emerge as stages in which the process changes from an external into an internal one. In other words, they turn out to be stages in the process of reflection or formation of a new psychic element of the consciousness of an individual.

At the very first stage of development of mental concepts, a great or even a decisive importance attaches to the formation of an orientating basis for the process. This term refers to a complex phenomenon consisting of a preliminary representation of the product of the process and of the process itself, together with a system of reference points which allow a task to be performed.

The second parameter is the degree of generalization. This represents the extent to which the essential properties are distinguished from the inessential ones.

The third parameter is the completeness of the act. It shows what operations are actually carried out and whether the child can perform the task either in a simpler manner, or, on the contrary, by means of a more complete set of operations[1].

The fourth parameter is the degree to which the act becomes the property of the individual. Although this is the least distinct of the parameters, its effect is shown by the fact that the act takes place as though along a well-worn path and, accordingly, with greater or less facility.

All these parameters are *relatively* independent of each other. The process may be generalized (may be applied to a wide range of objects),

---

[1] The gradual shortening of mental process in its general form was noted by P. A. Shevarev, B. M. Teplov, N.A. Menchinskaya and others in their investigations.

it may be abbreviated and well assimilated but may be carried out only in the presence of material objects or their physical images, i.e. only on a physical (or materialized) level. On the contrary, the process may occur only in the mind, but without any appreciable degree of generalization (it may be applied only to a particular object), and the details of the process may be difficult to elucidate[2].

For the formation of a complete mental act, the first concern is for the development of a correct set of reference points. Then, on this basis, the material (or the materialized) form of the act may be developed, and this may be modified subsequently in terms of generalization, abbreviation, and assimilation. The degree of assimilation of all the intermediate forms must be sufficient, but must not be excessive, so as not to interfere with the subsequent transition to the higher forms of the thought process. Further, the physical act must be completely reflected in verbal speech (without any dependence on material objects). Finally, it must be possible to transfer this personal speech form of the act into an internal mental arrangement, so that it becomes re-arranged in the form of the individual talking to himself, and the act becomes one of verbal thinking. Here, as a result of abbreviation and complete assimilation, the act attains its final form which although hard to follow by introspection is so important for an understanding of the psychical phenomena associated with it.

2

A study of processes has led us to investigate certain examples based on these processes which will serve to give further information about them. Among these examples (in the broadest sense of the word), particular importance attaches to concepts, and as far as their development is concerned, a study is required of the elementary concepts acquired at school. We are concerned here to find how they are associated with processes, and how they are based on them. But since processes are not in themselves anything simple or primary, but have to be formed, then the immediate question is how their formation is associated with that of the processes underlying them.

Many very different processes are associated both with the object and with the concept, but with which process are we concerned? In teaching elementary concepts referring to a particular science, this problem is simplified: in this case the attributes of the new concept serve firstly to

<hr>

[2] A more detailed account of the formation of mental acts is given in the article by P. Ya. Gal'perin [1].

determine whether a given phenomenon is included in the concept in question. By considering all that is included in the concept "the subject", it can be determined whether or not a given word is the subject of a sentence; if the attributes of the concept "perpendicular" are considered, it is possible to decide whether a given part of a figure is perpendicular etc. Consequently, the process upon which the acquisition of a new concept is based consists of the application of the set of qualities which it represents to a material object so as to establish whether any part of it can be included within the concept.

Accordingly, from among all the components from which the concept is built up we have distinguished those which are necessary and sufficient to determine whether a particular phenomenon is to be included in the concept under consideration. We have taken only those features which must be applied in the solution of a particular problem. We have called these "working features". It should not fall to the lot of the psychologist to distinguish these essential features which are necessary for the process, but unfortunately this work is not often carried out, and we have, therefore, to undertake it. Even in such a precise science as geometry, textbooks and teaching devices often fail to describe the characteristics by which many concepts may be recognized. Thus, for instance, usually no definition of a straight line is given[1] ; many properties of a perpendicular are given, but for the most part these are not used in Class VI[2], and are not therefore "working" properties; only incomplete definitions of adjacent angles etc. are given.

The next problem to decide is to what material the new concept is to be applied. Phenomena which may be referred to one concept or another may present various forms. The subject of a sentence, for instance, may be expressed by various parts of speech, by one or by several words (and then some of them may not be in the nominative case which is usually the distinguishing feature of the subject!); finally, the proposition may have no subject. A perpendicular may be presented either by a pair of lines, or it may be included in other figures, which may be of various degrees of complexity. If we wish to develop a concept which may be generalized to a certain extent, then it is not sufficient merely to vary the material (since variation over a range of one or more forms selected at

[1] In the school geometry textbook by A. P. Kiselev it is stated that examples of a straight line are a tightly stretched thread, or a ray of light passing through a small aperture. However, it is not pointed out that coincidence of a line with a stretched thread is a feature which may be used to determine whether a given line is straight.

[2] The pupils in this class would be 14 or 15 years of age.

random does not afford adequate generalization); what is required is a systematic variation in a definite order of the basic forms of the phenomena, to each of which a clear, unchanging definition of the new concept must be applied.

Further, a variety of problems may be set, and in these the conditions stipulated by the definition may be completely or incompletely fulfilled, so that a verbal set of stipulated conditions may or may not agree with the diagram presented. All of this is of the greatest importance in determining which part of the problem is essential.

In accordance with these requirements we have composed four separate tests. In the first type of problem, a complete set of conditions was given, and the drawing was appropriate to the stipulated condition. In the second type, the conditions were also given completely, but the drawing did not correspond to them. In the third type of problem, the conditions themselves were incomplete, but the drawing corresponded to the conditions. Finally, in the fourth type of problem, the conditions were incomplete and the drawing did not correspond to them.

The subject was told that the components of the concept were included in the conditions, but were not necessarily present in the drawing, and that only when the whole set of components of the complex were present would the phenomenon be included in the concepts under consideration.

We explained to the subject how he was to use the components of the concept to solve any problem presented to him, and how he was to apply each of these components to each part of the material, i.e. to all the conditions of the problem and to all the elements of the figure.

Finally, in considering the results of these investigations into the development of thought processes, we examined the stages by which the components of the concept were assimilated. This examination was chiefly concerned with the system of components, i.e. with the criteria of the concept. These components were listed and numbered in a column on a card, and were used by the subject in this form in solving problems. We call this form of the process the materialized form. It enables the components of the concept to be considered objectively, and enables the action of the subject in applying them to the experimental task to be controlled.

When the subject has thoroughly assimilated the contents of the card, it is removed, and he then begins to recite aloud from memory the components which he has been shown, and he also describes aloud whether these components correspond to the figure which he has been shown.

Finally, the same process is carried out in the same order, but the subject speaks "to himself", but announces the result aloud[1].

No special study was made of the other parameters, abbreviation and assimilation, as these were worked out "by themselves", in the course of the experiments.

In the tests, we made use of only the most elementary geometrical concepts such as those of a line, an angle, the bisector of an angle, adjacent and supplementary adjacent angles, and a perpendicular.

The subjects were 8 pupils of Class VI and 8 of Class VII[2]. Both groups were already acquainted with the concepts involved. In making our selection of pupils we chose only these who were described by their teachers as "hopeless"; in our screening experiment, they also failed in the problems set. In addition, we used 32 pupils from Class V[3], who had made no study of geometry and who in other subjects had been given marks as low as 2 or 3 out of 5[4]. The total number of subjects was 48.

We considered that a concept was completely formed when the subject changed over from searching for its separate components to applying it directly to the particular task in hand. This was shown by the way the child would glance quickly over the problem set, and then give the answer immediately. When asked the reason for his opinion, the child would usually turn once more to the problem, and indicate the necessary and sufficient components of the concept in the conditions of the problem.

The results showed that when the method as described above is used the *formation of the concept proceeds almost faultlessly* from the very beginning. Thus, during the formation of the concept "a straight line", 14 of our subjects solved 346 of the 360 problems correctly, and made mistakes in only 14 of the problems; in forming the concept of "an angle", of the 162 problems set, 152 were correctly and 10 incorrectly solved.

The following illustrates the typical method of solution.

Pupil L. (Class V) who is developing the concept of "a straight line", was set the following problem: "Three lines were drawn: a straight line, a kinked line, and a wavy line. A match fell on the drawing and some of it was burnt. Only the ends of the lines remained. Would it be possible

---

[1] A more detailed account of the principles of this method and of its results and their importance is given in a report by P.Ya. Gal'perin, "On the formation of sensory images and concepts" [2].

[2] The pupils in Class VII would be 15 and 16 years of age.

[3] The pupils in Class V would be 13 and 14 years of age.

[4] This refers to a 5-point scale of marking traditional in Russia. 3 is regarded as a bare pass.

to reconstruct the burnt portions if we had never seen what they were?"
A drawing is supplied:

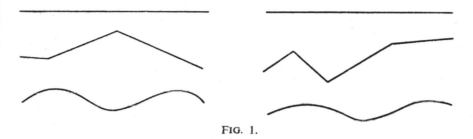

FIG. 1.

Pupil L.: Only the straight line could be reconstructed.

Experimenter: Why?

Pupil L.: Firstly, between two points only one straight line can be drawn, and then it can be drawn along a stretched thread. About the others, nothing can be said, since they bend in any sort of way.

Pupil V. (Class VI) who is developing the concept of "an angle" was given the problem: "Two lines proceed from a single point. What sort of figure is formed?" (An angle was shown in the drawing).

Pupil V.: I don't know what this figure is called, but it is not an angle. Probably, there are two kinds here.

Experimenter: What kinds?

Pupil V.: If these lines are straight, then an angle is formed, because then both conditions for an angle are fulfilled: a common point and two straight lines. But if these lines are not straight, then it is not an angle. Because then only one of the conditions of an angle is fulfilled—the common point. And then it is not an angle.

Experimenter: Please make a drawing of the problem.

The subject draws as follows:

(Both examples are taken from the work of S. B. Mashkova).

It must be noted that the subjects not only give correct answers, but also defend them. It is well known, that with the usual methods of teaching, the question "why" often presents difficulty not only to backward

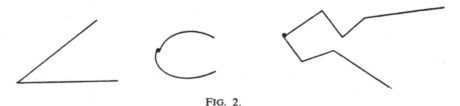

FIG. 2.

pupils with whom we were concerned, but also to the more advanced students. It must also be pointed out that our experimental subjects were easily able to deal with even the more difficult kinds of problem, in which the conditions were not completely defined, and in which the diagram did not correspond to the conditions of the problem; this is shown in the second set of examples.

If, in certain cases, the subjects gave incorrect replies, all that was required was to turn their attention to the conditions of the concept, and the correct reply was then forthcoming. The mistakes, as we have seen, were very few, and most of these were made when the thought process was internal, and occurred when the subject was operating under his own control. In some of these cases it was sufficient to suggest to him that he should repeat to himself the list of components, and that he should then once more look at the problem; when this was done, the mistake was corrected. If this procedure did not help him, the experimenter then suggested that he should recite the list of conditions of the concept aloud, and should look to see whether they were fulfilled by the conditions of the problem. Returning the process to the preceding level always led to a correction of the error.

The following example shows how this occurred. Pupil N. (Class VI) was set the problem: "Given two intersecting lines. What sort of figure do they form?" (The problem is given without a figure).

The subject first solves the problem "to himself", and only the answer is spoken aloud.

Pupil N: They form an angle (wrong answer).

Experimenter: Name the distinguishing features of an angle.

Pupil N: A common point and two lines.

Experimenter: Be more precise.

Pupil N: A common point and two lines going out from it (here she sees the mistake). The line must be straight. But here it does not say whether the line is straight or not. It is not known, it might form an angle and it might not. (This example is chosen from the work of N. F. Talyzina).

When the process returns to the level of the spoken word, the subject is able to correct the mistake for himself.

Naturally, in the formation of a concept by our method in which there was a distinction between the conditions and the drawing and in which the subjects were attending to the conditions, they were not in any way "bound by the figure". In problems where the figure did not correspond to the conditions, the subjects did not base their answer on the figure but on the conditions.

Thus, for instance, the same pupil N. (Class VI) in solving a problem in which the conditions specified adjacent supplementary angles, but the figure showed adjacent angles, was able to show without difficulty that the angles were in fact adjacent supplementary.

When the experimenter asked her to show on the drawing where was the side which represented the continuation of the other, she replied: "There is no continuation. In the conditions, they are adjacent supplementary angles, but they aren't on the drawings".

Experimenter: What are they on the drawing?

Pupil N: Adjacent (from the work of N. F. Talyzina).

In these cases, the subjects usually added that what was required was not to "look" at the figure, but at the conditions.

A further example. Pupil K. (Class VI) was set the problem: "Given a line, of which no part will coincide with a stretched thread. What kind of line is this?" (The figure shows two straight lines joined at an angle).

Pupil K: This is a curved line, since no part of it coincides with a stretched thread. The figure is incorrect, and a curved line should be drawn (draws line). (The example is taken from the work of S. B. Mashkova.)

We will give one further example. Pupil Kh. (Class V) was set the problem: "From a point O, two straight lines are drawn: OA and OB. What sort of figure do they form?"

The following drawing was given:

O————————A   O———————B

FIG. 3.

Pupil Kh: Here there should be an angle.

Experimenter: Why?

Pupil Kh: Because two lines should go out from one point.

Experimenter: But the drawing?

Pupil Kh: This is wrong, there should be an angle (from the work of E. V. Konstantinova).

As we have seen, the subjects do not regard the figure as a part of the conditions, but only as an illustration attached to them, and as one which may be untrue.

The results obtained allow us to confirm the *fact* which is *known* from the practice of teaching, that *in solving problems students "go beyond the drawing", and this is not due to any feature of the child's thought but is due to the method of instruction.*

In the experiments, it was also shown that with our method of instruction, the subjects recognize a particular geometrical figure in any spatial position. Furthermore, when asked by the experimenter, the children themselves will draw geometrical figures in a variety of positions.

Pupil Z. (Class V) when asked by the experimenter to draw various perpendiculars, drew as follows:

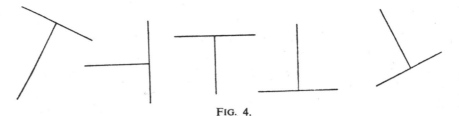

Fig. 4.

Experimenter: Why are all these perpendiculars?

Pupil Z: Because they are straight lines and they form right angles (from the work of E. V. Konstantinova).

In view of these results, we have set up special experiments directed to solving the problem of the *necessity for varying* the figure in developing geometrical concepts by our teaching method [1].

For this purpose, special experiments were carried out on 26 pupils of Class V, who had been shown a figure deliberately presented in a constant position (the perpendicular was drawn as composed of one horizontal and one vertical line running upwards from it). This position was given both on the card which was used as the standard of reference in solving problems, as well as on all diagrams associated with the problems. After 8–10 problems with the figure in this position, we presented it in a markedly different position, and without allowing the subject to read the conditions defining the problem we asked them to decide at a glance whether one figure, or another, conformed to the corresponding concept.

All 26 subjects whom we tested with the control experiments answered correctly. They described the figure accurately, and when asked why, they indicated the features which had been initially given as criteria.

We will give some examples.

A preliminary enquiry showed that as a rule the subjects called only the horizontal lines straight, and the oblique lines were considered as not straight but slanting. We deliberately left this mistake uncorrected.

---

[1] Detailed information on the necessity for varying the position of the figure in space in order to distinguish the essential features of geometrical concepts are given in V. I. Zykova's work [4].

After instruction in our method (during which the line was presented only in the horizontal position) in a control set of experiments, K. (Class V) was shown a straight line inclined at an angle to the horizontal. In reply to the experimenter's question as to what kind of line it was, she confidently replied that the line was straight, arguing the point as follows: "It coincides with a stretched thread".

The same girl, when given the problem in the control group where she was asked of what kind of line the figure consisted,

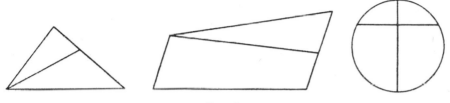

FIG 5.

answered as follows:

Pupil K: These are all straight lines, but this one (points to the circumference) is not straight.

Experimenter: Why?

Pupil K: Because all the lines coincide with a thread, but this one (points to the circumference) does not.

Pupil U. (Class V) is given the problem: "What sort of lines are these?"

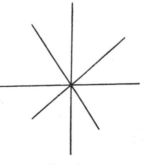

FIG. 6.

Pupil U: These are all straight.

Experimenter: Why?

Pupil U: Because they coincide with a stretched thread.

The situation was found to be similar in working on the formation of other concepts. Thus, for instance, after solving 9 problems on the application of the distinguishing features of perpendicular lines, where the lines were always shown in a standard position, pupil B. (Class V), at the request of the experimenter, drew a perpendicular in two different positions (Fig. 7).

FIG. 7.

Immediately after this the experimenter asked the following question: "What sort of figures are these?" (Fig. 8).

FIG. 8.

Pupil B: Also perpendiculars.

Experimenter: Why?

Pupil B: Because the straight lines form a right angle (indicates).

We can see, that in defining the straight line the idea of coincidence with a stretched thread is important to the subject; in defining a perpendicular, the conception is one of the existence of two straight lines forming a right angle, i.e. only the presence of those features which have been presented to them as necessary and sufficient criteria are referred to the given concept.

A precisely similar result was found in other subjects. Certainly, in 15 subjects, when solving the first problem of the control series designed to test whether they had assimilated the concept, of a straight line, it was found that there was some delay in the solution as compared with that of the previous problems. Three of the subjects had to return to the previous stage, i.e. they had to name aloud the distinctive feature of a straight line, and after this all the subjects promptly gave the correct answers. In 2 of them, the features were named only during the solution of the first problem, in the third—only when solving the first, third, and fourth of the 6 problems of the control series.

We will give an example of such a solution. Pupil R. (Class V), in reply to a question by the experimenter: "What sort of line is this?" (a slanting line is drawn), at first gives no reply. Then the experimenter asks: "Would this be a straight line?"

Pupil R: No.

Experimenter: Why?

Pupil R: (is silent).

Experimenter: Name the distinguishing feature of a straight line. The subject names the feature correctly, and then says "Yes, it is straight".

Experimenter: Why?

Pupil R: Because it coincides with a stretched thread. (The examples arc taken from the work of E. V. Konstantinova).

It must be noted that this independence from the particular features of the diagram is maintained even after a considerable interval of time. Thus, 5 months after she had already solved the problems requiring the application of the concept "perpendicular", we asked pupil N. (Class VI), how to determine which lines on a drawing were perpendicular [1]. On the drawing there were shown three perpendiculars in an unusual position, and one inclined line in the usual position (Fig. 9), so that the inclined

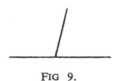

FIG 9.

line made only a very small angle with the vertical. Pupil N. replied: "It must be measured. Where there is a right angle, there it will be perpendicular". When the experimenter asked which lines appeared to her to be perpendicular, she pointed correctly to all four lines, but, referring to the inclined line, she said that this was not perpendicular (from the work of N. F. Talyzina).

These results give reason to suppose that a complete concept (complete in the sense of the clear distinction of its essential features) may be formed under certain conditions even without any variation in the diagrams. The difficulties encountered by the pupils in the case of unusual

[1] Other subjects were not tested in this respect.

positions of the diagrams, difficulties which indicate an insufficient degree of generalization of the distinguishing features of the concept, can be explained in terms of the way the teaching has been carried out. In these cases the pupils are not presented with clearly defined features of the concept, and are not taught to think objectively in terms of them, or to apply them to particular problems. Certainly, by no means all the pupils can think in this way. Naturally, for a certain proportion of the pupils, a definition which they may be able to reproduce faultlessly will turn out to be "non-functional", and it will be found that their genuine reference point for the solution of the problem is the figure, and that by the side of this there is the "non-functional" definition. With this type of teaching, it is very necessary that a wide variety of figures should be shown and that there should be a gradual distinction and generalization of the essential features of the concept[1].

It must be pointed out that, unfortunately, when dealing with geometrical concepts, not only the pupils, but also the teachers and the authors of textbooks are dependent quite frequently on a particular illustration, and not on the distinctive features of the concept. Thus, for instance, adjacent angles are usually defined as those which have a common apex and a common side. We ourselves have used this definition in a teaching experiment. But because we asked our pupils to make use of clearly defined features of the concept, we obtained results such as, for example, the following: Pupil N. (Class VI) gave as an example of adjacent angles, an angle and the part of that angle adjacent to one of its sides. When we attempted to refute her, she answered that the example was consistent with the definition. We were forced to agree, and then to introduce an additional feature: the common side must lie between the other sides of the angles (from the work of N. F. Talyzina).

From the very beginning, we gave the children definitions in a very clear-cut objective way, and instructed them to make use of these definitions in solving problems, and it was found that this freed the children from the influence of the incidental properties of the drawing.

---

[1] On account of the importance and the complexity of the problem it must be pointed out once more that variation in the material presented is necessary, not only in the actual content of the phenomenon, but also in its basic forms; also that this variation is required not only in order to enable the features of the new concept to be distinguished (because from the very beginning these may be presented in a clearly defined manner and as criteria of the concept), but in order that the concept itself may develop as a generalized form of reality. The features of the concept, and the concept itself are not one and the same thing.

The experiment has shown that there are *two ways of forming a concept*. In the case when the mental process of the subject is not controlled and organized to apply the definition to the problem in hand, the subject actually finds himself in the position not of a pupil, but of an investigator: he has to search for and establish for himself the essential and sufficient features of the new concept. Naturally, this takes place by means of trial and error, and the essential nature of the new concept becomes established only after it has evolved through a number of intermediate stages.

In the case when the correct approach by the subject is adequately controlled, and when the essential features of the concept are given clearly and objectively from the very start, and when he has been shown how to use these in the clearest possible way, the process of the formation of concepts takes place without any intermediate "hybrid" forms, and the path taken becomes very much shorter.

There are two possible methods of study which correspond to these two ways of forming concepts. They are distinguished chiefly by the extent to which each of the two methods organizes, studies, controls or facilitates the process which underlies the formation of the new concepts[2].

3

As has been pointed out above, the process of applying the definitions develops step by step. There is no doubt of the existence of the various levels of one and the same process. That this is so is shown firstly by the case which is well known from teaching experience, that one child will, for instance, carry out a certain process only when he has access to the actual object concerned, and another may be able to use merely the spoken word, but neither will be able to solve the problem mentally "to themselves".

Secondly, we frequently encounter processes at different levels in carrying out test experiments on pupils taught by the method used in schools. These levels have been found in the case of the processes involved in applying geometrical definitions. Finally, during our experiments, we frequently observed that a return to a preceding level of the process enables a subject to surmount the difficulty he has encountered. This circumstance is evidence not only of the existence of processes at different levels, but also of the fact that there is a certain continuity which indicates a certain internal logic in the process of evolution of psychic events.

2 This point is discussed in greater detail in the report by P. Ya. Gal'perin [2].

Thus, in our opinion, there can be no doubt that a single process may occur at several different levels.

But now another question arises: *to what is it necessary to develop all the levels* of the process (in applying definitions) *for the development of each concept.*

We investigated this question by carrying out special experiments on the development of the concept "perpendicular" in 8 children of Class VII (study by N. D. Kadymova). In these experiments, in some of the subjects, the process was developed by applying the definition of "a perpendicular" at first aloud, and then "to himself", i.e. by missing out the "materialized" stage of the process. In other subjects, the process was repeated with the "materialized" stage of the process preserved and the stage of thinking "to himself" included, but the stage in which the argument was voiced aloud was omitted. In 3 subjects, the instruction was carried out by developing the "materialized" form of the process and the spoken form, but no work was done on the stage of the pupil thinking "to himself". Finally, in a fourth group the development started immediately by the children thinking to themselves, i.e. "materialized" process and the verbal process were both omitted.

The results of these experiments showed that a concept may be assimilated when any stage is omitted provided that the remaining two stages are thoroughly developed. However, the effect on the course of the instruction will be differently affected according to the stage which is omitted.

Omission of the stage of thinking "to oneself" was not reflected (in the particular case!) on the rate of learning. Evidently, for the particular problem used, the basic conditions of the process "to himself" were included in the preceding stages. This is shown, for instance, by the fact that even at the stage of the spoken word, the subjects gradually began to answer immediately, and this was one of the indications that the process of the subject thinking to himself had become automatic.

Omission of the verbal stage had a marked effect on the stage when the subject thought "to himself". In this case the process of silent thinking continued very much longer in its extended form, that is to say the process took longer to become automatic. This was shown by the fact that when the subject went over to the method of silent thinking, the solution of the problem took a very long time, though this did not occur in the experiments in which the two preceding stages had been elaborated.

The omission of the stage with the card ("materialized" form of the process) had a particularly marked effect. In this case, the definitions presented verbally were first not used at all by the subjects, although they were described quite correctly by them. The experimenter also had to remind them constantly about the points in the definition, he had to tell the children to use them, and additional explanations were required. The stage in which the spoken word was used was considerably prolonged.

It was clear that in this case the card showed the points involved "in the hands" of the subject, and so represented the basis of the process. At the same time, the card played a part in the organization: the features shown on it were acquired by the subject in a definite order, and this was the order in which the points were applied. When no cards were used, the experimenter had to take over this function himself, and if he did not do so, the children failed to cope with the problem.

Omission of the first two stages, i.e. when the idea was developed by silent thinking, made it almost impossible to develop the concept. Even in the case of the most simple problems, the subjects either gave wrong answers or else did not attempt the solution.

In all these cases the experimenter had to intervene with an explanation, and this was tantamount to operating in terms of the spoken word.

The geometrical concept was mastered completely only in experiments in which either all the stages were developed or, to a lesser degree, in those in which the stage of operating with the aid of the actual experimental material was very thoroughly developed.

However, all that has been said concerning the necessity for step by step development of a concept applies to cases when only a single, in this case geometrical, concept is involved. The question then follows as to how necessary step by step development is in cases when not one, but several concepts are involved.

To investigate this point, 14 subjects including 7 from Class V and 7 from Class VI were taught the concepts of a straight line and of an angle by the step by step method[1]; after this we began to develop a third concept, that of the bisector of an angle. This last concept was taught directly by the method of the subject thinking "to himself" (work of N. F. Talyzina and S. B. Mashkova).

We instruct the children in the school definition of a bisector, and ask them to distinguish the features from which it was possible to recognize the bisector of an angle. All the children accomplished this task without

[1] We used the step by step method as applied to two concepts and not to one, in finding their effect on the formation of other concepts, because the notion of a straight line does not possess any clearly drawn comprehensible features, and because the utilisation of this concept does not involve reference to any set of distinctive attributes

difficulty. They were then asked to solve for themselves various problems which involved application of the concept of a bisector (the problems were of the four types described above). Altogether they solved 110 problems.

It was found that *all* the subjects succeeded in the task set. Of the problems, 106 out of 110 were solved by thinking "to themselves". All were correctly solved.

Our method of developing simple geometrical concepts affects the way in which the subjects apply others which are more complex. We will demonstrate this by reporting the solution of the same set of problems, involving the bisector of an angle, which were carried out both in a test experiment before the concepts of a straight line and of an angle had been elaborated, and in a control experiment after the subjects had mastered these two concepts.

Pupil K. (Class VI) was given the following problem, among others, in the test and in the control experiments: "From the apex of an angle, a line is drawn which divides this angle into two parts. Is this line a bisector of the angle?" The problem was presented without a figure.

In the test experiment the solution of the problem proceeded as follows:

Pupil K: Yes.

Experimenter: Why? You know how a bisector is described.

Pupil K: But here the angle is divided, so it must be a bisector.

Experimenter: Draw a diagram for this problem. (The subject draws a straight line in the position of a bisector of the angle.)

Experimenter: Into what kind of parts does this line divide the angle?

Pupil K: Into equal parts.

Experimenter: Is this stated in the conditions of the problem?

Pupil K: Yes... No, but all the same this is a bisector, because it says that the line divides the angle into two parts.

As we see, the problem is incorrectly solved, and the subject does not base her answers on the definition of the bisector, although she is acquainted with it; at the beginning of the test experiment, she gave an entirely correct definition of a bisector [1].

After the subject had developed the concept of a straight line and of an angle, the solution of the above problem proceeded as follows. The subject had scarcely read through the problem when she said: "No, this is not a bisector".

Experimenter: Why?

---

[1] Before being given the problems, the subjects were tested to find if they knew the definition of a bisector.

Pupil K: Because the conditions do not give all the properties of a bi-sector.

Experimenter: Which properties are given and which are not given?

Pupil K: Here there is only one property of a bisector—the angle. But it is not known into what sort of parts the line divides this angle, and it is not known what kind of line it is; it could be curved, or bent (draws both instances on paper).

The subject not only gives (mentally) a correct solution, but defends it: she has no difficulty in pointing out what properties of the bisector are present, and which ones are missing. Further, she indicates possible alternative arrangements.

The pupil M. (Class VI) was given the problem: "A straight line is drawn within an angle so as to pass through the apex and divide the angle into two equal parts. Will this straight line be a bisector of the angle?" A figure is given which does not correspond to the conditions of the problem: the straight line is drawn in a position widely different from that of the bisector.

In the test experiment the solution of this problem by a boy pro-ceeded as follows:

Pupil M: No, it will not be a bisector.

Experimenter: Why?

Pupil M: It is obvious.

Experimenter: How is it obvious?

Pupil M: Well, here is the drawing, and in it the straight line divides the angle into unequal parts.

In solving the problem, the subject depends not on the conditions, but on the drawing, and so solves the problem incorrectly.

After M. had been instructed in the concepts of a straight line and of an angle, he rapidly read through the problem to himself, and imme-diately replied: "Yes, this is a bisector".

Experimenter: Why do you think so?

Pupil M; Here, in the conditions, it says: there is an angle—this is the first condition for there to be a bisector, and the straight line divides the angle into two equal parts—that is the second condition that the line is a bisector.

Experimenter: But the drawing?

Pupil M: No, here it ought to be like this (draws a straight line in the position of a bisector).

It can be seen, that in solving the problem, the subject depends on the definition of a bisector (a straight line divides an angle into two equal parts) and looks for these features of the definition in the conditions of the problem, and not in the drawing.

A closely similar result was found in other subjects in both Class VI and Class V [2].

This, for instance, is how pupil Zh. (Class V) solved a problem of this kind. "Within an angle, and through its apex, a straight line is drawn which divides the angle in the ratio 3:8. Will this straight line be a bisector of the angle?" A drawing was supplied in which a straight line was drawn as bisector.

The subject read the problem rapidly to himself and then answered quickly: "Here the drawing is wrong. From the definition, this is not a bisector, but on the drawing it is; another drawing ought to be made".

Pupil Zh: It says in the conditions that the straight line divides the angle in the ratio 3:8, and not into equal parts. Here the second condition for a line to be a bisector is missing.

Here we see that the subjects now clearly distinguish the necessary and sufficient properties of a bisector, use these correctly in solving problems "to themselves", even in cases when the drawing contradicts the problem as stated; previously the children were misled completely.

Our subjects successfully solved the problems in the application of the definition of a bisector of an angle, even in cases when the bisector was presented in a system involving concepts with which the subject was not familiar.

Thus, for instance, subjects in Class V were given the following problem: "Given two parallel straight lines and a line which intersects them. A second intersecting line divides one of the internal corresponding angles into two equal parts. Will this second line be a bisector of the internal corresponding angle?" The subjects knew nothing of parallel lines or of properties of lines intersecting them. No drawing was supplied. This is how the problem was solved in this case. Pupil Sh. (Class V) reads the problem to himself.

Pupil Sh: What is an intersecting line?

Experimenter: A straight line which intersects another line.

Pupil Sh: That means an angle is formed. And it is divided by a second intersecting line, a straight line, into two equal parts.

---

[2] It must be remembered that in Class V, geometry has not yet been studied. We taught the definition of a bisector to these children before attempting problems on the bisector. They then recognized for themselves the features of the definition which could be applied.

Well, we have the characteristics of a bisector. That means that it is a bisector [1].

The problem was solved by pupil Sh. quite correctly, though the solution was made aloud and not "to himself" (just as in the case of problems where the bisector was given in a system with which the subject was familiar). Three other subjects also solved this problem aloud, while the remainder solved it "to themselves".

Thus, all the subjects gave correct solutions to the problems involving the concept of the bisector of an angle; in almost all cases the work was carried out silently. Not only did they solve the problems correctly, but they gave a reasoned argument in support of their solution, and pointed out the distinguishing features of the bisector. In doing so they invariably based their argument on the verbal formulation of the problem, and not on the diagram.

Thus it happened that in solving problems involving the concept of the bisector of an angle, the subjects discovered for themselves all the features which had been noted in solving problems involving the use of the concepts of a straight line and of an angle. Since we did not carry out any step by step development of the concept of the bisector of an angle, this effect may possibly be explained as follows: in developing the concepts of a straight line and of an angle, the subjects *acquired a definite method of applying definitions of concepts, and this method was them transferred to the new concept of the bisector;* this usually happened immediately, at the level of thinking "to himself", and in some cases at the level of thinking aloud.

After the problem involving the use of the concept of the bisector of an angle, the subjects were set first problems involving the concept of "supplementary adjacent angles", and afterwards some which involved the notion of a perpendicular. Neither of these concepts was developed by the step by step method. Just as in the case of working with the concept of the bisector of an angle, the experimenter gave a definition of the concept, and a drawing. The subjects independently distinguished the essential features of the concept (from its definition), and proceeded to solve the problems.

The results of these experiments showed that the great majority of the problems in the use of both concepts were correctly solved, and the method of solution explained [2]. Out of 176 solutions to the problems

[1] It must be noted here that no confusion was caused by finding a line which was both a bisector and an intersector, though this often causes confusion in school work [3].

[2] The children were given problems of the four types already described.

in the use of the concept of supplementary adjacent angles, only 3 cases occurred in which mistakes were made. Here, just as in the problems involving the bisector of an angle, the subjects made use of the features of the concept which were contained in the conditions of the problem, and not those represented in the figure.

We will give an example. Pupil Ch. (Class VI) was given the following problem: "Given a triangle. Will the angles at the base of the triangle be adjacent supplementary angles?" (a suitable diagram was supplied). In the test experiment, the solution of the problem proceeded as follows [1].

Pupil Ch: Adjacent supplementary.

Experimenter: Why?

Pupil Ch: We dropped a straight line form the apex. And here there will be angles (shows the angles at the base), but the triangle is right-angled.

Experimenter: How is it right-angled?

Pupil Ch: Like this (makes indefinite movements with the hands). The problem remained unsolved.

In the control experiment, the pupil Ch. reads the problem to himself and immediately replies:

Pupil Ch: No, these are not adjacent supplementary angels.

Experimenter: Why?

Pupil Ch: Not all of the essential features are given. There are two angles at the base—that is the first condition, one side of them is prolonged into the other, but the common side is not present.

The problem is correctly solved "to himself".

The solution of many other problems proceeded along similar lines. However, most of the problems involving the concept of "adjacent supplementary angles" were solved aloud (out of 176 problems only 56 were solved silently). Being unable to solve the problem by the silent method, the subjects went over to the method of analysing it aloud, and then were able to reach a correct conclusion.

We will give an illustration of one of these cases. Pupil B. (Class V) was given the following problem: "In a triangle, the bisector of an angle at the base is continued beyond the limits of the triangle. Will the angles subtended by the sides of the triangle be supplemetary and adjacent?"

Pupil B. after reading the problem "to himself", and after a short pause, replies. "They will. No... they will not: but here there is a triangle, and not an angle".

---

[1] Before solving the problems, both in the case of the adjacent supplementary angles and in the case of the perpendicular, the subjects were tested to see that they were acquainted with the appropriate definitions.

Experimenter: Read the problem carefully to yourself and decide whether the conditions for supplementary and adjacent angles are contained in the conditions.

Pupil B. (reads). . . . I do not know. No, there will be, because here there is a triangle.

Experimenter: Proceed.

Pupil B: These are the features: there is a common line; there is a continuation of one side into another—this is one side of the triangle; there is a common side—the bisector; yes, these are supplementary and adjacent angles.

At first the subject tries to solve the problem to himself. In spite of the fact that he is acquainted with the characteristic features of supplementary and adjacent angles, and that the experimenter points out that he is required to decide whether these features are contained in the conditions postulated, the boy is not sure of himself: he gives first one answer, then another. He even tries to avoid the solution by saying that he does not know. But as soon as he begins to describe the essential features of supplementary and adjacent angles aloud, there is a sudden change in the situation, and a correct solution which is adequately supported is then forthcoming.

(All these last examples are taken from the work of S. B. Mashkova).

Of the problems involving the concept of a perpendicular, the great majority were solved in silence (of the 198 problems, only 16 were solved aloud, and the remaining 182 were solved silently).

In spite of the fact that in the concepts which we used, that of "the perpendicular" was very much further removed from those which we had elaborated using the step by step method than was the concept of adjacent and supplementary angles, the transfer of the acquired thought process to the concept of "the perpendicular" was realized in most cases at the higher level (silently). Transfer to the concept "supplementary and adjacent angles" was effected at a lower level, the thought process usually being expressed aloud.

The results that we have obtained show that for the formation of many simple concepts, a step by step method is not necessary in each case. The formation of some of the following concepts may be started straight away at the level of thinking aloud, and some of them may even be elaborated as a purely mental process.

We are not yet in a position to say just why the transfer occurs at different levels, or what are the limits of this transfer process. This will be the subject of future investigations.

However, the results obtained give reason to suppose that with careful step by step development of initial concepts, during which methods of operating with these concepts will be acquired, no difficulty in the development of further conceptual systems will be experienced; this latter study may even be carried out more rapidly without having to develop each concept step by step.

4

As we have seen, working by our method requires that the teacher should take a considerable amount of trouble in preparing the lesson and the scheme of work, but that, on the other hand, the task of the student is made very much easier.

Firstly, the pupil is not required to learn anything by heart—the material ("materialized") form of the thought process makes it unnecessary to learn any special set task by heart. The learning by heart takes place of itself, i.e. unintentionally and incidentally during the study process.

Secondly, no homework was set in our experiments, and the only work that was performed was during the experiments. Nevertheless, the children not only assimilated a small number of concepts selected by us, but they also acquired the habit of working with other concepts.

A further reason why teaching by our method is easier, is that the formation of the new concepts is very economical in effort (as compared with the usual "inductive" method). The child is not required to seek for himself and establish what are the essentials and the relationships between the features of the new concepts. Owing to a clear presentation of these essentials, there is no longer any need to vary the material in order that they may be elicited and generalized. On the other hand, the systematic variation of the basic forms of the particular effect being studied allows a complete generalization (at the appropriate level) to be realized in the course of applying the definition of the concept to the problems supplied.

The gradual transition from the completely detailed material ("materialized" forms of the thought process to the "purely verbal", and thence to the stage of "thinking to oneself" has the effect that the content and the logic of the thought process in all its forms becomes understandable and accessible to the pupils. The applications of the features contained in the definition of the new concept to the problem in hand is so organized that any deviation form the procedure as indicated, such as may result from an incomplete understanding of the process and from private attempts to find methods of supplementing it, are virtually excluded: if they do in fact occur, then the conditions, which we have laid down to enable the process to be assimilated, allow these deviations to be revealed immediately, recognized, and corrected.

Since the thought process remains unchanged (both in its objective content, whose accurate representation is specially elaborated in each higher form, and in the way it is applied), a dynamic stereotype develops rapidly, and complete assimilation of the thought process occurs. Concepts of the same group encountered subsequently, may as we have seen, be assimilated immediately at the higher level, and this may even take place directly in the process of thinking "to oneself".

All these effects together produce a sharp, and, it may be said, even a striking facilitation of the process of assimilating new knowledge, i.e. of acquiring an understanding of new concepts, and developing the corresponding mental processes.

At the same time there is another side to this problem which we think should certainly be pointed out. If we organize the conditions of work so that the action on the part of the pupil is almost completely determined, then subjectively, i.e. from the point of view of the pupil, these conditions will appear to be those which are most favourable to his course of action, giving him freedom to adopt his own standpoint and to acquire confidence in himself. He finds himself in the position of a person who knows what should be done, and understands how to do it; he also understands that the work is of value, as he can see from the teacher's attitude to it. Although the task itself represents work for the child, it leads him successfully to his goal.

It is therefore not at all surprising that when taught by this method, the children begin to take part in the work very actively and willingly, whereas previously they were at best indifferent to it, or else showed actual displeasure, as though the work were definitely disagreeable.

Translated by H. ASHER, B.A.

REFERENCES

1. GAL'PERIN, P. YA., (1954). Opyt izucheniia formirovaniia umstvennykh deistvii, (An Experimental Study of the Development of Thought Processes.) Collection "Reports on the Conference of Problems of Psychology, 3–8 July, 1953", Moscow, published by Academy of Pedagogical Sciences, R.S.F.S.R.
2. GAL'PERIN, P. YA., (1957). O formirovanii chuvstvennykh obrasov i poniatii (The Formation of Sensory Images and Concepts). Collection "Proceedings of the Con-

ference on Psychology", Moscow, published by Academy of Pedagogical Sciences, R.S.F.S.R.

3. ZYKOVA, V. I., (1950). Operirovanie poniatiiami pri reshenii geometricheskikh zadach (Use of Concepts in Solving Geometrical Problems), Collection "Problems of the Psychology of Teaching", Editor N. A. Menchinskaia, *Bulletin of the Academy of Pedagogical Sciences*, R.S.F.S.R., issue 28, Moscow, published by the Academy of Pedagogical Sciences, R.S.F.S.R.

4. ZYKOVA, V. I., (1955). Ocherki psikhologii usvoeniia nachal'nykh geometricheskikh znanii (Outlines of the Psychology of the Assimilation of Elementary Geometrical Concepts), Moscow, State Training and Pedagogical Literature Publishing House.

THE ORIGIN AND DEVELOPMENT OF
THE CONSCIOUS CONTROL
OF MOVEMENTS IN MAN *

A. V. ZAPOROZHETS

Institute of Psychology, Academy of Paedagogic Sciences of R.S.F.S.R., Moscow

VOLUNTARY movements, in contrast to involuntary, are effected by man consciously. Control of movements of this type is effected through reflection, the image both of the movements themselves and the conditions determining them. In this sense, voluntary movements can be regarded as the "consequence of our thought", as the "consequence of afferent stimulation from our subjective representation" (Pavlov, [8, p. 481]).

Since the 'thirties Soviet psychologists (L. M. Shvarts, E. V. Gur'yanov, A. N. Sokolov, D. G. El'kin, A. Ts. Puni, P. A. Rudik and others) have been working systematically on the problem of the role of consciousness in the formation and performance of motor habits. Investigations have also been proceeding on the dependence of motor functions and their realization on the conditions and nature of the subject's activity (A. N. Leont'ev, V. I. Asnin, P. Ya. Gal'perin and others).

Continuation of the lines of these investigations and utilization of the outstanding achievements in the physiology of higher nervous activity together with the new spheres of knowledge such as the theory of the control of machines and living organisms now makes it possible to advance a little in our understanding of the genesis and nature of conscious forms of movement control in man.

The development of this control is evoked by vital necessity and is determined by the extraordinary complexity and constant variability of the external and internal conditions for human activity.

Biomechanical investigations carried out here in the U.S.S.R. by Ukhtomskii [11] and later by Bernshtein [3] and others on transporting and manual movements by man (particularly with tools), revealed that not even the most accurate dosing of the initiating effector impulses can

* *Voprosy psikhologii*, No. 1, pp. 24–36, 1958.

of itself ensure the execution of the required motor act in accordance
with the conditions imposed by the task because of the multiplicity of
the degrees of freedom in the kinetic systems of the human body, the
elasticity of the muscular connections between their links, and the extremely great and ever changing participation of "extra-muscular" (external and developing in the kinetic system itself) reactive forces in the
dynamics of movements of this type.

The purposeful control of these complex movements is effected solely
through "return afferentation" (P. K. Anokhin), by means of which the
nervous system is continuously informed of the course of a premeditated
movement and of all deviations from the required course.

Alone, however, the information supply cannot itself effect control
of motor behaviour. In order that the individual shall be able to evaluate
the incoming information correctly and to convert it in the appropriate
way into "executive information", into a system of adequate efferent
impulses, he must also know, even if only approximately, what he has
to do: he must have some programme of the actions to be undertaken.
Bernshtein very rightly states that the control of movements requires
collation of the *data* on the actual values of the movement parameters
to be regulated with the *given* values required of them, this latter system
constituting the programme for the motor act to be performed [4, p. 86].

Thus, even at this point the biomechanical analysis of movements
in man has shown that these cannot be effected on the simplified behav-
iourist system (stimulus—reaction) and that, for their control, the subject
must have some form of action programme.

The physiological substrate for this programme is apparently the supplementary afferent complex of conditioned excitation which Anokhin
[1] has designated the acceptor of effect. It can be assumed that the acceptor of effect has undergone profound qualitative changes in the course
of evolution. At early primitive levels in the organization of movement
only the final adaptational effect of the reflex act is accepted, and the
conditions for and means of its attainment are discovered blindly, so
to speak, by means of chaotic reactions, by trial and error. At later stages
of development the acceptor begins to reproduce not only the end adaptational effect but in addition the whole picture of the objective situation facing the individual and the actions which must be performed in
relation thereto. The psychical regulation of movements has arisen, regulation which is effected through reflection, through images.

Rudiments of the psychical regulation of behaviour are also to be
found in the animal world. Only the simplest form of such regulation,

however, is seen in animals and, more particularly, its most important component, the image of the movements to be executed, has not undergone any very material development in them. This is connected with the fact that the ontogenetic development of motor function in animals mainly follows the line of adaptation of already existing forms of motor behaviour, which have become fixed in the species experience, in relation to the varying external conditions of existence, which necessitates a certain degree of orientation to these external conditions but not to the features of the movements themselves.

In contrast to this, man is required, right from early childhood, to master what are for him completely new, communally determined forms of motor behaviour, which present themselves to him as models, as something requiring special orientation with a view to its mastery. The regulating role of images in the formation and performance of motor acts is increased immeasurably under these conditions.

At the same time, because of the existence of the second signal system, the images that are created in man acquire a generalized and conscious character, whereby movements executed on the basis of these images also become conscious and volitional in the strict and true sense of the latter word.

The problem of the image and its role in the regulation of motor acts is the central problem in the psychology of man's volitional movements. What is the nature of this image and how does it influence motor behaviour?

In general, the reflex theory of Sechenov and Pavlov and, more particularly, their doctrine on orienting and investigatory reflexes are of decisive importance for the overthrow of the false subjective idealistic conception of the image and for a correct understanding of its genesis.

According to the Pavlovian interpretation of the function of the orienting reflex as now developed by Asratyan [2], Anokhin [1] and others, this reflex plays an essential part both in the formation of any temporary connection and in the production of any already created system of conditioned behavioural reactions.

That the orienting reaction plays an essential part in the formation of the temporary connection can be illustrated by the experimental findings obtained by M. I. Lisina in our laboratory. She elaborated conditioned vasodilator reactions to the action of an electric current in adult subjects. The method used was similar to that elaborated by Pavlov's co-workers for investigation of the mechanism of volitional skeletal muscle movements. The experiment consisted of the following. Electrical stimulation, producing unconditioned reflex vasoconstriction, was delivered on the subject's arm. As soon as temporary relaxation of the spasm of the vessels developed and there was seen to be some enlargement of their lumen while the painful stimulation still continued, the current was then switched off. Thus, extraordinary conditioned significance—that of a means for abolition of the action of a negative external agent—was conferred on the vasodilator reaction (and on the afferent impulse coming from it) by withdrawal of the painful reinforcement. Despite a very large number of combinations, a conditioned reaction of this type could not be elaborated in any of the subjects in the first series of experiments. It was found that, because of the weakness of the interoceptive impulses coming from the vasomotor effects and their unaccustomed role as behaviour orientators, they did not attract the subject's attention and so did not evoke an orienting reaction directed to themselves, which made formation of the required connection difficult. In the several subsequent series of experiments the subject's attention was drawn to the activity of his vasomotor mechanisms by means of additional direct signalization (tactile, auditory or visual) which was varied in exact correspondence with the dynamics of the vessels or by verbal indications given by the experimenter, whereon the conditioned vasodilator reaction was elaborated relatively rapidly, and could be evoked thereafter by verbal instructions or by self-instruction.

The mechanism of orienting reflexes is, in living organisms, the analogue of the "follow-up systems" which play an important part in modern complex automation installations, the purpose of which is to furnish the required information to the control unit.

Here, in the sphere of the activity of living beings, is seen the general principle of control, the essence of which is, in the words of Sobolev et al. [10, p. 29], that "movements and activities of large masses or the transmission and transformation of large quantities of energy are directed and controlled by small masses and small quantities of energy carrying information".

This also explains the particular role of orienting reactions in the activity of living beings. The character of orientational activity changes in the course of evolution.

There exist, apparently, more elementary forms of orientation (both unconditioned and conditioned), which amount to setting reactions promoting better perception of stimuli and thereby facilitating demonstration of those among the stimuli which have unconditioned or conditioned significance for the organism. Orientation of this nature does not participate in the formation of new forms of behaviour and does not anticipate the paths for their realization. It merely tries to discover in the surroundings occasions for unconditioned and conditioned adaptational reactions existing in the organism.

Orientation activity in the course of which a copy of the object examined is built up is quite a different matter. The image developing from this type of orientation accepts the subsequent movement, regulates the course of its execution and facilitates the assimilation of new forms of behaviour.

Orienting-investigatory activity of this nature, leading to the formation of an image and, subsequently effected on the basis of the image, is now psychical activity.

A large number of physiological investigations have been devoted to study of the mechanisms of unconditioned and conditioned orienting reflexes.

The problem of orientation has recently begun to occupy the attention of psychologists also (E. I. Boiko, E. N. Sokolov, V. S. Merlin and others).

Some investigators, for example Leont'ev [6], Gal'perin [5], Luria [7] and others, have started to develop problems connected with the formation of the image in the process of the subject's orienting-investigatory activity.

In the Institute of Psychology, Academy of Sciences of R.S.F.S.R., and the Department of Psychology of Moscow University my co-workers and I have been engaged for a number of years on experimental investigation of orienting-investigatory activity and the images built up as a result thereof, and also the part played by these in the regulation of complex forms of motor behaviour at different stages in child development.

The works of T. V. Endovitskaya, Ya. Z. Neverovich, Z. M. Boguslavskaya, G. A. Kislyuk, A. G. Polyakova, V. P. Zinchenko, D. B. Godovikova, T. I. Danyushevskaya, O. V. Ovchinnikova, L. I. Tsvetkova and others deal with investigations on the effect of various forms of orient-ing activity on the formation and functioning of motor habits, the successive changes in orientation with increasing familiarity with the conditions of the task, and also the stages in the development of investigatory activity in children.

These experiments demonstrated that the process of motor habit formation depended essentially on the intensity and character of this activity. The particular features of the orienting-investigatory activity influenced both the rapidity of learning and the quality of the habit when elaborated.

Ya. Z. Neverovich's investigations, for example, showed that complex systems of manual (tooling) movements, elaborated in children showing different forms of orientation, acquired different internal structures and were characterized by different standards of execution.

It is well known that the mastery of complex motor systems connected with the use of tools (e.g. the skill of hitting a nail with a hammer) presents considerable difficulty to children between the ages of 3 and 7 years. Neverovich found that one of the causes of such difficulties was that, in the usual method of teaching the child's orienting activity was directed mainly to the result of the action. The actual methods employed for its performance and particularly the hand movements associated therewith were at the periphery of attention, and in consequence, the analysing of the signals coming from them and the establishment of the corresponding connections was rendered exceptionally difficult (Table 1).

The efficiency with which tool operations were mastered and the actual standard of their execution were considerably higher when orientation to the method of performing the action could be produced in the child in the course of training (Table 1).

TABLE 1. *Number of blows struck by children to drive a nail in (as a percentage of the number of blows required before training)*
(Investigation of Ya. Z. Neverovich)

Age of children	With orientation to the result of the action	With orientation to the manner of performance of the action
3–4 years	40	7
6–7 years	28	7

This was achieved in Neverovich's experiments by abolishing the results of the action (the child was asked merely to strike a board with the hammer) or again, by the introduction of a model which the child had to imitate.

The experiments of Kislyuk, Polyakova and others produced evidence that the elaborated skills attained varying degrees of generalization and were variously transferred to changed conditions, depending on the character of the orienting activity.

Polyakova studied the transfer of the skill of traversing a table model labyrinth which had been acquired on the background of different types of organization of the orienting-investigatory activity in children of different ages. In one series the skill had been elaborated simply by demonstration of the required movement by the experimenter, and in another series the child's attention was directed during training to orienting points on the path, their relative positions were pointed out to him and he was first of all made to follow the alleys in the labyrinth from point to point with his hand and with his eyes. When the habit was formed in both respects the labyrinth was turned through 180° and the subject had then to find the way out of the labyrinth in its new position. It was found that transfer of the skill was accomplished much more successfully in the children trained in the second series of experiments than in those trained in the first (Table 2).

TABLE 2. *Percentage of children effecting transfer of the labyrinth habit elaborated by means of simple demonstration of the required action and formed in relation to special organization of orienting activity* (Investigation of A. G. Polyakova)

Method of learning / Age of children	With simple demonstration of the required action	With special organization of orienting activity
3–4 years	10	50
4–5 years	50	80
5–6 years	90	100

It will be seen that the differences in the indices for the two series of experiments tended to disappear with increasing age. This is apparently explained by the fact that, even in the absence of special organization of their orienting activity, older children tended more and more to make such a detailed examination of the labyrinth on their own initiative and so achieved in the first series of experiments almost the same efficiency in the transfer of the skill as in the experiments of the second series.

This investigation also revealed the particular changes taking place in the orienting activity of the child in the process of development. In the early stages of ontogenesis motor-tactile orientation was of dominant importance in the process of familiarization with the surroundings. Later, the eye, which earlier had followed the hand as it felt objects, borrowed, as it were, on its accumulated experience and became able to fulfil the orienting function independently. This transition from tactile-motor to visual orientation can be illustrated by the results obtained by Boguslav-skaya, who studied the ways in which children of various ages familiar-ized themselves with strange objects (Table 3).

TABLE 3. *Percentage relationship between the various forms of orienting activity in pre-school children on first acquaintance with new objects*
(Investigation of Z. M. Boguslavskaya)

Forms of orienting activity	3–4 years	4–5 years	5–6 years	6–7 years
Feeling of the object	44	33	28	21
Manipulation of the object	26	22	19	14
Examination of the object	30	45	53	65

These findings indicate that, as age increased, the percentage of cases in which familiarization with an object was effected by touch and ma-nipulation decreased and purely visual orientation to new material in-creased gradually. At the same time it was observed that when older chil-dren were confronted with more difficult, completely unknown objects visual orientation was insufficient and there was need for their tactile-motor examination.

In the course of the child's development visual orientation becomes possible in relation to the learning of movements as well as in relation to objects. In this connection imitation plays an important part in the formation of motor habits.

S. A. Kirillova's experiments demonstrated that in the early stages of ontogenetic development the best training results were attained by "mechanical guidance" of the motor behaviour of children, by employ-ment of the method of "passive movements", and training by imitation gave relatively poor results. The importance, relative and absolute, of imitation in the mastery of motor skills increased as the child grew (Table 4).

Although the children followed the actions demonstrated to them with great attention yet, because of their limited motor experience and lack of the necessary visuo-kinaesthetic connections, their visual impres-sions were still incapable of determining their motor behaviour. In con-trast, the visual image formed in older children in the process of imitat-ing the actions of another individual had a regulating effect on their motor activity.

TABLE 4. *Average number of exercises required for the formation of a habit by the "passive movements" method and by imitation in children of different ages*
(Experiments of S. A. Kirillova)

Age of children / Nature of training	Passive movements	Imitation
3–4 years	8	12
4–5 years	8	8
5–6 years	5	5
6–7 years	3	1

The importance of speech, the second signal system, in the formation and performance of motor habits increases progressively with development of the child.

The experimental findings of Endovitskaya, Kislyuk and others afford evidence that the speech control of behaviour is effected through the medium of orienting-investigatory activity. At first speech can evoke orientation only in relation to objects directly perceived. Subsequently, at later stages in the child's development, systems of conditioned orienting reactions, already formulated in relation to named objects and associated with them by means of verbal designations, can be actualized in the absence of the corresponding objects by means of the verbal stimuli. There is development of mental orientation in the situation, which is immeasurably more abbreviated and generalized than direct orientation, and there is associated increase in the effectiveness with which preliminary verbal instructions, given without any visual indication of the conditions under which the action takes place, are carried out.

Analysis of the experimental findings concerning the function of orienting-investigatory activity in the process of habitual movement formation leads us to the conclusion that its main function is in the formation of the sensory part of the elaborated motor system, in the preliminary analysis and synthesis of the afferent stimuli in the system.

The "intensification of sensation" brought about by orientation, to which Sechenov drew attention [9, p. 430], is a factor of considerable importance for the separation of stimulations of a certain type from the general mass of agents acting on the analysers.

This intensification, by means of orienting reactions, of the effect of stimuli of a certain type was demonstrated very clearly in investigations carried out under our direction by E. N. Martsinovskaya.

Martsinovskaya elaborated two different motor conditioned reactions in pre-school children in response to two different compound stimuli (a bright red circle on a pale yellow background and a bright green circle on a light grey background). During elaboration of the conditioned motor reflexes the experimenter oriented the children by directing their attention to the strong elements in the compound stimuli (the colours of the central circles) in one series of experiments and to the weaker components (the background colours) in the other. These were followed by control experiments in which the components of the previous compound stimuli were delivered in new combinations (the red circle on the light grey background and the green circle on light yellow) to determine how the children reacted to the new signal combinations. The results of these experiments, which are given in Table 5, showed that all the children (with few exceptions) who in the course of training had been oriented to the strong elements in the compounds, reacted to these strong elements irrespective of the weak component with which they were combined. When the orientation had been to the weak elements in the compound the picture was materially changed, and the nature of the change varied in children of different ages.

TABLE 5. *Changes in the percentage relationships between the different types of reactions in children to a compound stimulus in control experiments as determined by orientation to the respective components during the elaboration of a conditioned connection*
(Investigation of E. N. Martsinovskaya)

Age of children	Orientation during instruction	Reaction to strong component	Reaction to weak component	Reaction sometimes to strong sometimes to weak component
3–4 years	To strong component	100	—	—
	To weak component	55·5	44·5	—
4–5 years	To strong component	90	—	10
	To weak component	20	80	—
5–6 years	To strong component	100	—	—
	To weak component	—	70	30
6–7 years	To strong component	100	—	—
	To weak component	—	90	10

It was difficult to re-orient the younger children to the weak elements in the compounds and so to override the influence of their strong components with the verbal direction of the investigatory activity used in these experiments.

In contrast, orientation to the weak components was easily produced in the older children by the same verbal methods so that the effect of the weak components was intensified and they attained functional predominance over the physically strong components. This intensification of the effect of stimuli by means of orienting reactions apparently plays a material part in the analysis of perceived effects, in the revelation of the signal significance of stimuli which are weak but not indifferent for behaviour.

The synthetic function of orienting-investigatory activity proceeds simultaneously with the analytic function, giving expression to the relationships between stimuli and thus enabling the temporary connection elaborated to be accurately co-ordinated with the stimuli.

The investigations carried out in our laboratory by T. O. Ginevskaya, T. I. Danyushevskaya and others demonstrated that the elaboration of conditioned reactions to ratios in pre-school children took place much more successfully when there was special direction of the orienting activity to examination of these relationships than under the ordinary training conditions (Table 6).

TABLE 6. *Elaboration of reactions to the relationships between the sizes of objects in children of different ages under ordinary conditions and with special organization of the orienting activity. The reactions to the ratios are shown as percentages of the total number of reactions for each age group*

(Investigation of T. I. Danyushevskaya)

Conditions of experiment / Age of children	3 6–4:6	4 0–5:6	5 0–6:6
Ordinary conditions	30	60	71
With special organization of orientation	67	78	84

It is interesting to note that a verbal reference to the ratios was sufficient to produce orientation in the older children, but that the younger children required more direct additional measures to direct their investigatory activity, such as alternate pointing with the hand to the objects concerned in the ratio, gestural indications of their different sizes etc.

The result of the preliminary analysis and synthesis of stimuli, which were effected by means of orienting-investigatory activity, was that an image was gradually built up in the subject, a representation of the situation and the actions which had to be performed in relation to it.

The process of image formation is characterized by a specific change in orienting-investigatory activity and the process goes through a number of successive stages. This process has been traced in our laboratory by T. V. Endovitskaya, Ya. Z. Neverovich, Z. M. Boguslavskaya, A. G. Ruzskaya, G. I. Minskaya, D. B. Godovikova and others. Recently, V. P. Zinchenko has made use of cinematography for the recording of orienting movements of the eye, which made it possible to examine the course of the process in greater detail.

(1) In the first stage of acquaintanceship with the conditions of the task the orientation is of chaotic character, in the sense that the orienting reactions are not yet carried out in a system corresponding to the stimuli operating. Each individual stimulis evokes orientation only to itself, quite apart from any connection with preceding or succeeding stimuli. The form of the orientation reactions has still not been developed to harmonize with the specific features of the object examined. In Ruzskaya's experiments, for example, young children, when familiarizing themselves with flattened figures by feeling them, at first turned them round with the finger, constantly losing contact with the object, so that it was impossible to discover their features by this method of orientation. A system of the orienting feeling movements necessary for examination of an object's contour had to be formed before the children could begin to distinguish the shapes of the different figures.

(2) The character of the orienting-investigatory activity changed in the next stage. Orienting reactions to extraneous stimuli were suppressed and the subject's attention gradually became concentrated on the actual conditions of the task. The most important change which took place now was the formation of conditioned orienting reactions and of corresponding differentiations. In the experiments of Godovikova, for example, a system of conditioned orienting reactions was gradually elaborated in children when a series of unreinforced indifferent stimuli (successively lighted electric lamps) was presented repeatedly without instructions of any kind. In addition to causing orientation to itself, each stimulus evoked conditioned reflex movement of the eyes to the point where a stimulus should appear the next moment. The elaboration of such a system of conditioned orienting reactions required different num-

bers of combinations of the indifferent stimuli in children of different ages (Table 7).

TABLE 7. *Average number of presentations of a system of indifferent stimuli necessary for the formation of a system of conditioned orienting reactions in children of different ages*
(Investigation of D. B. Godovikova)

Age of children	3–4 years	4–5 years	5–6 years	6–7 years
Number of presentations	7·6	7·9	6·7	4·6

The connections formed in the process of orientation to indifferent stimuli can be utilized subsequently for the elaboration of a system of executive motor-reactions. Thus, the children in whom a system of conditioned orienting reactions had been elaborated in the first series of Godovikova's experiments learned to press the corresponding reaction keys for such a system of signals much more rapidly than children who had not previously been made familiar with the system.

The formation of the system of conditioned orienting reflexes corresponding to the system of operative stimuli signified the emergence of the acceptor of effect which is the basis for the image formed of the situation and the actions to be carried out. It should, however, be remembered that the motor components of orienting reactions, as demonstrated in experiments such as those of Zinchenko, Godovikova and others constitute merely a part of the entire system. There are also other elements in its composition, among which strictly sensory changes play an important part, these changes also being reflex and capable of acquiring a conditioned character. It is only this complete aggregate of the components in the system of conditioned orienting reactions that can reproduce the picture of the external and internal conditions for action and can constitute a basis for the image of the situation.

The image arises, then, when there is such a degree of familiarization with the task, but this is a purely sensory image, which is reproduced only in the presence of directly perceived circumstances and which requires the development of orientation in these circumstances.

(3) In the next stage the system of orienting reactions, now created and associated with speech, becomes stereotyped and generalized. It can now be reproduced in the absence of direct perception of the object through verbal instruction or self-instruction.

Zinchenko succeeded in making cinefilm recordings of orienting movements of the eye when the object was presented to his subjects verbally. These oculomotor reactions were in general similar to the reactions to direct perception of the object. Later, there was a distinctive reduction in the effector links of the orientation reactions and the special features of the object were merely reflected by a distinctive constellation of excited and inhibited cortical areas which now developed without any external investigatory activity.

Gradually, therefore, through the medium of orienting activity, the development of the image of the situation proceeded and there was transition from sensory image to representation.

These various stages in the development of the image during the process of orienting activity are similar to the stages in the formation of mental activities as established by P. Ya. Gal'perin. This points to the common origin of the processes.

It should be noted that, although the preliminary orientation played a very material part in the formation of a motor habit, it can fulfil its function only when the subject had already had adequate experience of the action under similar circumstances or, in other words, if he already had a supply of appropriate temporary connections. If such experience were lacking or insufficient, then the preliminary orientation could not fully ensure the necessary result, and the formation of the image took place in the second part of the process of activity, when the subject proceeded from the orienting to executive activity, from the preliminary stage of familiarization with the task to its practical execution.

Strictly speaking, it is only executive activity, only practical contact with the object that can actually reveal new properties in it which are still unknown to the subject and clarify their significance in relation to behaviour. Even in this case, however, orientation fulfils an important function. Following on the performance activity, it ensures that the individual obtains the necessary information on the new properties of the surrounding activity revealed by this information.

There is thus continuous connection between orienting activity and performance activity and constant transitions from one to the other. Strictly speaking, they represent different parts, different components of a single, purposeful human activity. While originally orientation of necessity lagged behind executive reactions, it later acquired the power of anticipating the ways in which these reactions should be effected, of creating the image of what should be done.

When, either as a result of preliminary orientation or as a result of orientation in the course of the subsequent executive reactions, an adequate image of the situation and of the actions to be executed had been formed in the subject, there is a pronounced resultant change in the character of the behaviour.

We attach special importance to the objective signs of the development of the image which were demonstrated in the experimental investigations of Ya. Z. Neverovich, O. V. Ovchinnikova and others.

Prior to development of the image, the correct line of action is groped after blindly and erroneous lines are arrested only to the extent that the different trends receive positive or negative effective reinforcement, but the position changes with the development of the image. Correct movements are now fixed at once and erroneous movements are arrested from the very beginning, even before a positive or negative effect is attained, the former as corresponding to and the latter as failing to correspond to the established representation.

Coincidence of the completed movements with the existing image begins to function as a special form of conditioned reinforcement, with the result that the effectiveness of learning is greatly enhanced. Orientation is not suppressed on the development of the image but begins to perform a new function, namely, control over the execution of the movements by collation of the information received with the standard, the model created in the subject.

This trimming of the motor behaviour to the standard existing in the subject stands out very clearly during the learning of motor habits by imitation, which was investigated in our laboratory by A. G. Polyakova, S. A. Kurillova and R. I. Sharkova.

Tracing the ultimate fate of the developed motor skill, we found that if it was repeatedly reproduced under relatively constant conditions, there was gradual suppression of the orienting reactions. N. I. Poddyakova's investigation demonstrated convincingly that extinction of the orienting reaction was a very important sign of automatization of the action. Orientation was not, however, completely suppressed, was not suppressed to the entire system of stimuli acting on the organism at any stage of automatization. There was always some critical point which remained within the field of the subject's attention. In this special features of the stimuli and their significance for behaviour played a part.

Thus, it was observed in the experiments of S. M. Koslovskii on the late stages in the automatization of an elaborated motor habit that orientation to a whole series of triggering stimuli (except the first) succeeding each other in a stereotyped manner were extinguished, but agents which fulfilled the role of conditioned reinforcement continued to evoke active investigatory reactions.

Investigations carried out under our direction by A. I. Meshcheryakov, L. A. Venger, V. P. Zinchenko, D. B. Godovikova and others showed that there was contraction of the sphere of stimuli causing orientation and change in its character during the automatization of an action. Control following signals was displaced to the periphery of attention. For example, photic stimuli could now be kept track of through peripheral vision without any turning of the eyes towards them.

At the same time the earlier orientation-investigatory operations were reduced, became stereotyped and were converted into orienting-setting operations. The now "known-by-heart" complex of setting signals, without detailed investigation of them and without elucidation of all their features, at once evoked a system of tonic changes and created a state of readiness to act in a certain manner in a certain direction.

In this way orientation, which fulfils its basic function in the first stages of the mastery of a new movement, or in the initial period of change or rearrangement therein, retains all its importance in the course of its subsequent functioning.

There is an orientational factor even in the absolutely habitual, automatized motor act, which emerges in the form of orientational setting reactions regulating behaviour in relation to the task confronting the subject.

Translated by DR. R. CRAWFORD

REFERENCES

1. ANOKHIN, P. K., (1955). Osobennosti afferentnogo apparata uslovnogo refleksa i ikh znacheniye dlya psikhologii (The Features of the Afferent Apparatus of the Conditioned Reflex and their Significance for Psychology). *Vopr. psikholog.* No. 6.
2. ASRATYAN, E. A., (1952). K fiziologii vremennoi svyazi, cb. "50 let ucheniya akademika I. P. Pavlova ob uslovnykh refleksakh" (On the Physiology of the Temporary Connexion. In "Fifty Years of Pavlov's Conditioned Reflex Doctrine"). Moscow.
3. BERNSHTEIN, N. A., (1947). O postroyenii dvizhenii (On the Structure of Movements). Medgiz. Moscow.
4. BERNSHTEIN, N. A., (1957). Nekotorye nazrevayushchiye problemy regulyatsii dvigatel'nykh aktov (Some Pressing Probelms Concerned with the Regulation of Motor Acts). *Vopr. psikholog.* No. 6.

5. GAL'PERIN, P. YA. and PANTINA, N. S., (1957). Zavisimost' dvigatel'nogo navyka ot tipa orientirovki v zadanii (Dependence of the Motor Habit on the Type of Orientation to the Task). *Dokl. Akad. Ped. Nauk R.S.F.S.R.* No. 2.

6. LEONT'EV, A. N., (1957). Obucheniye kak problema psikhologii (Learning as a Problem in Psychology). *Vopr. psikholog.* No. 1.

7. LURIA, A. R., (1955). Rol' slova v formirovanii vremennykh svyazei v normal'nom i anomal'nom razvitii (The Role of Language in the Formation of Temporary Connexions in the Course of Normal and Abnormal Development). *Izd. Akad. Ped. Nauk R.S.F.S.R.* Moscow.

8. Pavlovskiye sredy (Pavlov's Wednesdays). Vol. 2. Moscow–Leningrad, 1949.

9. SECHENOV, I. M., (1947). Izbrannyye filosofskiye i psikhologicheskiye proizvedeniya (Selected Philosophical and Psychological Works). Moscow.

10. SOBOLEV, S. L., KITOV, A. I. and LYAPUNOV, A. A., (1955). Osnovy cherty kibernetiki (Fundamentals of Cybernetics). *Vopr. psikholog.* No. 4.

11. UKHTOMSKII, A. A., (1952). Cobr. soch. (Collected Works). Vol. 3. Leningrad.

THE NATURE OF THE CONTRAST ILLUSION

I. T. BZHALAVA

D. N. Uznadze Institute of Psychology, Science Academy of the Georgian S.S.R., Tbilisi

FORMULATION OF THE PROBLEM

IF a comparison of two objects held one in each hand and differing in weight or volume is repeated 10 or 15 times, the subject develops a certain "set" corresponding to the particular objects. This can be shown by further experiments in which pairs of similar objects are presented and which are perceived as differing in weight or volume.

From the conditions of the experiment, the object would be expected to appear heavier or greater in volume in the hand receiving the greater weight or greater volume during the development of the set. In practice, the object is interpreted as lighter or smaller in volume in the hand which was habituated to the experience of the heavier or larger of the two objects and likewise seemed heavier or larger in the hand which had had experience of the smaller and lighter. Here we are concerned with a paradoxical reaction often called the contrast illusion.

Until now there has been no clear understanding of the relation between the effects of contrast illusion and set, and D. N. Uznadze has therefore thought it necessary to point out that "the very common occurrence of the contrast illusion in our experiments throws doubt on the notion that we are dealing with the phenomenon of set in these experiments, and not with something else" [6; 21]. Uznadze's formulation of the reason for the development of the contrast illusion is as follows "... If the subject develops a stable set towards objects of large volume, a given object differing considerably from the one to which the set has been developed cannot be included in the set, which is therefore destroyed and replaced by an opposite set which can include the object and which shows it to be considerably smaller than it actually is" [4; 326].

Thus, according to Uznadze, an object which cannot be assimilated within the original set will cause its breakdown, and a new set will now

* *Voprosy psikhologii*, No. 4, 42–52, 1958.

be established and subsequent perceptions made in terms of it. Since originally the training given was in the instruction—"large on left—small on right", a set now develops acting in the direction—"small on left—large on right". Subsequent impressions proceed on the basis of this set, and will appear new and contrasting, although, as Uznadze has pointed out, the process represents one of assimilation.

There is also a further problem: if the action of equal stimuli breaks down a previously established set, why is it that the result is the emergence of a contrast effect and not the restoration of a true appreciation of the stimulus intensity? If the previous set has been destroyed and its nature was such as to alter judgements in a direction corresponding to assimilation, then the nature of the contrast illusion remains unexplained. Should not contrast effects also be present even when there has been no appreciable change in the set itself?

To resolve this problem, in addition to making use of the verbal reports of the subjects tested we based the experiment mainly on objective recordings using a cathode ray oscillograph.

METHOD

In one hand the subject was given a dynamometer requiring considerable force, while the other held another model which was more easily operated [1]. The electrical potential developed in the arm muscles was recorded on the oscillograph ($1 \text{ mm} = 25\mu\text{V}$). The electrodes were fixed with collodion to symmetrically placed points on the flexors of both forearms. The potentials developed were recorded on film; the difference between the recordings from the two hands could be seen with the unaided eye.

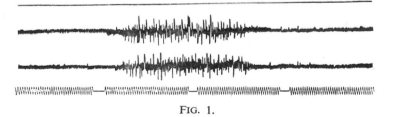

FIG. 1.

The tracing for the left arm is recorded parallel with the time tracing below; those for the right hand—above (Fig. 1). The subject was told to press with both hands simultaneously, and to make an equal move-

[1] For brevity we will refer to these as the strong or weak dynamometers.

19*

ment with each until the difference in pressure could be clearly felt. The left hand had the strong dynamometer (55 kg), and the right the weak one (35 kg). The same subjects were used for a second set of experiments in which the dynamometers were interchanged, the left having the weak, and the right the strong dynamometer. Two unequal dynamometers were used in order to establish a set by means of 15 repetitions of the movement.

This was followed by an experiment in which the subject operated two dynamometers each of 35 kg until he no longer noticed any apparent difference, i.e. until the set had been abolished. In each experiment, as well as making oscillographic recordings, the verbal reports of the subject were noted.

Two variants of this latter part of the test were employed: in the first the subject was instructed to stop pressing the dynamometers as soon as he noticed a difference between them, i.e. as soon as the contrast illusion appeared. In the second case he continued to press them after this, pressing hardest with the hand which appeared to encounter the greater resistance. The results of the two experiments are considered separately.

Forty-five subjects were used for these experiments.

EXPERIMENTAL RESULTS

1. As the myograms in Fig. 1 show, the experiment began with the hands completely relaxed. For almost a whole second the tracing is quite straight. This shows that the muscles are completely relaxed. Then the subject begins to press the dynamometers equally, and this continues thus for 2 seconds. It can be seen from the two myograms that the pressure is the same for both hands. It must be understood that there had been a preliminary period of training.

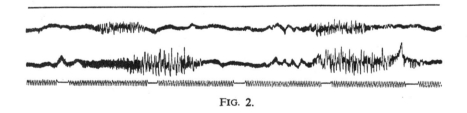

FIG. 2.

After some preliminary practice, a set is established by compressing dynamometers of different strengths, that in the left hand being the stronger of the two (Fig. 2). Since the subject has to overcome a greater resistance in the left hand, he contracts these muscles more strongly, and this is shown in the lower myogram by the greater frequency and amplitude of the oscillations; the right hand compresses the weaker dynamometer, and therefore moves it through the same distance with the exertion of a much smaller force.

The difference between the myograms of the two hands is very distinct: the left hand works more strongly, and so develops greater potentials. There was a pause of 1–1½ seconds between the two experiments. This period appears on the myogram by two almost straight lines, showing that the muscles return to a relaxed condition during this time, and show no after effect from the contraction. This shows experimentally that the set is not developed in the muscles, i.e. not peripherally.

The next experiment consists in compressing dynamometers of equal strength (Fig. 3).

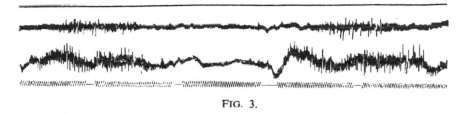

FIG. 3.

As has already been explained, before developing a set, the subject compressed the two similar dynamometers to the same extent (Fig. 1); but now, when he attempts to do the same thing, as is reported by the subject himself, it seems to him that the conditions of the experiment have changed. He is convinced that the left hand now encounters much less resistance than does the right, and he therefore says: "The left hand is performing the task very easily". It is clear that the origin of the difference is due to the development of a set, but the following point must be noted: the stimuli in the second experiment appear to the subject to be the reverse of those actually encountered in the previous one; while in the former the stronger dynamometer was in the left hand, it now seems to him that it is the right hand which is operating the stronger instrument.

It must be noted that the oscillograms (Fig. 3) do not correspond at all to the verbal description. It can be seen that in the second part of the experiment the subject continues to exert a greater force with the left hand; the myogram of the left hand differs from that of the right both in the greater amplitude and in the greater frequency of the oscillations.

That must have been the case, because the subject was using equal dynamometers and had a previously established set. This means that he contracted the fingers of the left hand more strongly than those of the right. The oscillograph records the effort expended by the flexors of the hand, i.e. it gives the objective measurement.

This experiment reveals a further point which can only be appreciated from the verbal report: the hand which produced the greater effort in the second experiment appears to encounter less resistance than in the previous experiment, and the subject therefore easily overcomes the resistance to the left hand, and it seems to him that the dynamometer in that hand is the weaker of the two. This is the experience which we call the contrast illusion.

It is therefore clear that the development of the contrast illusion depends on a previously established set. The latter so directs the work of the finger flexors that similar objects are perceived as dissimilar, i.e. an illusion develops. Thus the reason for the development of the contrast illusion is based not on a new but on an old set which governs the perception of the test objects in the second experiment.

Thus we have ascertained that the action of a set developed under controlled conditions is one of assimilation, and that it forms the basis of the contrast illusion which occurs when the subject is presented with equal stimuli. This continues until the subject, who is carefully following the instructions, stops pressing the dynamometer immediately the contrast illusion develops. But if we prevent this from happening, as we shall see presently, a characteristic break will occur during the course of the experiment.

In the second variant of this experiment, as has already been explained, the subject was not limited to experiencing the contrast illusion but continued to react by changing the effort expended according to his own subjective experience; in other words, he reacts to the illusory sensory input. This means that he expends a greater effort in compressing the dynamometer with the hand which appears to encounter the greater resistance, i.e. he flexes the fingers of the right hand more strongly. In this way the stronger contraction shifts from the left hand to the right, though this does not take place at once, but gradually. This makes it possible to follow the phases during which the change-over of the set occurs (Fig. 4).

It can be seen that at first the myogram of the right hand is the greater of the two, but that soon the difference becomes more marked and the subject begins to contract the fingers of the right hand more strongly. As the result, the myogram of the right hand shows electrical potentials from the flexor muscles which are greater in strength and in amplitude than those of the left.

Thus, after a set has been established by using dynamometers of different strengths, a strong one in the left and a weak one in the right hand, if the subject then squeezes a pair of equal dynamometers, he receives the impression that the one in the left hand is the weaker and that in the

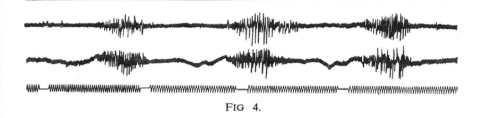

FIG 4.

right the stronger. By frequent repetition of this experience which, though illusory, seems perfectly real to the subject, a set in the opposite direction becomes established: a set towards the perception of a strong dynamometer in the right hand and a weak one in the left. This is the basis for the externally recorded effects which result in the dynamometer of the right hand being compressed the more strongly. A set in which the left hand contracts more strongly is replaced by one in which the opposite occurs. Thus the initial set gives rise to a new one which corresponds to the subjective impression of the subject. There is a change of set: the first one is replaced by another. It can now be understood why in both cases, despite the contrast illusion, we are concerned with an assimilatory action of the set.

In this way, oscillographic recording of the effects of set has made it possible not only to describe the illusion of force, which has not been known until now, but also to distinguish two stages in the action of the set. In the first stage, as we saw, the set acts by assimilation, and this is the basis for the development of the contrast illusion. The second stage begins with the development of the contrast illusion which is the impetus for the change in direction in which the set acts. The subject acts in terms of the contrast illusion and a set develops corresponding to it but experienced by him as a real distribution of stimuli.

2. Similar results were obtained with the illusion of volume. We will select one myogram as illustration.

In the first part of the experiment the subject holds and feels a large sphere in the left hand and a small one in the right. Fifteen repetitions of the comparison are sufficient to enable a set to be developed to the perception of a large sphere in the left and a small one in the right.

On flexing the fingers of both hands with equal force, as instructed, the subject encounters a strong resistance with the left hand and this stimulates a stronger contraction of the muscles and involves a greater expenditure of energy. This is reflected in the myogram (Fig. 5) which there is no need to describe, as the difference between the curves of the two hands is so very marked.

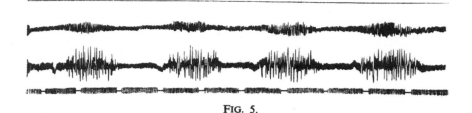

FIG. 5.

The experience of the subject is as follows: in the left hand be has a large object, and he perceives it as large, while in the right hand he holds a comparatively small object and perceives it as small. In short, there is complete agreement between the established set and the subject's experience.

In the second part of the experiment the subject acts in accordance with the established set. He therefore exerts the greater contraction with the fingers of the left hand which held the greater sphere in the first part of the experiment. (A succession of contractions with the left hand is shown in Fig. 6). The fingers of the right hand contract so little as to be

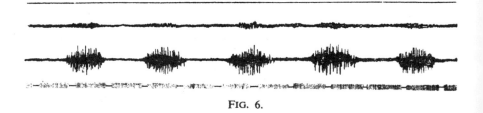

FIG. 6.

scarcely visible on the oscillogram. This can also be understood when we take into account that the impression of difference in the volume has suggested to the subject that he should cease contracting the fingers. He thus continues to perceive a difference between the two equal spheres. He was convinced that the sphere in the right hand was large and that in the left small. It was abundantly clear from his verbal account that he was flexing the fingers of the left hand much more lightly and against a much smaller resistance than those of the right. As a result of this, the sphere in the left hand seemed to him reduced in size while that in the right appeared increased. These conditions form the basis for a contrast illusion which would not have arisen unless the left hand had continued to exert a more pronounced flection as the result of the previously established set.

In this case too there is disagreement between the subject's impressions and the myograms.

The contrast illusion depends here also on the previous development of a set and at the same time it constitutes a signal for the change of the operative set.

The first stage of action of the set is effected in this way, after which a second stage is initiated which is directed to the establishment of a set corresponding to the contrasting illusory perception of the stimuli. This takes place at the time when the subject attempts to overcome the imaginary resistance to the right hand, contracting these fingers more strongly than those of the left hand, i.e. he is operating against the previously elaborated set. This represents the reason for the extinction of the previous set and the development of the new one.

3. We will now say a few words about the results of the experiment on the weight illusion.

The subject raises a pair of unequal weights 15 times, the left hand lifting 1000 g the right 200 g after which a pair of equal dumbells of 200 g each are substituted, and visual clues are excluded.

The second part of the experiment followed the same course as those already described and for this reason we have not included the myograms.

Thus from these experiments it is clear that the development of the contrast illusions concerning force, volume, and weight all follow the same course, and in all three cases the contrast illusion has the same base which is the development of a set in the individual.

DISCUSSION

Charpentier supposed that tactile sensation played the most important part in the contrast illusion. A large object comes in contact with a large surface of skin and so acts on a large number of receptors; a small object acst on a much smaller number of receptors. For this reason the large object appears light and the small one heavy.

Charpentier's mistake was shown very simply by Flournoit (1895). The weights were raised using rings placed on the finger. The illusion was still just as strong. Thus it still develops when the same number of tactile receptors are stimulated in each hand. Charpentier's view is also opposed by the fact that the weight illusion cannot be elicited if vision has been excluded.

G. E. Muller theory of "false expectation" is based on the following consideration: from frequent experience in every day life we develop a tendency to suppose that a larger object is heavier than a smaller one. "On account of this expectation, a large force is developed in the hand to raise a large object, which is then lifted very easily. Precisely the opposite situation obtains in the case of a small object. The impression developed on this account compels the subject to describe the larger object as lighter than the smaller one" [7].

According to Flournoit, the object which is thought to be the heavier is raised more quickly than the other. Claparède has shown that it is the rapid raising of the object which induces the contrast illusion. There is nothing essentially different in this view from G. Muller's theory of "false expectation".

It is not difficult to see the weakness in this theory, because as Seashore has pointed out, Charpentier's illusion is very stable. According to Nyssen and Bourdon [7] it occurs even when the subject knows that the two weights in front of him are equal. The occurrence of the illusion under these conditions shows that "false expectation" is not directly concerned in Charpentier's illusion.

The most effective criticism of the theory of "false expectation" is that of Uznadze. He developed a set in his subjects during hypnosis. On awaking, the subjects had completely forgotten the training experiment, but the contrast illusion occurred when they were presented with a pair of similar objects. In this case, the subject knew nothing of the experiment previously performed on him, and there could therefore be no reason to think that there was a "false expectation".

It has long been known that a phenomenon similar to the weight illusion occurs in the perception of a pressure when the finger joints remain motionless and the subject does not experience any associated movements [3]. "Essentially the same thing can be said of the volume illusion", writes Uznadze. "When a subject makes a haptic comparison of the size of two objects and expresses a definite opinion as to the relation between them, the rate at which they are raised plays no part in this judgement. Therefore it is wrong to base an explanation of these illusions on phenomena which can only occur in the case of weight perception. Since however all three illusions are of the same kind, a new explanation must be found which applies to all three modes of sensory perception" [5; 183].

Clearly a new explanation must be found in terms of the experiments which condition the individual and so induce the illusion. The results of our experiments apply here, both in connection with the perception of force and volume and in the case of weight. In all cases the illusion is preceded by the elaboration of the corresponding set. This allows us to suppose that, as Uznadze has pointed out, we are dealing with a general effect which lies at the base of quantitative judgements and is concerned in all similar conditions when a comparison of objects with respect to other quantities such as weight, volume, and force is made. This phenomenon constitutes the set, which, as has been proved experimentally, is established in respect of the relation between the two quantities and therefore remains the same no matter how the material actually used is changed or whatever sensory modality is concerned [1] [6; 39].

This standpoint will be found helpful in explaining the development of the contrast illusion.

When we develop in a subject a set to exert a greater force with the left hand than with the right, the subject continues to operate in the same way in the next part of the experiment. On this account the muscles of the left hand contract more and those of the right less strongly. The experience which the subject derives from this shows only that when using a greater force the resistance is overcome more effectively and therefore the left dynamometer appears weaker than the right, though in fact the two are equal. Contraction of the muscles of the right hand continues in accordance with the previously elaborated set, i.e. with less force, and therefore the subject experiences a feeling of greater resistance to the right hand.

A similar picture emerges in developing a set to the perception of different volumes. In this case too, a set is developed towards the perception of a large object in the left hand; as we have already shown, where a small object was felt by the hand, the fingers contracted with the force to which they had been conditioned previously, and therefore the object grasped by the hand trained to the large object seemed relatively much smaller than in fact it was. The reason is that in the second part of the experiment, when feeling the object, the left hand continues to exert the same force which it employed in the experiments in which the set was developed.

After developing a set to the perception of unequal weights, two equal weights presented to the subject subsequently will be interpreted as un-

[1] We consider the central origin of set to be self-evident and therefore do not consider it necessary to report experimental results which confirm this view.

equal, the one held in the hand conditioned to the heavier weight appear-
ing the lighter of the two. Precisely the same thing occurs in Charpentier's
phenomenon, when the larger object raised appears lighter than the small
one. The perception of a large and a small object establishes that set which
is induced by objects of different weight, since as far as our consciousness
is concerned a large object is interpreted as a heavy one.

It follows from this that the subject's relation to the test objects which is
based on the set which has been elaborated accounts for his experience which
is shown by the descriptive words he uses such as "flying up", "sticking
to the support", "compression", "swelling", "getting larger", "getting
smaller" etc. After elaboration of the particular set, raising of the small
object gives the impression of "flying up" if we raise it with a large force;
an object will appear heavy and as though "stuck" down since we raise
it with a smaller force. The same thing is observed in the volume illusion:
of two equal objects, one seems reduced in size and the other increased;
in the case of the illusion of force, one is interpreted as weak and the other
as strong. In these subjective experiences, that which has been called the
contrast illusion enters our consciousness, and there is therefore no reason
to invoke any other explanations.

As far as the significance of the situation for the subject is concerned,
we have seen that he begins to act so as to direct a large force at the point
where the greater resistance is felt. Thus the reason for the alteration of
the original set to an opposite one is to be found in the sensations developed on the basis of the old set, i.e. that which preceded the formation
of the new set. Until the new set has been developed, the subject is in
a transitory condition in which there is a disagreement between the operative set and the experience which he receives while under its influence.

This state of affairs may of course last for a considerable time, and
at a certain instant, as the experimental results show, the sensation of
contrast comes to control the situation and a set is developed corresponding to this new situation. In other words, the sensation of contrast is the
signal that the acting set shall be replaced by another which is appropriate
to the subject's sensations.

While under the control of this signal, the subject attempts to exert
a greater force with the hand which appears to encounter the greater
resistance. In our experiments this is the right hand, and it is therefore
clear that the subject will contract the fingers of this hand most strongly.
In this way a set is developed which is in the opposite sense to the operative one and which corresponds to the subjective experience of contrast. It may be thought that over a certain period there must be two sets

operating in opposite directions, so that for a time the illusion would be less clear. At one time the old set would predominate, and then there would be an equilibrium between the two so that there would then be a correct perception of two equal objects. This is the way that we interpret the extinction phase of the set, which as is well known, shows considerable variation from one individual to another.

It cannot be said that there were no difficulties, even when the experiment was carried out by the usual method without using oscillographs. The replies of the subject were often indefinite when describing the illusions; however, it was not clear what the nature of this difficulty was, since introspection usually revealed a contrast illusion, and the preceding period was not noticed. The fact that we could reveal it objectively made it possible to obtain a recording of the effect of the set.

The use of an objective method made it clear that the operative set does not come to an end immediately, but fades away over a definite period. A transitory condition in which the experience of the subject and the objective record of the old set are at variance occurs between the decay of the old and the development of the new set. This is resolved by the development of a set corresponding to "contrast perception" of the stimuli, i.e. to the contrast illusion.

In following the requirements of the general law governing change of set as established by Uznadze, we were able to make observations on the effect of the established set both before and after its disappearance. Before it had disappeared, the action was assimilatory, so that the force exerted by the left hand was greater than that of the right. This represents the reason for the disappearance of the set, because on pressing both dynamometers equally the subject continues to act in accordance with the established set, and therefore the dynamometer in the hand which has been trained to the strong one appears weak. Subsequently, by taking this into consideration, the subject exerts the hand in which he feels the greatest resistance. From this moment onwards a new set is formed which is opposed to the direction of the first: whereas before the set was such as to correspond to "large on the left, small on the right", now it is of the kind: "left—small, right—large". The basic reason for the change of the set, as Uznadze showed, is the marked difference between the stimuli. The greater the similarity between the training and the test objects, the less easy is it to destroy the set which has been established. Everything that has been said above naturally confirms a set which has been quantitatively established, because as Z. I. Khodzhav has shown, a set only works in a quantitative way in directing the assimilation of impressions.

In studying the physiological mechanism of "set", some investigators have attempted to find its origin in the phenomenon of contrast illusion, but this attempt has not been successful. The reason for this can be seen from the results of our experiments; it is also clear that the physiological mechanism underlying "set" must have an assimilatory action.

Our previous research has shown that the physiological mechanism must be regarded as either part of the system composed of the cortex of the two cerebral hemispheres or else as "the dominant": there is no appreciable difference between these two views [2]. Everything that we know about "the dominant" gives good reason to suppose that the general physiological basis of "set" is to be sought in this direction.

SUMMARY

Strength, weight and volume illusions were studied objectively by oscillograph records of the processes accompanying the development of the set.

It was found that after it has become established the set continues to act for a certain time in the initial direction, i.e. the phenomenon is one of assimilation. Meanwhile the verbal reports of the subject show that they are experiencing the contrast illusion.

The establishment of the set represents the essential basis for the perception of contrast in equal objects.

The contrast illusion represents the sensory input and has the effect of reversing the subject's response and so results in the development of a new set which corresponds to the illusory perception of the stimuli.

Translated by H. ASHER, B.A.

REFERENCES

1. BZHALAVA, I. T., (1952). The after-image and the establishment of "set", Communication to the Academy of Science of the Georgian SSR, No. 2. In Russian.
2. BZHALAVA, I. T., (1953). "Set" in relation to brain function, Communication to the Academy of Science of the Georgian SSR, No. 10, In Russian.
3. BOCHORISHVILI,, A. A., (1927). A pressure analogy to the weight illusion, Bulletin of the Tbilisi University, No. 3. In Georgian.
4. UZNADZE, D. N., (1930). The fundamental law of change of "set", volume III, issue 3. In Russian.
5. UZNADZE, D. N., (1956). The illusion of weight and its analogies, Collected works, volume 1.

6. UZNADZE, D. N., (1949). Experimental basis of the psychology of set, *Psikhologiya* volume VI. In Georgian.

7. NYSSEN and BOURDON, (1956). A new contribution to the experimental study of the size-weight illusion, *Acta Psychologiya*, No. 3.

STUDIES ON THOUGHT AND SPEECH PROBLEMS BY PSYCHOLOGISTS OF THE GEORGIAN S.S.R.*

R. G. NATADZE

Department of Psychology, Tbilisi University

SINCE the establishment of Soviet power, a considerable amount of experimental work in psychology has been directed to the study of the problem of thought and speech.

THE PSYCHOLOGY OF SPEECH

1. The first investigation into the psychology of language and speech was published in Georgia in 1923. This was the study by D. N. Uznadze of the psychological basis of the naming process [21]. After it had been published in German [25] there were considerable repercussions in the psychological literature, and as will be shown below, this was the start of further and more thorough experimental work in this direction at Tbilisi University.

This investigation played an important part above all in studying one of the chief problems of the psychology of speech—the problem of the relation between the word and its meaning; this is shown by the considerable space devoted to this problem in A. Willwoll's monograph [29; 32–35], where the results were considered and contrasted with the classical theory of O. Seltz, K. Buhler and others.

In his investigation, D. N. Uznadze showed experimentally that during the act of naming, the relation between the sound complex and its content was not of a chance mechanical kind; it has a definite psychological basis. This linkage is not brought about merely by the factor of association, i.e. not by a simple association between the sound complex and the meaning of the word but by a more diffuse factor involving the whole condition of the subject.

In this work the author did not reveal the precise nature of this factor, but it is clear to anybody acquainted with D. N. Uznadze's theory of

* *Voprosy psikhologii*, No. 5, pp. 91–107, 1957.

set that here he had in mind the condition of the subject which was later referred to by the term "set". This was confirmed in one of his later works in which he directly states that set is a factor which creates a single sound complex and significance in a word (see below, section "Internal forms of speech").

In experiments on naming, the subjects were given 42 meaningless "words" (groups of syllables), and from these they were told to choose names for a number of quite complicated shapes drawn on paper. It was found that altogether the subjects selected only 68 per cent of these words as names, while the remaining 32 per cent were rejected as unsuitable. Several words were chosen by many of the subjects as names either for the same figure or for figures showing a close resemblance to each other. The author considers that the psychological basis for the naming process is the "general impression" and the "emotional tone" as constituting the common factor between the object and the name given to it.

This investigation is also relevant to another important present-day psychological problem, that of intermodal "affinity" or unity. It must be emphasized that D. N. Uznadze's work was published before that of E. Hornbostel [27] who renounced the traditional mechanistic, atomistic, psychological theory of sensation which interprets the modalities as independent isolated mechanisms.

The experimental results of this investigation are advanced by W. Köhler in connection with (1) the evidence for the theory of the objectivity of the psychic "inner" world as part of the "external" world, and (2) the possibility of direct access to another's experience [28].

2. After D. N. Uznadze's death [1], his work was continued by A. G. Baindurashvili in the Department of Psychology of Tbilisi University [13; volume XI].

D. N. Uznadze was one of the first to show that the naming of objects is a systematic process, and that it has a psychological basis. However, the method he used was not quite appropriate, and the results he obtained, as we have seen, were never completely analysed. The psychological factor which is operative in the naming process was not completely elucidated. Naturally further study was required, and this was carried out by A. G. Baindurashvili, who succeeded in perfecting the method and extending the experimental work.

He proposed that the objects to be named should not be drawings having no significance, because under normal conditions a person is never required to name an object of this kind. He chose instead real phenomena for which there was no name in the subject's own language. In the experiments, the subjects were asked to give a name to objects which either had no name in Georgian or whose correct name was not known to the subject (altogether 21 objects were presented). For instance, he might be told to supply a name for the process which in Russian is conveyed by the word "yekhat"* (in Georgian "yekhat' " and "to go on foot" are represented by one and the same word, as in French); to supply a word having the significance of the German word "fressen", which means "to eat", but only as applied to animals; to think of a word combining the concept of bulls and cows (generalized concept); to supply a name to replace borrowed foreign words which have a different significance in their own language; to supply a single word for "student hostel"; to supply a single word meaning "a vehicle drawn by animals"; to supply a name meaning "a vehicle moved by a force of nature"; and to name a number of pictures of various kinds.

The experiment consisted of two parts. In the first part the subject himself had to invent the name for the object, and in the second part he was supplied with a list of 10 meaningless "words" from which he had to choose one to apply to the particular object. In the instructions it was emphasized that he was required to supply a name for a phenomenon for which no name existed.

The results obtained allowed the author to deal with many fundamental problems of the psychology of speech. They showed clearly that a set of qualities with which the naming process was concerned presented itself differently to the minds of different subjects; this can be more accurately stated by saying that different qualities occupied a central position. Although the central feature did not always coincide with the essential attribute named, it nevertheless played a decisive part in the choice of the descriptive word used.

The following result is significant. The need to use a new word for purposes of communication compels the subject not to restrict himself to his own knowledge of the object to be named, but to search in his own system of knowledge to find in it a corresponding place for such a set of qualities (to establish relations with other concepts), and to use this place as a starting point for the naming process. Thus in the naming process, there is not only the establishment of a link between the particular attribute and the name applied to it, but also the acquisition of meaning by the word given. This seems to us to constitute a powerful argument against the mechanistic explanation in terms of association, which de-

---

* *Translator's note:* This Russian word means "to go", but applies only to cases where the subject travels in or on some kind of conveyance (train, sledge, car, horse, etc.).

scribes the naming process as a simple association between the attribute and the name for it. The author quite correctly points out that the function of speech is not merely to effect communication, but has a cognitive significance.

In order that a particular sound complex and the meaning of the associated name should merge within the consciousness of the individual, he must experience and appreciate them as related to each other. Many of the proposed names were rejected by all the subjects as quite "inapplicable". Among the sound complexes proposed there were some which were selected from amongst a group of 10 by the majority of the subjects; one name was chosen by 100 per cent, another by 75 per cent, and a third by 64 per cent of the subjects. All this demonstrates that naming is a systematic and not a chance process. On the other hand, by itself the sound complex has no functional relation to any named attribute, so that the majority of the sound complexes are selected by different subjects as the names for different attributes.

The sound complexes are accepted as a name only when the subject accepts them as corresponding to a "set" for finding a name for the particular attribute.

It must be pointed out that the naming process consists of far more than finding the appropriate name: the sound complex which is accepted as "suitable" for naming a particular phenomenon exerts a reciprocal action on the experience of the attribute perceived and changes its structure in the subject's mind. The mutual relationship between these two processes continues, so that they no longer exist in the subject's mind independently of each other, and the name "assimilates" the attribute and vice versa.

The author of the article considers that the "set" of the subject represents the basis of the naming process and that this consists of finding the "corresponding" name and the subsequent assimilation of the name with the object named. The effect is that the objectively indifferent sound complex is "appreciated" by the subject as naming a particular attribute.

3. Work carried out in the Psychology Department of Tbilisi University by M. G. Kolbaya [3] concerns the relation between speech and thought; he showed experimentally that deaf-mutes not possessing normal speech could not grasp even concrete concepts, while others who had been taught speech in special schools could do so (see below, section on "The pathology of the thought process"). From this the author concludes that speech and thought are one.

4. D. N. Uznadze refers to the problem of the relation between meaning and sound in a later work "The internal form of speech" [16]. This

theoretical article presents the principal problem of the psychology of speech, the problem as to what is the nature of the so-called "internal form" of the language (this is a concept derived from Humboldt). He refers here to that form of the whole language which, although it is not audible and cannot be perceived, nevertheless underlies the overt form, and determines it; later authors have referred to it as the "feeling for the language", i.e. that which causes us to use a particular form of speech, for instance our native language, without being conscious of the rules which govern it.

From a theoretical analysis the author concludes that set constitutes this basic form of language. As a result of a set developing which corresponds to a particular situation, we begin to talk in a language, naturally in one which we know, which corresponds to the same situation: a stream of words and expressions now flows into our consciousness, and these are in the language appropriate to the given situation; this is the case even if the language concerned is foreign to us and therefore less firmly imprinted in our speech habits than is our own native language. The onset of speech is determined by a set to speak in a particular language; this activates the mechanisms in the subject concerned with this language, and he then produces speech without consciously searching for words and without being conscious of the rules which govern the language in question. The author stresses that set must not be conceived as a purely subjective condition, but rather as one which reflects an objective situation; he holds that a different interpretation of set would lead to an idealistic interpretation of the psychological basis of speech.

The author considers that this concept of the "internal form" of speech resolves the two chief problems of speech psychology—the problem of the unity of language and speech (these are united by the common factor of set), and the problem of the unity of sound and meaning, and these are related by the underlying concept of "the integral modification" of an individual who requires to communicate, i.e. by a unique set.

5. The problem of the psychological nature of the unity of thought and speech has been studied by Sh. A. Nadirashvili [4] in the Department of Psychology of Tbilisi University. This work includes a critical review of the chief foreign psychological theories concerning the problem of the relation between speech and thought. Then, from his own experiments, and using D. N. Uznadze's concept of objectivization, he tried to determine the nature of the unity of thought and speech. The subjects were given specially selected problems to solve, and were asked to "think aloud". The author considers that in this way he produces a very active

thought process, and the plan aims to reveal the underlying thought process. He concludes that the verbal process plays an essential part in the development of a new thought, and that the unity of thought and speech is manifested in the new thought which has been elaborated by the use of words, i.e. in the "objectivization" of the general signs associated with different phenomena (the word is the instrument which effects the "objectivization.

6. D. I. Ramishvili has published a number of papers on the basic problems of the psychology of speech. We must first of all consider her work on the psychology of the so-called everyday conceptions [13; volume IX], [15]. The author starts by criticizing foreign theories of speech which consider a word as a fusion of two independent component parts—the part which is sensed and the part which is thought. In order to establish what a word contributes to the development of a thought process, she carried out experiments in which definitions supplied by the subject of words expressing everyday (non-technical) concepts were compared with the way these words were actually used by the subject in various situations. The results showed that the use of a word is not decided by its content, as appreciated by the subject, but by a completely determined feature of which the subject is in no way aware. This feature is the role which the phenomenon named plays in the subject's experience of the environment. The recognition of this objective feature which is responsible for the systematic use of the word is extraordinarily difficult and sometimes almost impossible. As far as the overt "signs" which compose the particular phenomenon are concerned, they are distinguished in the first place when the phenomenon is perceived; they become the "centre of experience" and therefore enter consciousness in definitions given by the subject of the concept in question. However, it is remarkable that the use of the particular word is not determined by this "centre of experience", but by the role of the phenomenon designated as affecting the society concerned.

On this basis the author advances many arguments against the theory of language originating through gestures [13; volume X], [14]. She shows that this kind of origin is in keeping with the viewpoint of introspective psychology, according to which language is explained as starting from the consciousness of the individual, and its natural origin is thought to be the intention of the individual to convey to another the manifest content of his own consciousness. However, according to the author, the conscious state itself can only be realized through the expression of the general concept in the form of language. This essential process of the "crystallization" of the concept into a word through systematic use of a sign language is not within the compass of the natural sign language, owing to the specific features of its origin. It is for this reason that the history of mankind could not have originated from a sign language.

In a later study [13; volume XI], D. I. Ramishvili criticizes the interpretation of words as conventional signs, on the grounds that this presupposes prior existence in the subject's consciousness of two items — the lingual sign (sound), and the meaning. According to the author, it is just this which is implied by the verbal convention, though not always consciously. For this reason Ramishvili considers that psychologically a word cannot be treated as an agreed sign, since its existence is not derived from previous appreciation of the designation and of the object designated.

A study of different kinds of speech, including everyday, scientific, and artistic speech, led Ramishvili to investigate the special psychological mechanisms underlying the use of words and speech in general. The author considers that the mechanism concerned is that of set [13, volume VII]. It explains the possibility of the existence of verbal generalizations in the sense that the general attributes of the object can be reflected in it before they reach a conscious level in the individual. Set is the "preliminary reflection of the object in the subject's being, a reflection which determines every activity of the person and all his conscious processes". In the author's opinion, the laws governing set throw considerable light on the different characteristic forms of speech—the everyday, scientific and artistic forms.

7. As far as the special problems of the psychology of speech are concerned, the principal investigation in Georgia is that of D. N. Uznadze. This is an investigation into the impersonal form of verbs—impersonalia [17].

The author bases his argument on the fact that the impersonal forms are used as a rule to signify meteorological events (both in Georgian and in European languages this form is used to refer to rain, snow, thunder, frost, etc.), and raises the question as to what is the psychological nature of the reflection of these events in consciousness. His work includes a criticism of the theories of Siegwart and Wundt. He attacks these theories on the grounds that judgements are expressed in impersonal statements. Actually the impersonal statements quoted reflect and express not judgement but perception. It is the specificity of the perceived meteorological events which evoke the impersonal verbal form since they are perceived as impersonal. Thus representation of impersonal events is made in the impersonal form when the events as interpreted by the subject are expressed by the use of the third person. Uznadze considers that this kind of verbal description of events is not the result of an opinion held, but originates from some deeper-lying cause. There is no doubt that the latter constitutes that internal condition reflecting objective reality which the author subsequently refers to as "set".

8. A great many investigations have been made of the problem of the development of speech in children.

A. M. Avalishvili [13; volume VII] was the first to describe results obtained from observations on the development of speech in a Georgian child up to the age of 4 years; the observations were made on his own son.

The work of N. V. Chrelashvili [13; volumes IX and X] concerns the speech of the early pre-school and pre-school age child; it attempts to throw light on the psychological basis for the development of grammar in speech.

What is the psychological basis for the development of the laws governing speech? The author concludes that in childhood this process takes place without any conscious appreciation of grammatical requirements and that set, in the form of an unconscious appreciation of the objective situation represents the basis of the unconscious facility for correct speech.

K. D. Mdivani studied the development of writing in students of the Tbilisi Georgian School in Classes I to VII inclusively [13; volumes IX and X.

He demonstrated many steps in the development of the written language. In the first stage, the importance of the following two features was stressed. In Class I the chief feature is the "objectivization" of only the subject of the narrative, but not of the verbal form corresponding to it. The latter becomes noticed only in Class II onwards.

In the investigation particular attention was paid to the occurrence and subsequent development (particularly from Class V onwards) of a second feature—"the consideration of the reader" in carrying out written work. This feature determines to a large extent the logical method of exposition, the portrayal of inner connections in the subject of the narrative, as well as "the verbal structure" and even the written material of the text.

A. N. Mosiava [13; volume VIII] gives an interesting psychological analysis of the process of writing in connection with learning the alphabet; he has written many articles on the study of development of grammar from the point of view of the part played by "objectivization" in this process [13; volume VII].

There have been some accounts of the problem of the study of a second language (the study of Russian by Georgian children). Among these that of N. V. Imedadze [13; volume XI] is specially worthy of note. The purpose of the work is to describe psychologically the process by which the child comes to acquire two languages simultaneously, and the study is based on Russian and Georgian.

In spite of the idea, which is widespread abroad, that early acquisition of two languages is a factor which retards the development of speech and intelligence in the child, the results obtained give reason to suppose that the early acquisition of two languages favours the development of both these qualities, provided that two "independent spheres of influence" come to exist in the conscious mind. The possibility that such spheres shall be formed is due, in the author's opinion, to the elaboration of two verbal sets, each of which lies in a definite situation. Interesting instances are given of how a child learns the two languages at the same time.

The work of A. M. Avalishvili [13; volume VIII] gives results concerning the acquisition of a second (Russian) language by the pre-school child who has already mastered his native tongue.

A second work by the same author [13; volume IX] gives an analysis of typical mistakes made by Georgian children in writing Russian at the early school age.

G. N. Mchedlishvili [13; volume XI] has made a detailed investigation of the psychology of slips of the tongue. He gives a psychological analysis of these slips, criticizes foreign theories, and attempts to throw light on the "mechanism" of slips, chiefly from the point of view of the laws of the manifestation of set.

THE PSYCHOLOGY OF THE THOUGHT PROCESS

1. THE COGNITIVE SIGNIFICANCE OF PERCEPTION

The first experimental investigation in Georgia on the psychology of thought [18], [26] is that of D. N. Uznadze. The investigation concerns the part played by the object perceived and by its attributes as sensed by the observer in setermining the comprehension of its significance.

The subject, who has his eyes closed, is given the object to hold in his hand; he is asked to recognize it by feeling it, and while familiarizing himself with it he is asked to "think aloud". The results showed that during this perception of the object, the conscious thought content comprises sensory phenomena and "qualities of form" arising from the behaviour of the object. But this conscious content becomes a final concrete experience only when the subject "recognizes" the object, when he comprehends the significance of what has been sensed. The whole conscious thought content during the experiment is regulated by the search for the objective significance of the object perceived. This objective significance moulds and transforms the sensory attributes into their ultimate interpretation made up from a combination of sensations and perceptions. The following point is of interest: cases are known where the sensory content of a perception changes according to the way in which the subject interprets a particular object. This last observation is of great importance in connection with the problem of constancy of perception (as was shown by the author in 1940 in his "General Psychology"): the sensory content depends within certain limits on what the subject thinks the objects sensed to be.

In this regulation of the sensory content of the perception by the object, according to the author, the decisive part is played by the set of the subject. As a result of the action of the object, a set develops in the subject which determines how the conscious mind shall eventually comprehend the significance of what is perceived, i.e. a final consolidation of the attributed, as sensed, occurs.

2. THE PSYCHOLOGY OF COMPREHENSION

1. The most important experimental work in Georgia on the study of the thought process has been applied to the problem of what has been called "the education of comprehension", with special reference to the problem of the development of comprehension in individual children.

The first investigation in this realm was that of D. N. Uznadze. His well-known work on the development of comprehension in the pre-school child was published in German [23] and caused wide repercussions both in the Soviet (L. S. Vigotskii and others) as well as in foreign journals (V. Stern, B. Dumas, V. Blumenfeld).

The principal achievement of this study was, as L. S. Vigotskii correctly points out, that it reveals the psychological content of forms of the child's conscious mind, and these appear to represent the functional equivalent of comprehension, i.e. they effectively carry out the function of comprehension in different kinds of the child's thought processes, and at the same time in their psychological content they do not constitute "scientific" concepts. The traditional pedagogical psychology as applied to the child contained the false idea that the significance of words used correctly by the child represented a precise understanding of them; this profoundly wrong idea led to serious mistakes in pedagogical theory and practice. It was not until the end of the first quarter of the present century that the concept of "functional equivalents of comprehension" (Werner and others) developed; the result was to free child psychology from the error just described. But the nature of these functional equivalents of comprehension at the different stages of development was not known until Uznadze's investigations had been carried out. Here this gap was largely filled. He gives definite descriptions of many features of the functional equivalent of comprehension at various preschool ages from 2 to 6 years.

Although the method of forming an artificial concept used in this experiment scarcely differs from that of N. Ach, several essential features were introduced, of which one, known as the method of "graded help" received high praise from L. S. Vigotskii and is carried out as follows: when the child is unable to answer the question put, he is given a systematically planned set of problems which make the solution of the original problem more and more easy until the complete solution is forthcoming. This graded help makes it possible to reveal not only the level of the manifest capabilities of the child, but also the possibilities in the "zone of adjacent development of the child"; this in turn makes it possible to demonstrate in each subject certain essential features of the process, which are equivalent to comprehension.

In our opinion it is particulary important to note the result of Stage IV of the experiment—the stage of "mutual comprehension": these experiments, which were carried out on children, confirmed the observation first made by N. Ach, that new experimental words acquire an indirect meaning, i.e. they become meaningful words only after they have been used for the purpose of communication, when they serve as a means of communication between the experimenter and the subject. Before this social event, no matter how closely the complex of sounds was associated with the concept of certain objects, it was not perceived as a meaningful word, i.e. it did not merge with its own concept.

Many interesting features concerning the psychology of the naming process were revealed at the stage of the experiment when the subject was required to supply the name of a certain group of objects.

Almost simultaneously with this work, D. N. Uznadze published a study of the process of classification in pre-school children [24]. It is based on experimental material from the first group concerned in the above-mentioned investigation of the development of comprehension. The children were told to classify cardboard figures made in all possible spectral colours and in monochrome. These were clearly divided into groups consisting of large and of small figures. They could also be distinguished according to the number of colours: some consisted only of one colour, and some of two or three. The shapes of these figures were so varied that it was not possible to classify them on this basis. The classification could be carried out in terms of colour, size, or number of colours. The results obtained depend largely on the method of "graded help" which was mentioned above. Four types of classification were revealed, and these corresponded to the four degrees of development of classification at the pre-school age.

2. The work of D. N. Uznadze on the development of comprehension at the pre-school age was followed by a number of experimental investigations of this process. Most of these concerned the growth of this faculty at various stages of child development.

R. G. Natadze [5] dealt with this problem in a dissertation for a doctorate (1939). The methods employed in this investigation were used by him in many subsequent studies dealing with the particular problems of comprehensive thought. The essence of these methods consists in attempting to reconcile the contradiction in science between the two opposite kinds of studies of comprehension, a contradiction which L. S. Vigotskii had already pointed out, and which he had claimed represented an insuperable difficulty. This contradiction is between the methods of formation of new artificial concepts and those in which new real concepts are assimilated.

Natadze tried to work out a method of investigating concepts which, although they were new to the subject and had been formed during the experiment, were nevertheless quite real; in this way he overcame the difficulties and combined the positive side of these two opposite methods. During the experiment, the subjects had to assimilate concepts which were new to them (which had no place in their own native language), but which were quite real. The concepts are real, firstly because they fulfil the cognitive function of comprehension, that is to say they possess the cognitive value of a generalized representation based on the essential features of categories of phenomena such that their classification has a cognitive value, and secondly because they form part of the system of real concepts which the subject possesses. In the experiment, several concepts were elaborated by grouping together the appropriate material (for instance, pictures of different kinds of transport); then, by generalizing, the wider concept of a "second order" was developed, and then by generalizing further a still wider concept of a "third order" was introduced, and this could be, for instance, that of man's means of transport, corresponding to the German word Fahrzeug.

Thus these concepts, unlike the artificial ones used in other experiments, not only involve use of the cognitive faculty, but do not remain separated from the subject's perceptual system; at the same time they constitute a miniature system of experimentally induced conceptions which enables an explanation to be found of how the subject acquires a set of logical relationships between innate and specific contents, and which also allows us to study the process by which concepts of the second and third orders are indirectly formed. Natadze maintains that this method is free from the defects which L. S. Vigotskii quite correctly considered to be the fundamental weakness in the method of the formation of artificial concepts.

Natadze also considers an important feature of the method to be that it is possible to carry out the experiment in two opposite ways. The second way is to present the subject with the same conceptions, by describing them purely verbally and proceeding "from above downwards". The experimenter begins by defining the most general concept (without giving the child any examples which he can see), and then proceeds to the specific concepts using for their definition the generic concept whose definition has already been given in the experiment. Thus, this form of the experiment, together with the alternative arrangement in which the concept was developed by generalizing from material actually shown to the subject, throws light on the evolution during the life of a child of a concept developed from a basis of observation, as well as from an abstract verbal representation.

Among the principal features of the method it should be noted that the concepts presented to the subject are composed of *relative* indications (which is a characteristic of logical concepts) and not of manifest properties of the objects such as size, shape, colour, etc., as was the case with previous methods of the "development of concepts". In using the basic method, the subject develops a system of concepts referring to kinds of transport, and these are based on indications of the kinds of motive force used, the indications being united into the more general concept represented by the German word Fahrzeug, to which the nearest Russian equivalent is the word *ekipazh* (carriage). By using the second method, which was possible only for the older schoolchildren, a set of correlative concepts of relations between people was built up (people related by kinship, people internally related to each other through acquaintance, and people only externally spatially related, for instance brothers, etc.).

The results obtained by the methods which have been described enabled Natadze to follow the formation of concepts in subjects from 7 to 17 years of age, and to establish the existence of several stages in this process. There is no space here to discuss these results. The description given by

Uznadze in his "General Psychology" [20] of the development of conceptual thought in the schoolchild depends entirely on the findings of these experiments.

3. Work on the development of the cognitive function of concept formation was published by R. G. Natadze in 1942 in an abbreviated form [6]. The problem to be investigated was based on the following principle. In experimental psychological investigations of the development of a concept, usually no distinction is drawn between the manifestation and recognition of *common* as opposed to *essential* features. For instance, in the usual investigation into the development of a concept, the subject builds up the concept from *common* features which are a property of all the objects of a certain group. Nevertheless, psychologically the search for and the recognition of the *essential* feature, that feature which appears to be the essence of the development of the concept, is a process quite different from the search for a *common* feature and the abstraction of this *common* property of the particular category of objects. Not everything which is a common attribute of all the objects of a particular category is necessarily essential. For instance, every human being and only human beings have a vertical groove on the upper lip, but this groove is not an essential feature of a human being, although it is a specific property of such a being. Natadze maintains that in the methods of concept formation, up till now no account has been taken of the recognition of what is essential in concepts, or of the development of this faculty in children. For this purpose the author has developed a special method.

Children from 7 to 17 years of age are given a description of a man and are told in what ways he differs from an animal, and this description includes many specific but non-essential features, such as the groove on the upper lip, the typical ear lobe, etc.; other essential features such as wisdom, the power of speech, ability to work, use of tools, etc. are also described. After the subject has completely grasped the features described, he is set the following task. He is told about a newly discovered island on which beings are found which converse with each other, build huts, sow maize, etc. but which have no groove on the upper lip, no ear lobe, etc. The subject is then asked—"Are these people or animals?" They are then told about a second island, on which beings are found with the human type groove on the upper lip, with a typically human ear lobe, etc., but who cannot speak, who feed on wild fruits, live under trees in the forest, etc. They are then asked whether these beings are people or animals.

After this the subjects are invited to decide which is the better of the two definitions of a human being; in the first only the non-essential external typical attributes of a man (such as the groove, etc.) are mentioned, while in the second definition only the essential attributes such as speech, use of tools, etc. are mentioned.

The work gives a detailed description of the solutions of these problems by children from Classes I to X, and the typical development of the cognitive function of a concept is described. It was shown that there were many different stages in the development of the ability to recognize the essential features of a concept; at first the visible signs preponderated completely over those which could not be directly perceived, the latter being of no account in determining which features were essential. Finally, the ability to recognize the essential signs and to seek for that which was essential became completely developed. Well-marked discontinuities of development occur at the age of 11 (Class IV) and after 15 (Class VIII and above).

Another later investigation by the same author deals with the problem of appreciating the essential attributes of a concept [11]. The principal features of this work were presented at the All-Union Conference on Psychological Problems held in Moscow in 1955 [8].

In this investigation the external appearance (visible form) of an animal is contrasted with the essential features which cannot be directly perceived and about which the child is specially informed by the experimenter. In test experiments, the child is required to relate drawings of animals on cards to the appropriate concept; the animals are drawn in such a way that from their external appearance (phenotype) they can be related to one concept, for instance fish, while from their essential nature, i.e. from their essential signs, they should be referred to a different concept, for instance that of mammals. In the paper referred to, the problem is studied for the primary school age.

Later, in 1954, another paper was published [9], and this was a continuation of the same line of study. It describes observations made by the same method of the acquisition of the same essential conceptual features by schoolchildren from Classes V to IX.

4. In 1942 a shortened form of R. G. Natadze's work on the development of the generalization of concepts during the development of the individual was published [13; volume I]; this work depends entirely on the methods described above for the study of the development of new but real concepts (the concepts of kinds of transport and of the relations between people).

The chief result of these experiments considered as a contribution to psychology can be stated as follows. The process in which a concept becomes generalized—the way in which a unifying concept comes to be formed from the separate specific concepts—implies that what takes place is not an impoverishment of the concept, but a "deepening" in the sense that, owing to the generalization of the concepts, the knowledge of the object as imaged in the conscious mind becomes more profound. This more profound knowledge is obtained psychologically by the synthesis of the attributes of the specific contents in the general concept: during the generalization process there is no rejection of specific attributes of particular concepts, no loss, but on the other hand there is a synthesis which results in the attributes of the specific concepts being preserved in the generalized concept, where they do not remain isolated but are united in the synthetic form.

The author contrasts this conclusion with the traditional conception and with the results of other recent experimental investigations (N. Ach and others) which have been influenced by formal logic, which treats the process of generalization of specific concepts into a generic one, as a simple rejection or elimination of various of the attributes of the specific concepts.

A description is given of the development of different kinds of generalization of specific concepts in schoolchildren from Class I to X; these begin with simple "arithmetical summation", and develop through "collection" of a generalized concept, and end with a detailed generalization synthesizing the attributes of the specific concepts into the generic concept which unites them.

In 1943 R. G. Natadze published two short articles dealing with the problem of the development of generalized concepts in children of pre-school age [2; volume I]. In the first of these the author attempts to show that the discussion which has taken place abroad as to whether the general or the particular concept is developed first, is based on a false interpretation of the psychological attributes of the generalized concepts which the child "possesses" at the pre-school age. No matter how generalized these concepts appear to be from the logical point of view, their representation in the child's consciousness cannot be considered as a generalized concept. This would necessarily assume that the subject was aware of the unification of the specific concepts within the generic one. Nevertheless, as the material collected by the author showed, at the pre-school age, use is typically made of generic concepts lying outside the specific concepts contained within them, and that most frequently the child makes use of generic concept while not aware of its specific constituents; also that he may have difficulty in using a generic concept when the specific contents are well known to him. For instance, the child will use the word "fruit" to refer to species whose names he does not know, while he will apply the correct name to the varieties that he does know; again, while using the word "trees" to refer to varieties whose names he does not know, the pine is not considered as a tree but is named together with these trees as if it formed no part of that concept: "This is a drawing of trees and pines".

In 1942, R. G. Natadze published a paper on the development of the power of classification in schoolchildren [7]; this was based on results obtained in classifying different kinds of transport. A brief description was given of eight stages in the ability to classify as developed during the range of school ages.

5. In 1953, the same author published an article [13; volume VIII] in which a study is made of the development of the concept from context. Starting from the idea that the principal method of developing a concept in everyday life depends on *meaningful context* in which the concept is used during the process of communication or reading, the author proposes a method for the study of the acquisition of a concept from context, a method which he used in 1935–1936. The subject has read to him a text in which an unknown word consisting of a meaningless complex of sounds "Darvasi", and whose meaning he should be able to understand from the context; the meaning of this new but real concept is that of a device for defence against harmful naturally occurring phenomena and includes examples such as macintosh, protective goggles, galoshes, etc. The experiment was carried out on children from 7 to 17. Eight stages in this kind of development of a concept from context were distinguished. It was shown that by using this method, the same stages in the development of the concept occurred as were found in the method described above for the formation of new but real concepts. Also that the stages of development of the concept were much more clearly distinguished in those methods than when studying concept as derived from context.

6. In 1956 R. G. Natadze published a description of two ways of developing a concept [13; volume X]. Using the method we have previously described for the formation of new real concepts, the author follows the way in which these same concepts of kinds of transport change with age in two opposite ways: either by the usual method of generalizing factual material (pictures of different kinds of transport), and then by subsequent generalization of the concept obtained in this way ("the way from below upwards"), or by mere verbal definition of the same concepts, beginning with the more general and proceeding to the specific

concepts. Naturally, these two kinds of experiment are carried out on different children. The results published refer to the first five school classes. They enabled the part played by the material handled in developing a concept at the various stages, depending on the age of the child, to be determined. It was found that at the stage of Class I, the child cannot use a purely verbal method and that he cannot imagine the actual physical significance of the concepts described (cannot imagine what sort of objects are referred to), and this is so in spite of the fact that each word of those used in the definitions given to him are known to the child, and that the subjects which contribute to the concept are also familiar to him. In presenting these same concepts by generalizing from objects actually shown to children of the same stage of development (Class I), the children developed a practical grasp of the concepts so efficiently that they used them correctly in many problems. At a later stage, the child apprehends the meaning of the essential attributes more or less correctly, though it appears that the attributes themselves cannot successfully represent the concept if the child is unable to grasp the objective significance of the concept. During the acquisition of the same concepts by generalizing from objective material, a child of the same stage of development grasps the essential attributes of the concept, forms an objective picture of their significance, and interprets correctly the principal logical relations between the newly acquired specific and generic concepts.

At the stage represented by Class IV, the verbal approach is so well accessible to the child that the level of development of "concrete" concepts is almost the same irrespective of whether they are acquired by generalizing from objective material, or through definitions.

In the upper classes of the middle school, as can be seen from the unpublished results of R. G. Natadze, the second method of developing a concept (by understanding the definition of it) actually accelerates the process; this is because by defining the essential attributes which have already been distinguished they are presented, as it were, ready-made, whereas in the actual objective examples themselves, they can only be derived by a quite complex intellectual study by the subject.

7. In Georgia, the study of the development of conceptual thought is not confined to the general problems of the development of conceptions. Special investigations of the acquisition of certain kinds of scientific concepts have been studied. Mention must be made of the experimental work of E. V. Tabukashvili [13; volume X] in which the development of concepts of "subject" and "predicate" in the elementary school were studied. In the experiments, the logical and the grammatical subject and

predicate were contrasted, and this revealed the stage at which the child
failed to appreciate the formal grammatical scheme, although he understands the grammatical concept itself.

3. A PSYCHOLOGICAL AND PEDAGOGICAL STUDY OF THOUGHT PROCESSES IN THE PRESCHOOL CHILD

A *considerable* study has been made in Georgia of the thought processes of pre-school children, considered from the point of view of the theory
of teaching. Particular attention must be paid to the work carried out
by a group of research workers led by B. I. Khachapuridze [2; volumes
I, II, issue I] and those of F. S. Khundadze. B. I. Khachapuridze devized
special didactic materials for the kindergartens which aimed at stimulating the children to appreciate the concepts of colour, shape, and size.
He and his co-workers obtained information on how these concepts are
acquired by children through the use of these teaching aids [2; volume
II, issue 2]. Particularly interesting results were obtained concerning the
acceleration of development and the active acquisition of such operations as abstraction in perception, based on the colour or shape of the
objects, "objectivization", the properties of the objects, analysis of the
perceptions, etc.

In the papers by F. S. Khundadze [13; volumes IX, X, XI] a study
is made of the developmental trends of cognition in preschool children,
and a description is given of the general direction of their thought processes. It is shown that the "analytical" processes tend to preponderate
in the younger children and that there is a gradual development of the
"synthetic" activity in the later stages. A study is made of the development at the preschool age of their interest in the objective relations between
different objects and different phenomena, and later in the general laws
relating to these phenomena.

In A. S. Prangishvili's article [12] the problem of the development
of the thought process in the child is considered in relation to the idea
of the unity of thought and language. The author considers two kinds
of theories to be unsound—both those which treat the development of
thinking as a transition from non-verbal thought forms to a logical verbal
process, and those which represent it as a process which changes from
a type of thinking which is unrelated to the reflection of reality (super-
logical thinking) to logical thought. He attempts to show that the development of thought in the child is possible only in the form of verbal
thinking.

4. A STUDY OF TECHNICAL THINKING

In Georgia, the study of the thought process is not confined only to the so-called verbal thinking. Several studies have been made of the development of what is known as *technical thinking*. Particular attention should be paid to the work of D. N. Uznadze [22]. It is based on a large amount of material based on the solution of 34 problems involving the so-called technical faculty of more than 1200 students in Classes I–VIII. A description is given of the analysis of several types of problems, and *curves are given for the solution* of problems of different kinds. Interesting results are obtained on the differences in the development of technical thinking in boys and girls. Various stages according to age are distinguished in the development of technical thinking, and the psychological characteristics of each of these stages are described. Well-marked discontinuities in the rate of development of this method of thinking are found at the age of 11 and 14–15.

An unpublished work by K. D. Mdivani, which we will not describe, deals with the development of one of the "components" of technical thinking, that of spatial visualization.

R. G. Natadze [10] devotes a paper to the development of another "component" of technical thinking, namely estimation. This is based on observations of more than 1000 schoolchildren of from 8 to 17 years of age. A psychological analysis is given of the different kinds of problem, three chief psychological types are distinguished, and three different developmental curves of the ability to estimate are given.

5. THE PATHOLOGY OF THE THOUGHT PROCESS

Many of the works of the Tbilisi psychologists deal with investigations of pathological disturbances of the thought process. First of all it should be noted that in most of them, use has been made of the experimental methods of "concept formation" as described previously in this article.

1. In his studies of the process of concept formation in schizophrenia, K. D. Mdivani [13; volume V] used the method which was described earlier in this article and which was used by D. N. Uznadze in connection with the formation of a concept in the preschool child [19]. The principal result of Mdivani's investigation was that the great majority of schizophrenics retain the "mechanisms" for the elaboration of experimental concepts (based on visible clues of size and colour). All the principal operations, such as classification, abstraction of visible signs, their generaliza-

tion, naming, etc are scarcely affected in these patients. He found that the chief peculiarity of the schizophrenic patients was that for them the thought content associated with the experimental material alters, and they develop a set which is not appropriate to the experimental situation.

2. During the last war, R. D. Natadze used the method of forming a concept, as described above, to study disturbances of conceptual thought as affecting patients with speech disorders of various degrees of severity [13; volume II]. From the results obtained it appears that the chief disturbance consists of a reduction in the synthetic and integrating function of the thought process, i.e. a reduced power to generalize. According to the extent of this reduction in relation to the characteristic narrowing of the patient's conscious mind, there may be various degrees of interference with conceptual thought. The work describes many degrees of disturbance of this thought function.

3. A paper by M. D. Kolbaya [3] describes the ability of deaf-mutes to develop concepts. This was done using the method described above for contrasting the external appearance of animals, as related to definite scientific concepts, with essential features of these concepts [9]. According to the author, deaf-mutes not possessing normal speech were incapable of developing even simple objective concepts; they were not able to master even a simple classification of typical representatives of birds, mammals, and fish; it was not only that they failed to assimilate the essential attributes of objects, but failed even on general features of a group of objects. The ideas of deaf-mutes cannot be separated from the external overt nonessential properties of the object. A repetition of the same experiments in schools for deaf-mutes showed that the children in the higher classes of these schools are able to master objective concepts, and are capable of recognizing general features of objects, etc.

4. During the war, an investigation was made of alterations in the critical faculty caused by mental disorders (R. G. Natadze [13; volume IV]). The main conclusion was that a mental disorder produces a reduced critical faculty, and that this reduction is necessarily associated with a fundamental specific interference with the thought process which results from the disorder, and which consists of a reduction in the ability to synthesize and to integrate. On the basis of the results obtained, the author raises the question as to whether the critical faculty consists of the ability to contrast opposing features—in the ability to appreciate two features in a single relationship.

Translated by H. ASHER, B.A.

REFERENCES

1. BAINDURASHVILI, A. G., (1955). *The Psychological Nature of the Naming Process.* Author's abstract of dissertation, Tbilisi. In Georgian.
2. *Issledovanniya novykh didakticheskikh materialov dlya detskogo sada, (Development of New Teaching Aids for the Kindergarten)*, Vol. I, Tbilisi, 1943 and Vol. II, issue 1, Tbilisi, 1945, in Georgian. Volume II, issue 2, Tbilisi, 1946, in Russian.
3. KOLBAYA, M. G., (1953). *The Part Played by Speech in the Thought Process.* Author's abstracts of dissertation, Tbilisi. In Georgian.
4. NADIRASHVILI, Sh. A., (1955). *The Psychological Nature of the Unity of Thought and Speech.* Author's abstract of dissertation, Tbilisi. In Georgian.
5. NATADZE, R. G., (1940). The Formation of a Concept. *Transactions of the Tbilisi University*, No. 12. In Georgian.
6. NATADZE, R. G., (1942). The Development of Conscious Function in the Individual, *Transactions of the A. S. Pushkin Teacher's Training Institute, Tbilisi.* Volume II. In Georgian.
7. NATADZE, R. G., (1942). The Development of Classifying Ability in the School-child, *Georgian Science Academy Bulletin*, volume III, issue 3, Tbilisi. In Georgian.
8. NATADZE, R. G., (1951). *Ob ovladenii konkretnymi estestvennonauchnymi ponyatiyami v shkole, (The Development of Scientific Concepts in the School)*, Collection "*Materialy soveshchaniya po psikhologii*" (*Report of the Conference on Psychology*), Moscow, Academy of Pedagogical Sciences Press, RSFSR.
9. NATADZE, R. G., (1954). *The Acquisition of Simple Scientific Concepts at the Class V–VIII Level, Komunistura agzdisatvis*, No. 9, Tbilisi. In Georgian.
10. NATADZE, R. G., (1936). *The Development of Estimation in Schoolchildren*, Tbilisi. In Russian.
11. NATADZE, R. G., (1944). *The Development of Scientific Concepts in the Primary School, Transactions of the Tbilisi Pedagogical Institute*, Volume I, Tbilisi. In Georgian.
12. PRANGISHVILI, A. S., (1954). *Psychological Problems of the Development of Thought, Komunistura agzdisatvis*, No. 7, Tbilisi. In Georgian.
13. *Psikhologiya (Psychology)*, Volume I, Tbilisi, 1942; Volume II, Tbilisi, 1943; Volume IV, Tbilisi, 1947; Volume V, Tbilisi, 1948; Volume VII, Tbilisi, 1950; Volume VIII, Tbilisi, 1953; Volume IX, Tbilisi, 1954; Volume X, Tbilisi, 1956; Volume XI in press. In Georgian, summary in Russian.
14. RAMISHVILI, D. I., (1956). *Nepryemlemost' teorii pervichnosti yazyka zhestov s tochki zreniya psikhologicheskikh zakonomernostei, (A Rejection on Psychological Grounds of the Theory of the Origin of Speech through Gestures)*, Academy of Pedagogical Sciences Bulletin RSFSR, issue 81.
15. RAMISHVILI, D. I., (1954). *O psikhologicheskoi prirode donauchnykh ponyatii' (The psychological nature of pre-scientific conceptions)*, Reports at the Conference on Problems of Psychology, 3–8 July 1953. Moscow, Academy of Pedagogical Sciences Press, RSFSR.
16. UZNADZE, D. N., (1948). *The Internal Form of Speech, Psikhologiya*, Volume V, Tbilisi. In Georgian.
17. UZNADZE, D. N., (1923). *Impersonalia, Chveni metsniereba*, No. 1, Tbilisi. In Georgian.
18. UZNADZE, D. N., (1927). *The Internal Form of Speech, Psikhologiya*, Volume V, Tbilisi University, Volume VII. In Georgian.

19. UZNADZE, D. N., (1956). *The Development of Concepts in the Preschool Child, Trudy*, Volume I, Tbilisi. In Georgian.
20. UZNADZE, D. N., (1940). *General Psychology*, Tbilisi. In Georgian.
21. UZNADZE, D. N., (1923). *The Psychological Basis of Naming, Chveni metsniereba*, No. 2, Tbilisi. In Georgian.
22. UZNADZE, D. N., (1942). *The Development of Technical Thinking at the School Age, Psikhologiia*, Volume I, Tbilisi. In Georgian.
23. UZNADZE, D. N., (1929). *Die Begriffsbildung im vorschulpflichtigen Alter, Zeitschr. f. angew. Psychol.* No. 34.
24. UZNADZE, D. N., (1929). *Die Gruppenbildungsversuche bei vorschulpflichtigen Kindern, Arch. f. ges. Psychol.*, volume 73.
25. UZNADZE, D. N., (1924). *Eine experimentelle Beitrag zur Problem der Namengebung, Psychol. Forschung*, volume V, Nos. 1–2.
26. UZNADZE, D. N., (1927). *Zum Problem der Bedeutungserfassung, Arch. f. d. ges. Psychol.*, volume 58, Nos. 1–2.
27. HORNBOSTEL, E., (1925). *Die Einheit der Sinne*, Melos.
28. KÖHLER, W., (1930). *Gestaltpsychology*, London.
29. WILLWOLL, A., (1924). *Begriffsbildung*, Leipzig.

AUTHOR INDEX

SUBJECT INDEX